Generydes.

A ROMANCE IN SEVEN-LINE STANZAS.

BERLIN: ASHER & CO., 53 MOHRENSTRASSE.
NEW YORK: C. SCRIBNER & CO.; LEYPOLDT & HOLT.
PHILADELPHIA: J. B. LIPPINCOTT & CO.

Generides

Generydes,

A ROMANCE IN SEVEN-LINE STANZAS.

———◇———

EDITED FROM

THE UNIQUE PAPER MS. IN TRINITY COLLEGE, CAMBRIDGE

(ABOUT 1440 A.D.),

BY

W. ALDIS WRIGHT, ESQ., M.A.,

HONORARY FELLOW AND BURSAR OF TRINITY COLL., CAMBRIDGE,

EDITOR OF 'BACON'S ESSAYS,' 'THE BIBLE WORDBOOK,' ETC.; JOINT EDITOR OF THE
'CAMBRIDGE SHAKSPERE,' ETC.

LONDON:

PUBLISHED FOR THE EARLY ENGLISH TEXT SOCIETY,

BY N. TRÜBNER & CO., 57 & 59, LUDGATE HILL.

MDCCCLXXVIII.

55 & 70

CLAY AND TAYLOR, PRINTERS, BUNGAY.

v

PREFACE.

THE present version of the story of Generydes is printed from a MS. in the Library of Trinity College, Cambridge, where it forms part of the Gale collection, and is marked O. 5. 2. From the fact that in the same volume are Lidgate's *Siege of Troy* and his *Siege of Thebes*, the whole volume was catalogued as *Lidgate's Poems*, and consequently the existence of an entirely unknown poem was not suspected. When Mr. Furnivall was engaged upon his edition of the Helmingham MS. of *Syr Generides* for the Roxburghe Club in 1866, my attention was directed to some printed fragments of another version of the story in seven-line stanzas which had been discovered by Mr. Bradshaw in the binding of an old volume in our Library, *Michaelis Menoti Sermones Quadragesimales*, Paris, 1525; a volume which had formerly belonged to Edmund Castell, the well-known Oriental scholar. After copying these for Mr. Furnivall, I found some other fragments of the same version among the papers of Sir John Fenn, the editor of the *Paston Letters*, which were in the possession of Mr. Philip Frere of Dungate, who had inherited them from his father, Sergeant Frere, the nephew and adopted son of Lady Fenn. These also I transcribed and forwarded to Mr. Furnivall, and a week later, accidentally opening the volume of *Lidgate's Poems* among the Gale MSS., my eye was attracted by the name 'Generydes,' and to my great satisfaction upon further examination I discovered that the MS. contained all but one leaf of the seven-line stanza version. It is a large folio, measuring 17¼ inches by 12, vellum, and was written about the middle of the 15th century. No inference can be drawn from the fact that it is bound up with Lidgate's *Sieges of Troy and Thebes*, for it appears, upon closely examining it, to have been originally in a volume by itself, or to have formed a part of

another volume.   The evidence of this is that the edges of the book
are adorned with coats of arms, but these ornaments do not extend
over the portion occupied by the story of Generydes, which was
therefore, in all probability, originally distinct.   At the end of the
Siege of Troy occurs the signature ' Antonius Thwaites me possidet,'
and at the end of the volume ' Henry Thwayts' and ' Henry Thwaites.'
Anthony Thwaites may have been the son or descendant of John
Thwaites of Hardingham, Norfolk, who married Anne, daughter of
Sir William Knevet, and died 22 Henry VII., leaving a son Anthony
(Blomefield's *Norfolk*, v. 1198, folio ed.).   The book has evidently
been in the Thwaites and Knevet families, for their arms are found
in various combinations on the margins; and as the Thwaites arms do
not appear in the first part, which contains the story of Generydes,
whereas the Knevet arms are of frequent occurrence, it is possible that
this may have belonged originally to the Knevet family, and may
have been bound up with the Lidgate portion after the above-
mentioned marriage of John Thwaites with Anne Knevet.   The other
coats of arms I have been unable to trace with any certainty.   To
do so would involve a minute and curious, but certainly lengthy
investigation, and is altogether foreign to the purpose of this preface.
As a further proof that the Generydes portion of the volume was
originally distinct from the rest, I may add that the signatures of
the quires, which, except the last, consist of eight leaves, are quite
separate from those of the quires that follow, which evidently began
a volume.   Of the Generydes part there were originally 38 leaves, but
one of these has been cut out, leaving a gap of 187 lines in the MS.
after l. 4619.   There are two columns in a page and an average of
45 lines in a column.   The handwriting is very like that of the *Siege
of Troy* and the *Siege of Thebes*, which follow, and all may have been
the work of the same scribe.

The questions of the authorship of the English version and the
source of the story are as obscure now as they were when Mr.
Furnivall's edition of the other text appeared.   I have applied to
both M. Gaston Paris, and M. Paul Meyer, but neither of them has
met with any French version of the story.   It must have been
sufficiently popular to have been twice translated into English, and

possibly may still be lying hid in some unexpected quarter. The
disappearance of the original is scarcely more remarkable than the
almost as complete disappearance of the printed edition, of which
only a few mutilated fragments are known to exist. These, in all
probability, belong to that which was licensed to Thomas Purfoote,
as appears by the Registers of the Stationers' Company for the year
22 July, 1568—22 July, 1569, where the following entry occurs
(*Arber's Reprint*, i. 389) :—

purfoote   Recevyd of **thomas purfoote** for his lycense for pryntinge
of a boke intituled *GENERYDES*   **iiij**ᵈ

From the poem itself we get no clue as to the original. The
translator, to eke out his verse, occasionally introduces such phrases
as ' the story tellith it me ' (651), ' Mynne Auctour seith ' (686), ' myn
Auctour tellith me ' (967), ' as the writeng seyth ' (1081), ' myn
Auctour doth witnesse ' (1166), ' the story doth witnesse ' (1348),
' the Story tellith me ' (1648), ' the story makith mynde ' (2131),
' I me reporte onto the letterys blake ' (4526), ' as my Auctor doth
write ' (6002), ' in the story leke as I do fynde ' (6732) ; but he tells
us no more. In the Roxburghe Club version there is a French
original spoken of, and a Latin translation from it by a clerk at
Hertford, but here the information ends.

> ' Now of a geste that was sum tyme,
> That was radde in frensh ryme :
> A clerk itt in to latyn̄ tooke
> Att hertford out of a booke,
> There in latin was it wretin,
> As clerkes wele knowen and weteñ.'

In order that those who read the story may not be interrupted by
the gap which occurs in consequence of the loss of a leaf from the
MS., I give in brief the missing portion from the other version.

After the slaughter of Sir Yuell, Generydes makes his way to the
ship in company with Clarionas and the lavender, and reaches Persia
in safety, where they are welcomed by the Sultan, who makes a great
feast in honour of their return. After the first course had been served,
appear three messengers from Auferius to the Sultan, begging him
to send his son Generydes to assist him in recovering his lost kingdom

of India from Sir Amelok. The Sultan, who now hears for the first time that Generydes is a king's son, offers him half Persia and his daughter Clarionas in marriage. Generydes in return asks for a hundred knights, that he may win his father's heritage, and desires that his marriage with Clarionas may be put off till he comes back as a conqueror and can make her Queen of India. The Sultan grants his request, and allows Darel and those who were knighted with Generydes to accompany him. But when the plan was communicated to Clarionas she was filled with dismay.

The story then goes on as in the text.

I have in almost all cases printed the MS. as it is written, except where there was an obvious error destructive to the sense of a passage. In such instances I have sometimes corrected the text, putting the MS. reading at the foot of the page, and sometimes have introduced the correction in the Glossary. But I have not always attempted to fill up the defective or correct the irregular lines, and have sometimes left the reader to amend the text for himself. Professor Zupitza, in the first volume of *Anglia*, pp. 481—483, has printed some conjectural emendations, some of which I had already made in the margin of my own copy. They are included in the following list of correction :—

In 34 after *pite* insert *was*. In 39 for *lesse* read *lest*, as Professor Zupitza suggests. In 146 for *sothe* read *soche*. In 307 for *also* read *al so*. In 308 Professor Zupitza conjectures that we should read *preyse* for *plese*. In 335 omit *be*. In 414 omit *to*. In 454 for *hem* read *me*, as Zupitza suggests, where the MS. has *he*. In 601 for *fourth* read *fourth with*. In 707 for *renew* read *remew = remeve*. In 864 the MS. has *tell vs att it is*, for which I originally conjectured *telle what it is*, or *telle all as it is*. I now think the true reading is *telle it as it is*. Zupitza conjectures *as att* (= that) *it is;* but when *at* or *att* in this poem is used as a relative it is always preceded by 'that.' See 347, 591, 4388. In 1042 for *send* read *sendeth*. In 1163 the reference to the foot-note is omitted before *Ayre*. Omit full-stop at end of 1190. In 1330 for *obeyed* read *obeye*. In 1383 after *all* insert *that*, and omit *that* in 1386. In 1446 omit the second *he*. In 1455 Zupitza conjectures *wrought* for *sought*. In

1460 Zupitza suggests that *Anasere* should be printed instead of *Anasore*, because it is made to rhyme with *prisonere* and *ther*. Perhaps he is right, though in another passage, 2061, I had changed *ther* to *thore* for the sake of the rhyme, as the form *thore* occurs in 3394, 4316. The same correction would apply to 1725 (MS. *Anasare*), 2059, 2592, 2858, to which may be added 5575. In the present text, however, the forms of the name vary between *Anasore* and *Anasare*, while in the Roxburghe Club version we find *Anazaree* and *Anazare*, and I do not feel certain that after all the instances noticed by Zupitza may not be cases of imperfect rhymes. In the various readings given from the printed fragments at p. 224 it will be seen that in 2059 the printed text has *Anazere*, but then in the next line the reading is altered to *that there were*. To proceed with the correction of the text : in 1556 omit *hoole*. In 1633 Zupitza conjectures *ye rebuke* for *he rebukith ;* perhaps the single change of *he* to *ye* would be sufficient. In 1765 put a comma at the end of the line. In 2130 read *traytourly*. In 2481, 2482 something is wrong. Zupitza proposes to omit *That* in the first line. I would suggest the insertion of *it ranne* after *bak* in the second. See 2678. In side-note against 2524 for *Mountenor* read *Mountoner*. In 2576 the MS. has *hyn*, which I have corrected to *hym*, a form of *hem* which occurs more than once in the poem. Zupitza suggests *hem*. In 2682 *withoute moo* should not be between inverted commas. See Zupitza's note on Guy of Warwick, 719. In 2831 for *man of age* we should probably read *maner age*. In the side-note opposite 3018 for p. 60 read p. 69. In 3087 Zupitza suggests *left* for *lost*. In 3125 there is a corruption. We should probably read *Thus* for *This*, and the next word may be read *towardly* in the MS. In 3246 for *on* read *on to*. In 3297 for *to fight* read *for to fight*. In 3347 for *his* read *he his ;* but there is still a corruption in the passage, as is seen from the faulty rhyme. Perhaps we should read *whanne he him understode*. In 3392 for *knew* read *knew how*. In 3412 for *take* read *to take*. In 3414 after *councell* insert *the ;* and in 3416 after *sone* insert *be made*, as Zupitza suggests. In 3570 for *specially* read *speciall*. In 3635 for *swiff* read *swift*. In 3695, 3696 transfer the comma from

voyse to *courte.* The number of leaf 20 should be opposite 3712. In
3761 for *said* read *saide,* as MS. In 3780 omit *Iuell* and the full-stop
at the end of the line, and in 3781 insert *ride* after *cowde.* At the end
of 3859 omit note of exclamation. In 3921 the MS. has *on on;* perhaps we should read *and on.* In 4069 for *after now* read *now after.*
In the marginal note opposite 4201 for *Four* read *A few.* For 2467
read 4267 (p. 136). In 4489 the line should be amended by reading
at all aventure. In 4702 for *be* read *he,* as MS. In 5333 for *noo*
read *non.* In 5628 for *lorde* read *lady ;* and in 5651 omit *on* after *lay.*
In 5664 omit *mayde ;* and in 5705 for *hir* read *his.* In 5718 after
please insert *it.* In 5821 insert *on* before *apace.* In 5858 for *ganne
yei fall* read *yei fill.* In 5894 omit *ought.* In 6029 for *thorough*
read *thorough out.* In 6087 for *euerychone* read *euerych ;* and insert
so before *stronge* in 6091. In 6195 for *them* read *hym.* In 6271
the metre may be amended by reading *Ther to Abide to tyme,* &c.
In 6296, 6297 there is some corruption, probably due to the omis-
sion of some lines. At the end of 6443 omit comma. In 6569
for *swounyng* read *swoune.* On p. 211, l. 9614 should be 6614 ; and
in the following line *non* should be inserted after *of.* In 6619 insert
the before *tideng.* In 6640 for *place* read *pales* = palace. In 6693
for *in* read *in to.* In 6718 insert *was glad* or *was fayn* before *of.*
There is a corruption in 6821, but I do not see my way to a restora-
tion of the text. In 6966 read, for the sake of the metre, *All as
myn Auctour doth reherse.* In the marginal note, 3435, for *untrew*
read *untrue ;* and add ERBYS, *sb.* herbs, 6821, to the Glossary.

Besides these there may be many others, but they are not such as
to cause a reader any difficulty, and the remedy is generally very
obvious.

The Glossary will, I trust, be found fairly complete.

W. A. W.

Trinity College, Cambridge.
  December 7, 1878.

GENERYDES.

In olde Romans and storys as I rede,   **1**
Of Inde Somtyme ther was a nobyƚƚ kyng,
Ientiƚƚ, curteys, fuƚƚ trew in worde and dede,
Wyse and manly preuyd in eu*er*y thyng,   **4**
To his people fuƚƚ good and eke lovyng,
Mighty and ryche, a mañ of nobyƚƚ fame,
And Auferius this was the kynges name.   **7**

This worthy prince hadde weddyd in s*er*teyne   **8**
A fayre lady, and comne of nobyƚƚ kynne ;
And what pleasure he cowde for her ordeyne,
That shuld be do, ther was noo lette therin ;   **11**
In eu*er*y thyng he dede hyr loue to wynne,
He hadde nomore to lese and that he knewe,
ffor afterward she was to hym̄ vntrewe.   **14**

Hire fader was a mañ of grete powre,   **15**
And kyng of aufrike as I vnderstonde,
his dougħter quene of Inde as ye shall here,
kepyng right grete estate withynne the lande,   **18**
And aƚƚ the reme obeyed to hyre hande ;
And of hyr name to telle withoutyñ lese,
The story seytħ she higħt Serenydes.   **21**

This kyng of ynd, of whom̄ I spake before,   **22**
hadde a Styward a mañ of grete renowñ,
he gou*er*nyd the contre bothe lesse and more,
Also he hadde the Rule of eu*er*y towne,   **25**
And namely tho that longyd to the crowne :
him for to plese the pepiƚƚ were fuƚƚ fayne,
And s*er* amelok his name was for sertayne.   **28**

Marginal notes:

[leaf 1]
Auferius, king of India,

a man of noble fame,

married a fair lady, Serenydes, daughter to the king of Africa,

who was unfaithful to him.

His Steward, Sir Amelok, who governed the country,

was very intimate with her.

Not long after ther felle suche aqueyntaunce 29
Betwix the Quene and hym̄, that allway stiłł
hire mynde, hyr thought, was sette to his plesaunce,
All his desire hooly for to fulfiłł, 32
And whenne he lyste she was ałł atte his wille;
Gret pite that she in suche a wyse
Shuld sette hyr wurchippe atte so litiłł prise. 35

One day the king,

Vppoñ a day the kyng¹ for his disporte 36
An huntyng¹ went onto a fayre forest,

with four or five attendants,

Whanne he was sadde to putte hym in coumfort,
he lefte his meñ at home bothe most and lesse, 39
Save iiij or v suche as hym̄ semyd best,

rode a hunting into a fair forest,

And forth he gothe ther as the hartys hye,
his houndys were oncopelyd by and by. 42

An hert was fownde among the holtys hye, 43
And vppe vppoñ his fete he was a noñ;
The houndys went after witħ a mery crye,
The kyng rode after ałł hym̄ self alone, 46

and was separated from his companions.

Tyłł he hadde lost his knyghtes euerychone,
The houndes and the hert that was be fore,
Withynne a while they harde of them̄ nomore. 49

So rode he fourtħ as noo thyngge he rougħt, 50

He lost his way,

hys game was lost, his knygħtes forþe be hynde,
And specially on them was ałł his thougħt,
For hougħe they were he wyste not them̄ to fynde, 53
Thus rydiħ he sore trobelyd in his mynde;
The day was gonne, wherefore rigħt hertely
To god he prayd to send hym͛ some remedy. 56

but rode on till he came to a road which led to a house,

And, As god wold, hym͛ happyd in a waye, 57
Whiche brougħt hym͛ streyte to a goodly place;
And as his goodis is redy to purvaye

ffor good people in eu*er*y nedefull case,　　60
With that counfort he rode a better pase,
And whenne that he was come nygh hande *the*rate,
A fayre mayde ther openyd hym the gate.　　63

(margin: when a fair maiden opened the gate)

She seid he was welcome to that ostage,　　64
There were nomore but she and other twayn,
One of them was a man right ferre in age,
The toder was hyr mayden in s*er*tayne,　　67
To make hym chere they dede ther besy payn,
To hyr chaunbyr she brought hym verily,
Whiche was arayed right wele and richely.　　70

(margin: and welcomed him.)

(margin: She and her maid and an old man were the only inhabitants,)

(margin: and she brought him to her chamber,)

In that chaunber ther was an hanged bedde,　　71
Of sylk and gold full curyously wrought,
And ther vppon a shete of launde was spredde,
As clenly dressed as it cowde be thought :　　74
'And nowe,' q*uo*d she, 'that ye be hedyr brought,
Yow to counfort is holy myñ entente,
This howse is all atte your comaundement.'　　77

(margin: where was a bed with curious hangings.)

Anone vppon as she these wordis saide,　　78
Ther come an hert in att the chaunber dore
All embosed ; the kyng¹ was sore dismayede,
Semyng¹ to hym, as it passid in the flore,　　81
It was the same he chased in the more ;
This is, thought he, for me some man*er* trayne,
And ther with [all] she seyde to hym ageyn :　　84

(margin: A hart came in at the chamber door,)

(margin: which the king thought was the same he had chased.)

'Be not a ferde of this sodeyñ aventur ;　　85
It is for no harme, it is all for your beste,
This old fader he knowit very sure,
Of vij Saugys callid the wysest　　88
That was in Rome, but *ther* he myght not rest,
ffull wekydly he and his vj felawes
In to the see were cast among the wawis.　　91

(margin: 'Be not afraid,' said she, 'it is all for the best,)

(margin: as the old man knows, who is the wisest of the 7 Sages of Rome.)

When he was cast adrift with his fellows, he was thrown on the coasts of Syria, where my father is king,

And as the grace of god it wold ordeyne,   92
In Surre was this goodmaɴ) cast a lande,
Where my fader is kyngᵗ and souerayne,
Seke and wery ye may wele vnderstonde ;   95
And whanne that he was founde oɴ) the sand,

and became the chief of his council.

he sent for hyɴ) to come and not to fayle,
And whenne he came was made chefe of his counceꝉ.

He sayde the land of Surry shuld be lost   99
By a Gyaunte, and aꝉ for love of me ;

By his advice I was sent here,

Wherefore be his avyse in to this cost
I am come here, in lyke wyse as ye see ;   102

and I pray you now pardon me for what I shall say,
[leaf 1, back]

And forthermore I praye yow take in gre,
That I shaꝉ in your presence declare,
As fortune wiꝉ for youre ease and welefare.   105

And in this case to telle the mater playne,   106
Of very trougtħ and make no more delayes,

for to-night a child shall be begotten between us that shall do wonders.

This nyght *ther* shaꝉ be goteñ betwix vs twayne
A childᵗ that shaꝉ do mervelys in his dayes,   109
And moche a do he shaꝉ haue many wayes
Witħ grete *traveꝉ*, and aꝉ eskape rigħt wele,
This old fader canne teꝉ this eue*ry* dele.   112

For this cause the hart led you hither.

Only for this, and for noñ other thyng,   113
The hert that ye haue chased aꝉ this daye,
he was trewly the cause of yourᵖ comyngᵗ,
And to this place he gidyd yow the weye ;¹   116
This is the very trougtħ as I yow saye,

Yet you must know that the queen is untrue to you,

Yet most ye knowe a thynge that is be hynd,
Touchyng the quene, whiche is to yow vnkynd   119

And vtterly ontrew in eue*ry* thygᵗ ;   120
She and the Stiward bothe of oɴ) assent,
Witħ ther sotilte and false Imageninge,

¹ MS. *weþe*.

Yow to distroye that is ther hoole entente,   123   *and with the Steward has plotted your death.'*

ffor she is hoole at his commaund[e]ment ;

And aH to do yow hurte and hynderaunce,

Whiche afterward shalbe to *your* plesaunce.'   126

For these tidynges the kyng abasshid sore,   127   *The king was sore abashed,*

But ayenward whanne he thougħt oŋ that mayde

Anone his cher amendid more and more,

Remembryngꞏ the wordis that she sayde   130

Of his abidengꞏ ther ; thenne he hyr prayed   *and asked to know the real cause of his being there,*

To late hyɱ wete the very certente,

And she answerd ayeŋ that mygħt not be.   133

' This old fader that is my felaw here,   134   *but she said the old man could tell him,*

he canne telle that as wele as eny wigħt.'

The kyngꞏ hast[ed] to here of this materꞏ,

And prayed that maŋ that he wold telle hyɱ right.

he answered hyɱ and saide, ' as for that nygħt   *and this he promised to do next day.*

Go to your rest, for that is my counceħ,

To morow shaH ye knowe withoute fayle.'   140

Anoñ vpoŋ ther soperꞏ was redy,   141

She s*e*ruyd hyᴍ, in[1] like wyse as hyɱ ougħt,   *At supper the lady waited upon him, and*

And eu*er*y thing Accordengꞏ by and by,

For his plesurꞏ trowly ther lakkyd nogħt,   144

With aH deyntes trevly as cowde be thougħt ;

Hyre chere, hyr porte, it was in sothe awyse,

That more goodly that cowde nomañ devise.   147

After soper, withynne a litiħ space   148

She brougħt hyɱ to his bedde witħ torche ligħt,   *after supper brought him to his bed.*

And eyther stode so wele in otheris grace,

That she witħ hyɱ layde in armys rigħt ;   151

And what plesure they hadde as for y*t* nygħt,

P*er*avent*ur*e fuH good, who so it wist,

I canne not saye, deme ye as ye list.   154

[1] MS. *and in.*

But how that eu*er* it was be twix them thwayne, 155

It so happened that a child was begotten,

It happitħ, so the writeng¹ dotħ expresse,

That nygħt ther was a child goten certeyn;

After his hunteng¹ and his besynesse, 158

ffor his traveħ and his grete werynes

after which the king fell asleep, but the lady lay awake sighing,

he felle a slepe, and for to saye yow more

She sleppyd not, but lay and syghid sore. 161

With hyr syghenyng¹ a non with Aħ she wept, 162

letting her tears fall on his shirt; so that he awoke,

And on his armys dede the terys falle,

That thorough his shirte he felt it as he slept;

Right sodenly he brayded and wooke with Aħ, 165

And curtesly on hyr he beganne to calle,

saying he feared she repented of his coming.

'I drede me sore,' qu*o*d he, 'in myn entente

That of my comyng heder ye repente.' 168

'Nay,' said she, 'but my sorrow is for your departing.'

'Repente,' qu*o*d she, 'nay, nay, I yow ensure, 169

Your² departeng¹ is cause of aħ my smerte,

Only for that I do this payne endure,

ffor I shaħ lose the plesur² of myn hert, 172

And aħ my Ioye, I may it not asterte,

Withoute socour² or help*e* O warentice,

My disteyney hatħ shape it in this wyse.' 175

'Fair lady,' he said, 'I hope we shall not part so soon,

'My fayre lady,' qu*o*d he to here Ageyne,¹ 176

'I haue good hoope we shaħ not parte so sone,

And if we do, I seye yow certeyn

My chefe counfort is aħ to geder doon; 179

To morow shaħ we wete or it be none,

but to-morrow the old man will tell us.'

This old fader that ye kepe with you here,

he shaħ telle vs the trougtħ of this mater.' 182

When it was day and it was tyme to rise, 183

This old fader on to the kyng¹ he gotħ,

And whanne he cam he spak in this wise;

¹ MS. *Aveyne.*

'That I shaỻ sey, leve me withoute othe,   186   At daybreak the
This nygĥt is geteñ a sone betwix yow both,   old man
                                                          told him that he
Whiche shalbe suche, myꝛ auctour doth expresse,   must leave,
That aỻ contres shaỻ speke of his prowesse.   189

Here may ye a byde no lenger in this place,   190
ffor very trougtĥ for causes more thanne oñ ;
But of youꝛ shirt I must telle yow the cause,   and that the
                                                          tear-stained shirt
Vppoꝛ the whiche hir terys feỻ vppoꝛ :   193   could only be
                                                          washed by the
Ther shaỻ noꝛ wassĥ themꝺ owt but she alone,   lady herself.
Not be no maner of craft, take this of me,
But she sette handes therto it wiỻ not be.   196

And now to yow, madame, thus I saye ;   197   The lady he
                                                          warned to return
Yow must departe, and I shaỻ telle yow whye,   to her father,
The kyng youre fader is rigĥt seke this day,
And lythe neꝛ vppoꝛ the poynte to dye ;   200   who was dying.
And but ye ryde this day rigĥt hastely,
And leve aparte aỻ other thyngᵗ therfore,   [leaf 2]
Ye are not lyke to speke with hymꝺ nomore.'   203

Wheꝺ he seid aỻ that he thougĥt to seye,   204
Ther nedid noo displeasuꝛ to be sougĥt ;
The kyngᵗ knewe wele ther was noñ other way,
They must departe, and that was aỻ his thougĥt ; 207
Thenne were they bothe so ferre in sorow brougĥt,
Be cause of therꝛ so sodenly departengᵗ,
They cowde not speke a word for erthely thyngᵗ. 210

He toke his leve in sorowfuỻ maner,   211   The king took his
                                                          leave in sorrow,
hym for to be holde it was a grete pite ;
And furthe he ridetĥ with fuỻ heuy chere,
With his knygĥtes to mete and it wold be :   214
And at the last it happyd hym̄ to see,   and in a fair
                                                          valley fell in with
Where as they rode in a fuỻ fayre vaile,   his knights,
he sporyd his hors and theder toke the way.   217

They hym̃ perseyued sone, and forthe they went, 218
A none they mette the kynge vppoñ the waye,

who saw that he was sad.

he was no thyngᵗ mery to ther entente,
That wist they wele yet durst they noo thyngᵗ seye, 221
Withynne his brest he kept it day be day ;
And whanne that he came home, I yow ensure,
Of his councelł ther wist nom̃ erthely creature. 224

Now to this lady lete vs turne ageyn, 225

The lady went her way to Syria with the old man and her maid,

Whiche to Surry hatħ take hir viage,
And in hir companye no mañ but twayñ,
hir mayde and the old mam̃ ferre in age ; 228
So atte last they come to the village,
Ther for to rest as for a nygħtis space,
A dayes Iurney owt of the kynges place. 231

She Rode to court in grete heuynesse, 232

and came to her father,

And furtħ witħ alł she came to the kyngᵗ,
Whicħ was febyłł and sokyd witħ sekenesse ;
Yet not for thy he hadde trew knowleginge 235

who gave her his blessing,

Of his dougħter, and gave hyr his blyssyngᵗ,
his land, is good, withoute eny stryffe,

and died,

And so to god he passed owt of his lyffe. 238

There was wepyngᵗ and many a hevy chere, 239
Amongᵗ them alł grete sorow ganne they take,
And as it is the custom̃ and maneᵗ,
Anone they were arrayed in clothis blake ; 242
And sone[1] vppoñ ordenaunce ganne they make,

and was royally buried.

In alł the hast posible as for his beryengᵗ,
In Ryałł wise accordyngᵗ to A kyngᵗ. 245

This yongᵗ lady so goodly and so faire, 246
The lordes alł and the Comyns of the lande,
Be cause she was his doughter and his ayre,

[1] MS. *sone A.*

They toke hir for ther quene I vnderstonde,   249
And crowned hir witħ septer in hyr hande ;
And afterward, as is the rigħt vsage,
The lordys aħ to hir dede homage.   252

She was fuħ wele belouyd in certeyne   253
Of hir lordes and of hir comenaute,
And of hir name she was callid Sereyne,
ffro the first day of hir natiuite,   256
ffuħ humbly they hir be sougħt that she
Wold be maryed, for that was ther a vise,
But that she wold not in no maner a wyse.   259

The tyme came that hir wombe be ganne to grow   260
Som dele gretter thanne it was wont to be,
But yet she wold not it hadde beñ knowe ;
here mayde she callid furth in priuite,   263
Meden she higħt, the story tellitħ it me,
To whom) the quene hadde a rigħt fey[th]fuħ trost,
ffor to that mayde she mygħt sey what here lyst. 266

And whañ she came, she told here aħ the case,   267
lyke as it was of aħ here aventur :
'Madame,' quod she, 'I shall witħ goddes grace
ffuħ trewly kepe your counceħ be you sure :'   270
So went she fourtħ hyr seosynne to endure,
Tiħ atte last, be goddes purvyaunce,
The tyme was come of hir delyueraunce.   273

Thenne was ther noñ of counceħ saue Medeyn ;   274
Ther was no noyse, nor ther was noo cryengʼ,
I canne wele thynk the gretter was hir payne ;
her meny hadde noñ other knowleginge,   277
But hir sekenes was of some other thinge :
So this lady, fuħ debonerly and myld,
Brougħt furtħ a sonne whiche was a threfte child. 280

His daughter
was crowned
queen,

and was well
beloved,

but refused to
marry.

Her name was
Sereyne.

At length, when
her womb began
to grow, she took

counsel with her
maid Medeyn,

who promised to
be true to her,

and so it went on
till the time of
her delivery
arrived.

She brought forth
a son;

but none knew save Medeyn, who took it to a lavender to be brought up.	Medeyne it toke and in hir lappe it leyde,	281
	She brougħt it streyght on to a lavender ;	
	'This is sothely my Suster sonne,' she sayde,	
	'I wold it were kept in good man*er*.'	284
	'Maistres,' seyde she, 'care not for this mater,	
	I shaH it bere oñ to A good noryse,	
	Whiche shaH it kepe right wele o warantyce.'	287

A nurse was found for the child,	First to a norise, as fast as eu*er* they canne,	288
	They brougħt the child withoute eny lese ;	
	And thanne to chirch to make a cristenmañ,	
who was christ- ened Generydes.	And callid it be name Generydes ;	291
	Thenne his moder, after aH hir dissese,	
	Askyd medeyñ if she hadde done wele	
	And she seid yae, and told hir eu*er*y dele.	294

As soon as he could speak	Whenne the tyme was come that he cowde speke and goo,	
	And vnderstonde what folkys did hym) calle,	
the queen sent for Medeyn to bring him to court.	The quene anoñ, withoute wordes moo,	
	Callid Medeyñ, and she came furtħ witħ aH :	298
	'Medeyñ,' quod she, 'my wiH in [1] especiaH	
	Is for to haue my sone Generydes	
	In courte [2] witħ me his honour to encrese.'	301

[leaf 2, back]	To curte he came a pratye yong[1] seru*au*nt,	302
	But what he was ther wyst noo creature,	
	Saue only this that Medeyn) was his Aunte, [3]	
He came, and grew up at court,	And so fourtħ in courte he dede endure,	305
	TiH he was wexen) of a goodly stature,	
	And ther witħ also IentiH and curteys,	
	That [4] aH the countre [5] right gretely did hym) plese.	308

till one day he asked Medeyn of his father.	Vppoñ A day he axkid of Medeyn)	309
	Of his ffader, and hougħ is moder was,	
	She answeryd hym), and this she sayde ayen),	

[1] MS. *is in.*   [2] MS. *contre.*   [3] MS. *Aumte.*
[4] MS. *Thall.*   [5] *? courte.*

'I yow beseche of respite in this case   312
Till on the morow, and thenne with goddes grace
All that ye haue desired now of me,
Sone shall ye knowe the very serteynte.'   315

Of his desire the quene hadde knowleginge,   316
She sent for hym and seid, 'Generydes,

The queen told him she was his mother, and the king of India his father.

Of ynde suerly your fader is the kyng,
And I your moder am withoute lese ;   319
But ye must kepe this mater husht and pece,
ffor ther is non that knoweth it saue we twayne
In all the court, but if it be Medeyn.'   322

And whenne he knowe this mater very right,   323
Streyght to the quene he seid for eny thing ;
Besechyng hir of licence that he myght

He begged that he might go to India to his father,

Se the courte where his fader is kyng :   326
ffor as hym thought it were right wele semyng,
ffor to do hym seruice as in that case,
And rather ther thanne in a stranger place.   329

And he wold so demene hym furth with all,   330

promising to keep the secret of his birth.

That in the countre ther shuld no maner weight,
But if it were the kyng in especiall,
Wete what he[1] were be countenaunce or sight.   333
The quene Answeryd and seyd, 'all is but right
That ye desire, and therfore be myn Assent
Is and shalbe to forder your ente[nt].'   336

And furth with all she callid Natanell,[2]   337
A Ientill man right connyng and courteyse ;
To hym she told this mater euery dele,

The queen entrusted him to the care of Natanell,

Of hyr and of hir sonne Generydes,   340
And who is fader was withouten lese,
And how that his desire in eny wise
Is for to do his fader some seruice.   343

    [1] MS. *I*.   [2] MS. *Natavell.*

'Therfore,' quod she, 'I prae yow feithfully,   344
That ye will do the pleasure that ye may
Onto my sone, and teche hym throughely
That att longith to hym to do or saye ;   347
ffor his expencez and for his aray,
ffor hors or men that maye be for your spede,
he shall not lakke no thyngͥ that hym nede.   350

whom she warned
to beware of the
Steward,
But be well ware that the Stiward knowe not this, 351
Whiche is ontrewe and hath be many a daye ;
ffor if he may knowe who is sonne he is,
he will suerly distroye hym and he maye :   354
Wherefore whanne ye come ther this shall ye seye,
A Dukes sone he is and born in Greke,
To se the kyngͥ and wurchippe for to seke.   357

And whanne ye maye fynd good leyser and spase, 358
That sekerly ye may speke with the kyngͥ,
Ye shall me recomaunde on to his good grace
and to convey a
ring from her to
the king.
ffull humbly, and take ye hym this ryngͥ,   361
he gave it me atte ourͬ last departengͥ ;
When he it seth it shall his thought renewe,
And suerly knowe that your massage is trew.'   364

This Ientill man gave answere[1] in this wise :   365
Natanell pro-
mises to obey
her wishes.
'Madame,' quod he, 'my will is and shall
To do yourͬ sone pleasure and seruice,
As ye shalbe right wele content withall,   368
With goddes grace and what that euer befall,
Better or werse or what aventure be tyde,
Ye shall will wete I will with hym a byde.'   371

Furthe on his way Rideth Generydes,   372
lakkyngͥ no thing that cawde be hadde in mynde ;
And of his labourͬ wuld he neuer sese,

-----
[1] MS. _an answere._

Till he come streyght atte Reme of ynd,   375   They come to
                                                                   India, to the
Thenne for*ther*more as reasone wold hym bynd,   chief city
Of dyuerse folke he asked where laye the kyng :
Att parentynne, they seid withoute feyning,   378   Parentine,

Off all the land named the chefe Citee :   379
Then Natanell as sone as eu*er* he myght,
The best loggyng of all that he cowde see,   where Natanell
                                                                  took a lodging,
ffor his maister he dede it redy dight,   382
And ther he toke his rest as for that nyght,
And on the morow in good and riche araye,   and on the
                                                                  morrow they
he went to see the kyng ther as he laye ;   385   went to court.

And Natanell with hym in companye.   386
The kyng was sette and s*er*ued in the hall,   The king was in
                                                                  the hall among
With knyghtes and Esquyers throughely,   his lords.
In grete astate among the lordes all ;   389
Thanne Natanell the porter ganne to calle,
he came anon withoute taryeng,
And curtesly gaue them ther welcomyng.   392

Furthe anon in to the halle they ganne goo,   393
And to the kyng they made Reuerence,   They made
                                                                  their reverence
lyke as it was accordyng for to do.   to him,
Thenne Natanell in opyn audience,   396
Before his lordes in his hye presence,
ffull connyngly in all his demeanyng,
Right in this wise he seide onto the kyng :   399   and Natanell
                                                                  said

' Ryght noble p*ri*nce, this Ientilman present   400
To yow is come ferre out of his contre,
A dukes sone of Greke born by disente,   that Generydes
                                                                  was the son of
here in your court desireng for to be,   403   a duke of Greece,
To lerne connyng and wurchipp*e* for to see :   [leaf 3]
The Duke his ffader wold he shuld do so,   who desired to
                                                                  be in the king's
And be right gladde ye leste excepte hym so.'   406   court.

When) he hadde seid and made his Reuerence,   407
The kyngᵗ anon) thanne answeryd to Nataneꝉ,

The king gave
them welcome,

And seid he was welcome to his presence,
Be holdingᵗ wele his face and euerydele ;   410

and was re-
minded of the
lady who had
harboured him
so well,

Thenne that lady that harboryd hym) so wele
ffeꝉ in his mend, and thougħt be his visage
he was fuꝉ lyke to be of hire lenage.   413

He loked fast oñ to hym) in stede fast wise,   414

thinking Ge-
nerydes might
be his son.

And thought alway his sonne that he shuld be :
Whenne mete was do the kyngᵗ be ganne to ryse,
To nataneꝉ his maister thanne saide he : ¹   417
'This yongᵗ Esquyer is rigħt welcome to me ;
he shaꝉ lak nogħt, I say yow for certeyn) ;'
And he rigħt lowly thanked hym) ageyn).   420

They hadde mantellys and aꝉ of on) makyngᵗ,   421
Whiche were right sone departed bothe in fere ;

Generydes gives
his mantle to
the butler,

Generydes withoute taryengᵗ
Gaue his mantiꝉ on to the Boteler²,   424
Thenne Natanell, in rigħt curtes maner²,

Natanell his
to the porter.

To the porter he gaue that was his owne,
In thankefuꝉ wise the better to be knowen).   427

And so they live
in court.

Thus in the courte dwellid Generydes,   428
Rigħt wele belouyd of euery creature,
So weꝉ wexen that he was doutelys
A very goodly man), I you ensure :   431
Witħ good vesage, fuꝉ metely of stature,
his porte, his chere, and all his behavinge
ffuꝉ like a Ientilman) in euery thyngᵗ.   434

After a time,
as the king was
alone in a gallery,

It happyd so withynne a litiꝉ space,   435
The kyngᵗ a lone went in [a] Galery ;
Thanne Nataneꝉ aspied where he was,

¹ MS. *he saide.*

And to the kyng⸗ he went trewly,   438
To late hym) wete his erand by and by,
lyke as he was comaunded for to sey,
And thus he seid withoute more delay :   441

' Syr, if I durst be bold as in this case,   442
My message wold I say, if it yow please,
The quene Sereyne commandith hir to your grace,
And sent yow here your' sonne Generydes :   445
Be cause ye shall think it is noo lese,
She chargyd me to take yow this ring⸗,
Ye gaue it hir atte your bothe departyng⸗.'   448

The kyng⸗ toke gode avise vppon) the reng⸗, 449
It was his owyn), and that anon) he knowe ;
To Natanell he seid withoute feyni[n]g⸗,
' Gramercy, frend, for your massage is trew, 452
Ye haue brought hym) that doth my ioye renew ;
Whanne he come first hem[1] thought it shuld be he,
Wherefore I prae yow bryng⸗ hym) on) to me.' 455

Thanne furth with all departed Natanell,   456
Generydes he brought on to the kyng⸗ ;
Whanne he was come the kyng be held hym) well,
And liked hym) right wele in euery thyng⸗, 459
God wote he was so gladde of his comyng⸗,
That ther cowde noman) deme betwix hem) twayne,
Whiche of them) bothe were gladder in certayne. 462

Whanne this was do he went to his seruice, 463
The kyng dede call on to hym) Natanell,
And charged hym) in eny maner wise,
Aboue all thyng⸗ that he shuld kepe hym) welle ; 466
Thanne seruyd he the quene att euery mele,
Bothe att hir mete and soper decently,
The whiche he dede full wele and manerly. 469

[1] MS. he.

(marginal notes)
Natanell gave him the ring and message from Sereyne.

The king recognized the ring

and thanked Natanell.

Generydes was then brought to the king,

and both were glad.

After this Generydes attended upon the queen,

Withynne a[1] while it happyd in y^is wise, 470
The quene beheld Generydes so weH,

who liked him
so well that all
her love was
set upon him,

And liked hym) so wele in his service,
That aH hir loue on) hym) was euery dele, 473
And in hyr self she cowde non) other' fele ;
Withoute that she mygĦt have his loue ageyn),
She were on don) for euere in certayne. 476

and one day,
when the king
was gone a-
hunting, she
told him all,

Not long after the kyng' on) hunteng' went, 477
Generydes that day abode behynd,
The quene knew that, and sone for hym) she sent,
And told hym) aH that lay sore in hir mynd ; 480
' Generydes,' quod she, ' if I myght fynd
That ye wold loue me best and so endure,
I shaH do yow the same I you ensure. 483

Full long agoo I was in this purpose, 484
Butt thenne I myghĦt not telle yow what I ment,
Desireng' yow to kepe this mater close,
And lete me haue knowlage of your' entent ; 487

promising him
great worship
if he would
assent.

I promys you if ye wiH assent,
In grete wurchippe I shaH yow wele avaunce,
And alway do that may be your' plesaunce.' 490

Generydes stode stiH in grete musyng', 491
And to the quene gaue answere in this case :

Generides said,
' I am the king's
man, and can-
not be untrue
to him,'

' Madame,' quod he, ' I am bounde to the kyng',
To be his man) her' and in euery place ; 494
And I so moche am hold to his grace,
That for to haue his Reme myself alone,
I wold not be ontrew to his person).' 497

and took his
leave.

With that he toke his leve and furtĦ he went ; 498
And whanne she sawe it wold non) other be,
She threte hym̄ sore, and seid he shuld repent,

---

[1] MS. ai.

She rente hir here, a wonder thyng' to see,   501   The queen en-
raged, tore her
And brougħt hir self clene owt of charite ;   hair and threatened vengeance,
The Stiward came and sawe aħ was amys,

'Madame,' quod he, 'what grete affraye is this?'   504

'Afraye,' quod she, 'so may ye wele it calle.'   505   telling the
Steward
'But who did this?' quod he, 'I prae yow saye ;

Telle me the sothe, and late me dele withaħ,

ffor I shaħ sone a wreke aħ this arraye,   508

What euer he be he shaħ repente the daye

That he was bold, in ernest or in game,   [leaf 3, back.]

To do to yow this villany and Shame.'   511

'It is,' quod she, 'that fals Generydes,   512

Be cause he mygħt not haue his wiħ of me ;

ffor by noo prayour' he wold neuer sese,

But thus he hatħ arayed me as ye se.'   515   that Generydes
had offered her
And whanne the Stiward hard that it was he,   violence.

'Madame,' quod he, 'be ye no mor' displesid,

ffor in this case your' hart shaħ sone be eased.'   518

He toke a naked sward and forth he goth,   519   The Steward
took a sword
Generydes to slee if that he mygħt ;   and went forth
to kill Generydes;
But he wist wele beforⁿ the quene was wrotħ,

Wherefore be tyme he went owt of hir sigħt :   522

To his chaunber' the Stiward gotħ fuħ rigħt,

In euery place he sougħt hymⁿ vppe and donⁿ,

And he was atte his logging' in the townⁿ,   525   but he had gone
to his lodging
in the town,

Owt of daunger, and witħ hymⁿ Nataneħ   526

To whomⁿ he told this mater aħ in feere ;   and told Natanell, who
Quod he ageynⁿ, 'here in we shaħ do weħ   advised him to
await the king's
Tiħ that the kyng' come home we wilbe here,   529   return.

Thanne wiħ it be good tyme to draw yow neer',

And do seruice like as ye did be foore,

What euer faħ they shaħ preyse yow the more.'   532

The king came
home, and Ge-
nerydes served
in the hall,

The kyng came home, with hym his knyghtez aH, 533
Generydes, as he was wont to do,
ffuH wele and goodly seruyd in the haH :
The Stiward hadde fuH grete enuy therto, 536
And in his hand he bare a staff also ;
So goth he furthe in myddes of the prese,
In grete anger threting' Generydes 539

Withoute reason, and seid, 'what dost y^u here? 540
here is noman content of thii seruice.'
Generydes he gaue hym non answere ;
'Why spekist thu not?' quod he, 'thu art not wise.'
And with that word, in fuH creweH wise,

when the Steward
took him by
the hair and
smote him.

he toke hym be the heere ther as he stode,
And smote hym so that his nose braste on blode. 546

The king, wroth
to see his son
wronged,

And whanne the kyng' perseyuid aH the case, 547
Thow he were wrothe ther ougft noman hym blame,
To see his sonne so wrongyd as he was ;

called to the
Steward,

he callid on to the Stiward bi his name, 550
'Traytour',' quod he, 'god geve ye uery shame,
This yong' Squyer suerly dede non offence,
And thou hast smetyn hym here in my presence. 553

Not only now thu dost me villany, 554
Butt here afore thu hast do many moo :'

and stabbed him
in the arm.

And with his knyff he smote hym[1] hastely
Thorough the arme, and when he hadde so do, 557
'Out of my sigft I warne the that y^u goo.'
With that the quene was wroth in hir maner,
Thougft she anon this towchith me rigft ner'. 560

The Steward went
to his castle

Owt of the court the Stiward went his weye, 561
To his casteH he toke the wey fuH right,
And made hym strong' of men and of array,

[1] MS. *hym hym.*

And euermore his thought was day and nyght   564
To avenge hym) of the kyngᵗ if that he myght ;   *and plotted vengeance.*
To that purpose he sette aH his entente,
And moche people he hadde of his assent.   567

Now late vs leue aH this as for A space,   568
And to Generydes I wiH returne,   *Generydes was so discomfited*
So rebukyd and skomfite as he was,
he cowde not make no chere but alwey mourn),   571   *that he could not remain,*
And lenger ther he thought not to sogeourne,[1]
But hastely to make his departengᵗ,
And furth withaH he came to the kyngᵗ.   574

He knelid down) and seid right in this wise ;   575   *and begged the king*
' Ser, if it please your goodnesse for to hire,
With yow I haue contynued my seruice
In pese and rest, and now yᵉ[2] Stiward herᵖ   578
hath smete me in fuH crueH maner,
And hath putte me to Shame in yourᵖ presence,
And wile I wote I dede hym) non) offence.   581

I may not ease my hert as in this case,   582
That doth me harme whanne I remembre me,
here afterward I shaH, be goddis grace,
Think ther vppon) whanne I a seasone see,   585
I wiH no lenger dwelle in this contre,
Wherefore, I you beseche, sithe it is so,ᵗ
That ye wiH graunte me licence for to go ;   588   *to let him go.*

And whiH I leue yourᵖ trew man shaH I be,   589
Where euer I traveH to and fro,
To do yow pleasurᵖ that at lithe in me,
ffor right gretly am I holden) therto.'   592
And whanne the kyngᵗ knew weH that he wold go,   *The king*
And that ther was non) other meane to fynde,
God wote he was right heuy in his mynd.   595

---

[1] MS. *sogeourur*.   [2] MS. *now is yᵗ*.

and all his
knights were
sorry
The knyghtes all, and the squyers truely,   596
Were full sory of his sone departeng⟨,
Notwithstondyng ther was noo remedy,
But furth he goth withoute more taryeng⟨,   599
Right vmbly he toke leue of the kyng⟨,
And so fourth he went thorough owt yᵉ hall,
when he took
leave.
ffull curtesly he toke leue of them) all.   602

Generydes and
Natanell
Generydes and also Natanell   603
To ther logging⟨ they toke the redy waye,
trussed up their
harness
And trushed ther' harnes euery dele,
Whanne that was do Generydes ganne saye,   606
'Now late vs here appoynt for our' Iurnay
and resolved to go In to what land or contre we shall goo.'
Quod natanell, 'that hold I wele to do :   609

[leaf 4]
To Surry ward, hough seye ye now be that ?   610
The quene Sereyne wold right fayne se you *ther*.'
'All that is sothe,' quod he, 'but wote ye what ?
In stranger' place fayne wold I that we were,   613
ifor I am now of age harmes to bere ;
And to be knyght as I see other be,
The more wurchippe the better think[eth] me.'   616

'All this is very sothe,' quod Natanell,   617
'To your entent I canne right wele agree ;
Ther is a land I am remembryd wele,
to Persia.
Men) call it Perse, a plenteuous contre,   620
Ther and [yow] will the Sowdon) may yow see,
The whiche is knowyn) bothe ferre And nere,
A myghti prince, a man) of gret powre.'   623

Generydes thanne answerd in this wise :   624
'To that contre I rede we take the waye,
ffor ther we may not fayle of good seruice,

As ye suppose, teH me what ye seye.'   627
'Kepe stiH,' q*uo*d he, 'your' p*ur*pose I yow praye,
To myɒ entent ther is best abydeng*ı*,
I wote he wiH be gladde of your comyng*ı*.'   630

Ther hors, ther meñ, were redy eu*er*ychoɒ,   631
To that contre they toke the wey fuH rigꞜt,
And onɔ hir wey so ferre fourtꞜ were thei gooɒ,
That of the Citee sone they hadde a sigꞜt,   634
Theder they came be thanne it was nygꞜt,
And fourtꞜ withaH to ther loggyng*ı* they went,
The best that they cowde fynde to ther' entent.   637

It was the best Citee of aH the lande,   638   They came to the
And mounten*er* it higꞜt withoute fayle,   chief city,
                                                          Mountener,
Therin the Sowdoɒ was I vnderstonde,   where the Sultan
In a casteH fuH riche of appareH.   641   Goffore dwelt,
Generydes thanne after his grete appareH,
And NataneH they bothe in good aray,
To the Sowdoɒ they toke y*e* redy way.   644

And whanne they came ther' as the Sowdoɒ was,   645
Ther' wer' knygꞜtes and Squyers many onɔ,
hymɔ self walkeng*ı* in his disporteng*ı* place,   and found him
                                                          walking in his
They aH awaiteng*ı* vppoɒ his persone,   648   pleasure ground.
Generydes and NataneH anooɒ
Avaunsed them the sowdoɒ for to see,
Goffore he higꞜt, the story tellitꞜ it me.   651

Whanne[1] he hymɔ saw he did to hyɱ obeseaunce,   652
ffuH manerly and seyd rigꞜt in this wise ;
'Ser, if it be your' wiH and your' pleasaunce,
her am I come to offer' my ser*u*ice   655   Generydes offered
                                                          him his service,
To your' lordshipp*e*, rigꞜt as ye list to devise,
Now please it yow to take me for your' manɔ,
And I shaH do suche ser*u*ice as I canne.'   658

                    [1] MS. *Thanne.*

The Sowdoñ stode and hard hym̄ eu*e*ry dele,   659
he toke good hede att hym̄ in eu*e*ry thing';
And dought ye not he lekid hym̄ right wele,
Bothe his p*e*rsoñ and all his demeaneng',   662
And furthwith gaue hym̄ his welcomyng'
ffull curtesly, and seid in Ientill wise ;
'I am̄ content of you to haue se*r*uice :   665

What¹ is your' name ? I p*r*ae yow tell it me.'   666
'My name,' q*uo*d he, 's*er*, is Generydes.'
'Generydes,' he said, 'wele mote ye thee ;
A Ientilman̄ ye seme withouten̄ lese,   669
And in wurchipp*e* right lekely to encrese ;
and was accepted. Wherefore of suche as do to me se*r*uice
I will that ye be nexst in eny wise.'   672

The Sultan's   The Sowdoñ hadde his doughter and his ayre   673
daughter,   In his palys vnder his gou*e*rnaunce,
And for certeyne she was right inderly fayre,
And, as the writeng' makith remembraunce,   676
ffull womanly of speche and countena*u*nce ;
In suche wise hir' name beganne to sprede,
That eu*e*ry man̄ spake of hir' goodlyheed.   679

And as the Sowdoñ was sett att his mete,   680
Generydes softely he beganne to calle,
The best deynte that before hym̄ was sett
he toke it hym̄, and badde hym̄ goo with all   683
To his doughter : 'my lord,' q*uo*d he, 'I shall.'
So fourth he goth ther as this lady was,
Clarionas,   Mynne Auct*ou*r seith she hight clarionas.   686

loved Generydes, This fayre lady behelde Generydes,   687
In stedefast wise oñ hym̄ she cast hir eye,
All his man*e*rs so wele it did hyr plece,

¹ MS. *That.*

That she constreyned was in certeyn)te   690
To loue hym̄ best, it wold noñ other be ;
She though̄t it dede hir good on) hym̄ to thynk,
And of hir cuppe she offeryd hym) to drynk.   693

He toke it of hir' hand fuH curtesly,   694
And ferthermore, as I this mater fele,
In) his conseyte, I say¹ yow certeynly,
hym) liked neuer creatur' so wele :   697
his mynde, his thought, was sett oon hir yche deell ;   *and his mind was set on her.*
And, as I cowde perseyue in myn) entent,
There hartes bothe were sone of on) Assent.   700

Generydes he toke his leue anon),   701
To sone she though̄t as after hir avise,
Yet or² that he departed was and goon),
To kysse hym) she forgate not in no wise,   704
he thanked hir and offerid hir seruice,
To be hire man) and alway to be trew,
So to endur' and neuer to renew.   707

Vppe from) hir mete arose clarionas,   708
And on) hir bedde she leyde hir fourtḧ witḧ AH ;
hir mayden) had grete merveH what it was,
And fuH softely on) hir' she be ganne to calle,   711
' Madame,' quod she, ' what thing' is now be faH ?
Of your' dissese I prae yow telle it me,
To wete yow seke it is a gre[te] pite.'   714   [leaf 4, back]

Ther witḧ the lady gaue answere ageyn)   715   *She told her maid, Mirabell,*
Vnto hir maydeñ, MirabeH was her' name ;
' Of my dissese,' quod she, ' yf I shuld layne   *of her disease,*
Only to yow, I wis I were to blame ;   718
I haue founde yow, in ernest and in game,
Att aH tymes fuH secrete and fuH trew,
And soth to saye I neuer other knewe :   721

      MS. *saw.*   ² MS. *of.*

And for to telle you plenly of my dissese, 722
This is the cause ; ther is on) specialy
hatħ don) me harme, god wote causeles,
I neu*er* offendid hym) truly ; 725
And me think ther is noo remedy,
ffor I was neu*er* seke on) this maner,
A fore this tyme now knowe ye aħ in fer. 728

'Not aħ,' q*uo*d she, 'madame, that may not be ; 729
ffor yet I haue no knowlage whiche he is.'
'It is,' q*uo*d she, 'a yong Squyer, parde ;
he is but late come to my lord, I wis, 732
A very goodly man), so haue I blisse.'
'Aħ this may be, and I beleue the same ;
But good madame,' q*uo*d she, 'what is his name?' 735

and that unless
she could see
Generydes,
'To seye yow sothe,[1] Generydes he higħt.' 736
Q*uo*d she ageyñ, 'now wote ye eu*er*y dele ;
Butt I of hym) right sone may haue a sigħt,
it would not
long be well
with her.
Witħ me I wote it wiħ not long be wele, 739
ffor hym) only is aħ that eu*er* I fele,
And alway more and more it dotħ encrese ;
God wote I am no thing' in hertys ease.' 742

'Madame,' q*uo*d she, 'dismay yow neu*er* a dele, 743
Be of good chere, hurt not yow to soore ;
Dougħte ye noo thing' Aħ this shalbe right wele,
ffor I shaħ trewly do my part ther fore 746
Witħ right good wiħ, and for to say yow mor,
ffor [2] this mater I shaħ do wele ordeyne
That ye suerly shaħ speke with hym̄ ayen).' 749

With that anon) clarionas be ganne 750
To take hir chere mor comfortably,
Notwithstondyng' she was bothe pale and wanne,

---

[1] MS. *the sothe.*   [2] MS. *And for.*

And to hir ma[y]de she seid fuH soberly,   753
'love MyrabeH, I thank yow hertely,
ffor of myꝺ payne now I haue some respite,
And if I leue I shaH it yow wele aquyte.'   756

Now late vs leue apart clarionas,   757
And to Generydes turne we ageyꝺ,   Generydes, on
Whiche for hir sake stonditħ in hevy case,   his part,
As fuH of thougħt as he mygħt be certayꝺ;   760
Out of the cowrt he went for very peyꝺ,
Streigħt to his logging¹ hastely he hym spedd,
Whanne he came ther he leyde hym̄ onꝺ his bedd. 763

His maister had merveH what it ded mene   764   told his master
So sodenly to see hym̄ in that case,   of his case.
AH distemperyd and out of colour' clene,
he mused sore what maner a thing it was;   767
And whanne that he mygħt gete a metely space,
Rigħt thus he seid to Generydes,¹
'I prae yow, ser, Telle me your' dissese.'   770

'Mayster,' quod he, 'aH that lythe in my hert,   771
What euer it be, to yow I wolle not layꝺ
Why and wherefore I suffer aH this smert,²
Clarionas she causith it certayꝺ,   774
ffor hir only I suffer aH this payne,
And for to sey the very certaynte,
I wote not why she shuld do this to me.'   777

'Ye wote what, ser, after myꝺ avise,   778   Natanell pro-
Be mery and that is my counceH,   mises to speak
In this mater I shaH do yow seruice,   with Clarionas.
And peraventur' sumwhat it shaH prevaile;   781
To morow I shaH be ther withoute faile,
And speke witħ hir' as touching this mater',
And what she seith ye shaH haue pleyne answer'.' 784

¹ MS. _Geroerydes._   ² MS. _this certeyn smert._

'Maister,' quod he, 'I thank you hartely,   785
To yow only is all my very trost,
And what ye think that I shall do trewly,
In this mater' demeane me as ye list ;   788
hough I shall spede fayne wold I that I wist.'
'Wele, ser,' quod he, 'I canne noo ferther saye,
To my power I shall do what I may.'   791

With that he partid fro Generydes,   792

Next day he goes
to court and sees
Mirabell,

And on the morow, whanne he hadde tyme and space,
Onto the court he went withouten lese,
Therfor to speke with fayre clarionas.   795
Whanne he¹ was come ther as she was,

who asks after
Generydes.

Myrabell came and this to hym ganne seye,
'Where is,' quod she, 'your' maister, I yow prae?'   798

'He is at his
lodging full ill
at ease

'Att his loggyng¹, foll ill att ease,' quod he,   799
'And so a be a sithe afore yester day ;
What hym aylith I woote noo thing¹ parde,
His comfort and his chere is all awaye,
Butt after myn entent this dare I saye,   802
All this is grow, to tell the mater clere,

since he was last
here.'

Sithe he now last was with my lady here.'   805

Mirabell per-
ceived his
meaning,

Whan Mirabell perseivid what he ment,   806
And what desire he hadde thanne was she fayn,

and thought
all went well.

All this goth wele, thought she, to myn entent.
'Wele, ser,' she saide, 'to yow I will be playn ;   809
Sithe your' maister was here, I will nott layne,
My lady hath be seke bothe day and nyght,

[leaf 5]

ffor she hadd neuer rest I yow be hight.   812

Yet not for thy, if ye haue ought to saye,   813
ffor your maister be his comaund[e]ment,
Goo forth anon with owt more delaye,

¹ MS. she.

And telle hir aH the trougth of your' entent,   816
To speke with yow she wilbe wele content.'
So furth withaH, after his purpose was,
Streight fourth he goth on) to Clarionas.   819

Natanell sought the princess,

'Madame,' quod he, ' my lord Generydes   820
To you hym) recomaundith for certayne,
A wofuH man), clene owt of hartes ease,
And for to telle yow aH the mater playn),   823
If it please yow ye may respite his payn),
Of your' goodnesse to graunt hym) that licence,
That he may come on) to your' nobiH presence.'   826

and told her of Generydes,

who begged that he might come into her presence.

Whenne she had herd these wordes euerydele,   827
' Come nere,' she said, ' Mirabell, I you p[r]aye.'
' Madame,' quod she, ' I vnderstonde hym) wele ;
As me semyth with your' wurchippe ye may   830
Send me for hym and here what he wiH saye,
his maister here right sone for hym) wiH goo.'
' I am content,' quod she, ' that it be so.'   833

Mirabell advises that he should be sent for,

MyrabeH came and toke hym owt Aside ;   834
' Do after me,' quod she, ' as in this case :
Att this wyndow my lady shaH abide,
ffor thorough owt the gardeyn) he shaH pace,   837
And ther he shaH haue good leyser and space,
To saye what that hym) list in secrete wise ;
Now goo furth for this is myn) avise.'   840

into the garden.

Furth on) his way departith NataneH   841
To his maister, and founde hym) passeng¹ sadde :
'What tidynges now,' quod he, ' wiH it be wele ?'
' Right wele,' quod he, ' be ye noo thyng¹ adred :   844
Whanne ye knowe aH I wote ye wiH be glad,
As for the first, now take this of me aloon,¹
She wiH that ye come speke with her anon).'   847

¹ *aloon* added in another hand.

Who was glad
now but Ge-
nerydes?

Now who was gladde, and who was weℓℓ apayde,   848
And endly mery but Generydes,
Remembryng⸍ what Nataneℓℓ had seid?
So furtℏ he gotℏ, and neue*r* wold he sese,   851
Into the courte in myddes of the prese,

He went to the
garden to
Clarionas,

And so furtℏ on vn to Clarionas,
In the gardeyn⸍ where apoynted was.   854

Whañ he hyr saw, he fayled countena*u*nce,   855
Where witℏ suerly he was not wele apayed ;
And in like wise, to sey yow in substance,
On here behalf she was somwhat dismayde ;   858

and told her

Yet atte last rigℏt thus to hir⸍ he saide,
'Madame,' q*u*od he, ' be cause I hadde licence,
I am more bold to come to your⸍ presence :   861

And for to sey yow myñ entent I wis,   862
As for my self this is the mater playn⸍,
ffor I must suerly teℓℓ vs att [1] it is ;

of his pain of
heart for her
sake.

My hert is oue*r*come witℏ very payn⸍   865
Aℓℓ for your⸍ sake, and so hath beñ certeyñ
Sithe I was here oñ massage sekerly.'
' hoo so ?' q*u*od she,[2] 'I haue grete wounder why.   868

What [3] cause haue ye to putte me in this witte ?   869

The truth was
soon known on
both sides

As for my part I do no thyng⸍ nee sey,
I rede putte s*u*che thougthes in respite ;
Where I haue not offendid be this day,   872
Wherby ye shuld be hurt by eny way :
Wherefore,' q*u*od she, ' in ernest and in game,
To putte in me the defaute ye are to blame.'   875

' Trewly, Madame,' thenne seid Generydes,   876
' Of me ye ougℏt no magry to purchase,
And for to con⸍ yow thanke for my dissese,

---

[1] So MS. ; perhaps for *telle what*, or *telle all as.*
[2] MS. *he.*   [3] MS. *That.*

Now trewly that were a strange case.   879
Yet be the meane of fauo*ur* and of grace
Ye may me help*e* aƚƚ only and no mo,
O trewtħ it were your' wurchipp*e* so to do.'   882

Quo*d* she ageyñ, 'if it were for to blame,   883   *though after*
My wurchippe were amendes for to make ;   *some bashfulness*
And in like wise ye augħt to do the same,   *on Clarionas's*
                                                                  part,
If ther were eny suche that for your sake   886
had so sufferyd payn or heuynesse had tak ;
Peravento*ur* I mygħt be on) of thoo,
What will ye sey,' q*uo*d she, 'and it be so ?'   889

'Madame,' q*uo*d he, 'I here yow speke rigħt wele, 890
ffuƚƚ fayne, god woote, I wold that it wer' soo.'
'Trewly,' q*uo*d she, 'it is thus eu*er*ydele,
I yow ensure, I may not goo ther' fro ;   893
But my wurchipp*e* may not avowe it soo.
This is the very troutħ withoute feyning,
ffor loue wiƚƚ haue his course for eny thing'.'   896

Wheŋ Myrabeƚƚ had hard aƚƚ this array,   897
'After this werr',' q*uo*d she, 'god send vs pece :
I canne wiƚƚ think it wiƚƚ not lest alway.'
'Now god defende it,' q*uo*d Generydes ;   900
'I must depart,' q*uo*d she, 'withoutyŋ lese,
As for A tyme your' pleasur' for to spare,
Of eviƚƚ speche it is good to be ware.'   903

And shortly for to say you as it was,   904
A fuƚƚ [a]corde was made betwix theŋ twayŋ :
he gaue a ryng' oŋ to Clarionas,
And she toke hyŋ Another for certeyŋ ;   907   *and they ex-*
With trew promys eyther for ioye or payŋ,   *changed rings.*
In stedefast wise ther hertys to ensure,
Neuer[1] to chaunge but alway [to] endure.   910

                    [1] MS. *Nouer.*

And by that tyme fer passid was the day,   911
Mirabell seyd, 'it is hye tyme for to goo.'
Thanne wist he wele ther was noñ other waye,

[leaf 5, back] he must departe wheder he will or noo :   914
he toke his leue, wherewith he was full woo ;
And as for hir she was nott wele contente,
Yet not for thy she kist hym or she went.   917

Full of[te] tymes ther[1] were betwix hem[2] twayne, 918
They often meet in secret. Dayes apoynted to mete in secrete wise :
Notwithstondyng I say yow for certeyn,
To hir wurchippe was thought noo preiudice,   921
Butt only to owe hir his seruice,
As feythfully as cowde be thought or ment,
Ther was noñ other thyng in ther entent.   924

So furth he goth full streyte in to the halle,   925
To do seruice hym thought it for the best ;
And for to sey yow soth among them All,
In court there was none like Generydes, Thorough owt the court he was the goodliest, 928
In his demeaning the most Ientilest,
And with a spere to renne in warre or pece,
Ther was noñ like oñ to Generides.   931

Havkyng, hunteng, he cowd good skill ther oñ ; 932
And what that eny Ientilman shuld do,
ffor very trougth in all the courte[3] was noñ,
Knyght or squyer, so wele willyng ther to : 935
and all loved him save Malichias. Thorough owt the courte[3] he hadde the love also
Of euery creatur, bothe more and lesse,
Saue of A knyght callid ser Malichias.   938

As [for] a tyme leue we Generydes,   939
His father's (the king of India's) Steward And late vs now speke of the kyng of ynd,
And of his Stiward whiche wold neuer sese,

---

[1] MS. *they*.   [2] MS. *hym*.   [3] MS. *contre*.

But of malice compasing' in his mynd   942
Aᴴ maner weyes som treson[1] for to fynd ;
Witᴴ aᴴ the helpe that he cowde gete certeyɴ),
ffor to distroye his lord and souereyɴ).   945   plotted against
                                                               his lord,

And to perfourme aᴴ that he hadde take in hand, 946
This fals Stiward he had gaderid people grete,   and gathered an
                                                               army
To the nowmber' of iiij or v thousand,
Of meñ of warre the best that he cowd gete ;   949
And in A busshment fuᴴ sone he had themɴ) sett
Nyhand the towɴ), his tresoɴ) to be gynne,
And be that meane the cite for to wynne.   952   to win the city,

Off his tresone the quene knowe wele also,   953   The queen knew
                                                           the treason.
It to perfourme she did aᴴ hir entent,
And of hir counceᴴ ther were lordes[2] moo,
And certeyɴ) of themɴ) were of hir' dissente :   956
Of aᴴ this werk the kyng' was innocent,
And of ther falsed no thing' perseyuyd,
The more pite he shuld be so disseyued.   959

And shortly to procede whañ this was do,   960
There were iij lordes came oñ to the kyng',
Desireng' hymɴ) on huntyng' for to goo,
ffuᴴ ontrewly ther witᴴ ymagenyng' ;   963
To ther desire the kyng' was welewillyng',   While the king
                                                           was hunting with
So fourth oɴ) huntyng' he rode certeynly,   three lords
The iij lordes witᴴ hymɴ) in companye,   966

And ij Squyers, myɴ) Auctour tellith me ;   967
And while he was most besy in his game,
This fals Stiward had gotenɴ) the Citee,   the Steward took
                                                           the city
The whiche was callid pareyntyɴ) be name,   970
And made hymɴ) self proclamed in the same   and proclaimed
Aᴴ openly bothe kyng' and souereyɴ),   himself king.
Ther was no maɴ) that durst saye ther ageyɴ).   973

            [1] MS. *tresom.*   [2] MS. *londes.*

The king heard
thereof from a
forester,

Þe kyng⋅ hym̄ self knowe noo thyng⋅ of this case, 974
Till atte last a forster came rideng⋅ ;
And, wete ye wele, so sorowfull he was,
That he onnethe myght speke to the kyng⋅, 977
And ther he told hym euery maner thyng⋅,
Of his Stiward and of his fals treasone,
And what people he hadde withynne the town. 980

'I must,' quod he, 'telle yow myn avise and entent ;
The quene is cause of this on happy case,

and that the
three lords were
traitors also.

ffor these iij lordes ar⋅ of hir Assent,
That are Abideng⋅ with you in the chase ; 984
And whanne the kyng⋅ perseyuyd hough it was,
All his huntyng⋅ was don and his besynesse,
An hevy mañ [he was] and coumfortles. 987

In this musyng⋅ he rideth furth a pase, 988
The iij lordes they mette hym on the waye :
'Traytours,' quod he, 'god geve yow euyll grace
ffor your⋅ seruice that ye haue don to me, 991
So vntrewly your⋅ prince for to be traye,
Whiche neuer hurt nor harme on to yow ment,
I trost to god ye shall it sore repent.' 994

All his wordes they sett Att litill price, 995
ffor whye they drede hym not the soth to saye :
And to the kyng⋅ [they seyd] right in this wise,
'Take it in gre the fortune of this day.' 998
And whanne he saw ther was non other way,

He drew his
sword and slew
one.

he drow his swerd And smote on of them so,
And[1] from the grownde he myght noo ferther goo, 1001

Butt felle down̄ dede then in continent. 1002

The others fled,

his felawes fledde as fast as euer they myght ;
The kyng⋅ sawe that, and after them he went,

[1] ? *That*.

And ouer toke them) long or it was nygħt. 1005
So ferthermore to saye yow the very rigħt,
he slew them) bothe And sayde, ' traytours erante,
Of your falshed ye shaⱧ yow neuer avaunte.' 1008

but the king
overtook

and slew them
too.

And vppon) this he turned bak ageyn) 1009
To his squyers, whiche were rigħt ferre behynd,
And in this wise he dede to them) complayn) :
' I have,' quod he, ' founde yow bothe trew and kynde,
Now lak I good where witħ I shuld yow fynd,
And for to coumfort me now in my nede,
I canne noo more but Ihesu be your' spede.' 1015

Whenne his squyers had hard hym) thus complayn), [leaf 6]
They answerd hym ayen) in goodly wise ;
' Ser, think you not but we shaⱧ do our' payn)
To coumfort yow, and do yow suche seruice, 1019
As our' connyng' And Powre may suffice,
And thougħ your' hart be now noo thing' in rest,
With goddes grace AⱧ shalbe for your' best.' 1022

The kyng was plesid wele witħ ther coumfort, 1023
And as hym) thougħt he prayed them) for to saye
To what contre it were best to resorte,
That for hym self he mygħt some what purvaye. 1026
One of them) seyde, ' lo yender lygħt the waye ;
Streygħt to the Reme of Trace it wiⱧ yow bryng',
Wherein dwellytħ a prince, A¹ nobyⱧ kyng'.' 1029

With his two
squires
he took his way
to Thrace,

Toward that land he toke the waye fuⱧ rigħt, 1030
Whiche was callid a plentevous contre ;
Whanne he came ther, as fast as euer he² mygħt
To ṣe the kyng' he went in certayn[t]e, 1033
In humble³ wise, besechyng' hym) that he
Migħt do hym) seruice witħ his squyers twayne,
In like wise as his pleasur' wold ordeyne. 1036

¹ MS. a A.   ² MS. she.   ³ MS. humbly.
GENERYDES.   3

The kyng⟨ was wele contente of his comyng⟨,   1037

And of seruice he seid he shuld not fayle ;
What he shuld do he told hym euery thing⟨,
That myght only to his wurchippe prevaile ;   1040
And so alway, after thought and travaile,
God send rest and coumfort, be ye sure,
To euery wele disposid creature.   1043

Thus in that contre abideth still alway   1044
The kyng⟨ of ynd, vnknowen) in euery wise,
With his ij squyers, a wayteng⟨ day be day
hym) for to serue as they made ther promys ;   1047
And so this prince contynued in seruice,
Right well be trost and cherishid with the kyng⟨,
ffor he cowde please hym) in euery thing⟨.   1050

All that he dede was done so wittely,   1051
his demeanyng⟨ was suche thorough owt the place,
That euery man) hym) preysid by and by,
And he so wele stode in the kyngges grace,   1054
That he hym) gaue, withynne a litill space,

Of all his lande the Stiwar[d]shepe to holde,
And full power to rewle it as he wold.   1057

When he dede as wele as cowde be thought,   1058
Onto the kynggez honour⟩ in certayne,
Iustice was kept like wise as it owt,
Ther was noman) be resan) myght complayne ;   1061
And for he shuld his charge wele susteyn),

The kyng hym) gaue clerly an) Erlys lande,
The whiche but late was com in to his hand.   1064

Now of this mater⟩ a while let vs sese   1065
As for a tyme, And speke of quene sereyne,
That was moder on to Generydes,

And hougħ that she hadde herd the tidenggez playɲ,
hougħ ontrewly his fader be a trayɲ
Of his lordes made after ther entente,
he was putte owt of his land by ther Assent.   1071

Sereyne heard how the king of India had been put out of his land.

Off hyɲ and of there sonne Generydes   1072
Was vtterly her mend and aH here thought;
And trewly to leue in hartes ease,
That cowde she nougħt tiH that she hadde hym sougħt;
Of her estate no pleasure she ne rougħt,
Saue only for to knowe the certeynte
Of auferius the kyng where he shuld be.   1078

And fourtħ with aH she ganne aɲ erle to calle,   1079
The whiche in sothe hadde widded hir Cosyɲ,
Rigħt as the writeng' seytħ in especiaH,
A fayre lady and nexst of AH hir kynne;   1082
The Erle to truste was noo daunger in,
ffor he was ware and wise I yow ensure,
And therwith trew as eny creature.   1085

and sent for an Earl

She told hyɲ AH the grounde of the mater   1086
In euery thing', and how it was be faH,
Of auferius and of hir sonne in fere,
And hougħ the kyng betrayed was withaH,   1089
' Wherefore my purpose is in especiaH
To take oɲ me the labour' and the payɲ,
Where euer he were to fynd hyɲ in certeyɲ.'   1092

Theɲ¹ to the Erle she seid in this maner: 1093
' Ye shaH here haue the rewle and gouernaunce
Of this contre, with aH my full powre;
My meɲ shaH be vnder your' obeiseaunce,
And hougħ it be be disteyne or chaunce,   1096
What euer falle, if I come not Ayeɲ,
Ye² shaH be here botħ lord And souerayɲ.'   1099

to take the rule of the country while she went in search of Auferius and Generydes.

¹ MS. *When*.   ² MS. *he*.

'Madame,' he seid, 'to gouerne this contre 1100
It is noo liteH thing' to take in hand;
ffor yow it is moche bettyr thanne for me;
Yet neuer the lese, sithe I vnderstonde 1103
Your' purpose is to depart owt of the land,
I wolle fulfille your' pleasur' in this case,
And trewly as I canne be goddes grace.' 1106

Queen Sereyne set off,

Now Gothe quene Sereyn) fourth on) hir Iurnaye, 1107
And in hir company she hadde a knygĥt,
A trosty man), and othe[r] squyers twaynne,
With but few moo ther hors for to digĥt; 1110

came to India

So to the Reme of ynd they went fuH rigĥt,
And sone vppon) ther labour' and traveH

to Parentine,

To parentyne she came witĥ owt fayle, 1113

A towne whiche is rehersid here by fore. 1114
Anon) withaH was purveyd a logging

[leaf 6, back]

ffor this lady; and, for to say yow more,

and lodged with the faithful forester,

hire oste was sumtyme dwellyng with the kyng, 1117
The same forster that brought to hym) tidengge,
Of his Stiward and of his fals treson),
As he rode in the forest vppe and down). 1120

As for a nygĥt ther toke she hir' loggyng, 1121
And made on) calle the good man) of the place,
'Good ser,' quod she, 'telle me where is the kyng;
I haue grete nede,' quod she, 'on) to his grace. 1124
Sumtyme a lady weH att ease I was,
And now be force,' quod she, 'siche is my chaunce,
I am putte ow[t] of myn) enheritaunce.' 1127

'Madame,' quod he, 'here is noo remedy: 1128
The kyng suerly is putte owt of his rigĥt
By grete tresone, I saye yow certenly,

By his Stiward and by the quenys myght, 1131
Whiche I may soore repent bothe day and nyght;
ffor now A dayis I lese all that I wanne,
Where here before I was[1] a threfty man. 1134

Wherfor to hym I will, this is noo naye, 1135   whom she
Where euer he be, I say yow certaynly.'   prevailed upon
Thanne sayd the quene, 'good ser, I yow pray,
That ye will come with me in companye; 1138   to come in search
hym for to fynd I purpose vtterly,   of the king.
And I shall paye your costez euery dele.'
Quod he, 'madame, I gre me wele 1141

In your presence to travell day by day.' 1142
So on the morow departed quene Sereyne,   On the morrow
As erly as she cowde on hir Iurnay,   they departed
With hir to goo the forster was right fayn. 1145
So many dayes she laboryd certayn,
That of the Reame of Trace she had a sight,   for Thrace,
And thederward they toke the wey full right. 1148

When they came ther the[y] sawe a faire cite, 1149   and came to
As full a pepill as it cowde suffice,   a fair city
The fayre Reuer grete pleasur for to see,
With shippez grete of dyuerce merchaundise, 1152
All goodly thing that eny cowde wele devise;
And as the Story makith remembraunce,   of which Auferius
kyng Auferius had ther the gouernaunce. 1155   was governor.

And ther he was purposing to Abyde, 1156
As for A tyme for materys for the kyng:
The quene Sereyn was be the Ryuers side   The queen lodged
Right Wele loggid, and whan she hadde tideng 1159   by the river side.
A[nd] trew knowlage of Auferius the kyng,
hough he but late was come to the Citee,
God wote full wele therof apayed was she. 1162

    [1] MS. wis.

For hir' disporte she gotħ to take the Ayre,   1163
And to the Reue*re*s side she ganne hir dresse;

Ther was a brygge fuħ strongly made and fayre,
And ther she sawe, myɳ Aucto*ur* dotħ witnesse, 1166
iij lavenders ded aħ ther besynesse
A sherte to wassħ; thanne seid she to them) iij,
'What do ye here, fayre susters myɳ?' q*u*od she.

Q*u*od oɳ of them), 'that were good to be knowe, 1170
It is a wonder wark withouteɳ dougħt;
We wassh a shirte, and eu*er* shaħ I trow,

ffor this ij yere we haue beɳ it abougħt,   1173
And yet we cannot gete the spotte[s] owt,
Wherefore they calle vs noo good lauenders,
And we haue vsid it thus many yerez.'   1176

'Shewe me y*e* shirte,' thanne seid the quene Sereyɳ,
'And I shaħ se what I shaħ do ther to:
Whanne I haue do, ye shaħ haue it ageyɳ,
And do ther witħ what ye list to do.'   1180
She toke the Shirte withoute wordes moo,

And wesht it onys and ryneshed it so clene,
That afterward was noo spotte oɳ it seeɳ.   1183

Wheɳ she had doɳ, she toke it them) ageyɳ,   1184
Or tyme that she departed fro the place;

To hir logging went the quene Sereyɳ,
The lavenders hadde wonder of that case,   1187
They mused sore and mervelid how it was:
And home they went the womeɳ eu*er*choɳ,
Whanne it was drye they bare it fourtħ anoɳ.   1190

To auferius the kyng where as he laye,   1191
In a casteħ fuħ goodly to behold;
And whanne he sawe his shirt in that aray,

¹ MS. *Araye*.

Withoute spotte, he beganne to be cold,   1194   who called to
To thynk hough that a good old man) hym) told,   mind what the
Bothe of [the] shirte and other thingez aH,   old man had
Whiche sith that tyme fuH trewly hath be faH.   1197   told him.

The same forster that came with quene Sereyn),   1198   The forester
To the castiH he toke the way fuH right,   who came with
To se his lord, god wote, he was fuH fayn).   the queen went
Whanne he came ther of hym) he hadde a sight,   1201   to the castle
And spake to hym) as sone as euer he myght ;
The kyng hym) knew, wherof he was fuH glad,
Not withstondeng he fond hym) passyng sadde.   1204   and found the
                                                         king sad.

' Ser, if it please your' lordshippe,' thanne quod he,   'Sir,' said he,
' I yow beseche teH me your heuynesse :   'why is this
To wete yow in this plight it grevith me,   heaviness ? '
ffor if I myght I wold it fayne redresse ;   1208
And oftentymes it hath be sene expresse,
In grete materys, withouten) eny fayle,
A sympiH mannys counceH may prevayle.'   1211

To hym) Ayen) seid Auferius the kyng ;   1212   The king
' I knowe your' trowth, and soo hath doon) Alway,
And for to sey yow [sothe] withoute feyneng',
AH this is come to me sithe yester day,   1215
And hough and in what wise I shaH yow saye :'
And so fourth he told' of quene Sereyn),   told him of queen
And hough a child was gote betwix them) twayne, 1218 Sereyn,
                                                       [leaf 7]

And of his shert where on) hir[1] terys felle,   1219   and of her tears
That non) shuld wassh them) owt saue only she :   on his shirt which
' Now is it clene, whiche lekith me fuH ille,   none but herself
ffor thus I thynk It canne non) other be ;   1222   could wash out.
But she is dede in very certente.'   'But she is dead.'
' Nay,' quod he, ' ser, I trow it be not soo,   'Nay, Sir,
ye shaH here better tydengez or ye goo.   1225

        [1] MS. his.   But see ll. 162, 193.

I saw but late vppon) the Ryueres side   1226
One wassh a shert, I wote not whose it is.'
Whanne he[1] hard that he wold not long' abide
But askid more, 'now telle me who did this,'   1229
Quod auferius, 'so haue ye Ioye and blysse.'
'A fayre lady,' quod he, 'I yow ensure,
And for to chese a goodly creature.   1232

I came with hir owt of the Reme of ynd,   1233
And atte myn) howse ther toke she[2] hir loggyng';
She askid me where that she shuld yow fynde,
And I told hir I hadd no knowlachyng';   1236
So fourth she went and left all other thing',
At a venture your' welefare for to see,
And so came I with hir to this citee.'   1239

'Now, for my loue, helpe that I may hir see   1240
In eny wise,' quod Auferius the kyng;
'ffor I canne think right wele that it is she,
Whom) that I loue aboue all other thing'.'   1243
The forster seid, 'ser, on) to hir loggyng,
When) euer it please yow, I shall be your' gyde;
ffor she is here by vppon) the Ryuerez side.'   1246

In this mater ther was no more to saye,   1247
No lenger avise nor lenger abyding,

Butt furth he rideth vppon) his hakeney,
Vppon) the Reuerys side to hir logging':   1250
And whanne she had knowlache of his comyng',
Remembryng' hough that she shuld hym) see,
Wete ye right wele a glad woman) was she.   1253

When) he was come and knewe that it was she, 1254
ffor very glad he wist not what to saye;

Whenne she hym) sawe it wold non) other be,

[1] MS. *she*.   [2] MS. *che*.

Butt furth with all in swounyng⸱ ther she[1] lay. 1257   *she fell down in a swoon.*
As sone as he hir sawe in that arraye,
God wote he was an) hevy man) therfore,
And ther with [all] abisshid more and more. 1260

Yet Atte last full Ientilly he went, 1261
And toke hir in his armys for sertayn),
hir to commfort he did all his intent ;
With that she came vnto hir self ageyn). 1264
Thanne was ther ioye betwix them) twayn),   *Then was there joy betwixt them.*
ffor to telle yow all it were a wounder,
And ofte they kist or they wold part A sonder. 1267

Thanne was ther not ferre owt of the Citee 1268   *Not far from the city was a fair castle.*
A fayre castell, and thederward he went
Owt of the Citee, not[2] ferre past ij myle or iij,
That was his owen) att his comaundment. 1271
Whanne [he] came ther for moche people he sent,   *He sends for*
The whiche held of his lordshippe and fraunchesse,
That *th*ei shuld come to hym) in eny wise. 1274

And so they dede meche people in certayn) ; ⸀ 1275
Whanne they were come he told them) all the case,
Desireng⸱ them) to goo for quene Sereyne   *Sereyne thither,*
To the Citee, and bryng hir⸱ to this place ; 1278
ffor he purposith sone, with goddes grace,
In as short tyme as he cowde wele devise,
hir for to wedde in honorabill wise. 1281   *that he might marry her.*

To this castell they came with quene Sereyn), 1282
Right wele a compayned in eu*er*y wise,
Of hir comyng⸱ the peopill were full fayn),
And offeryd hir right lowly ther se*r*uice ; 1285
Atte hir pleasur⸱ and atte hir owyn devise,
In that castell she tared for to rest,
Onto the tyme they purvayed for the fest. 1288

[1] MS. *se*.   [2] MS. *nor*.

In this meane while, the kynges massenger   1289
To Auferius he came withoute fey[n]ing^t.
Curlus he hight and seid in this maner :
'My lord,' quod he, 'ye must come to the kyng^t   1292
In all the hast, and make noo taryng^t ;
I drede me sore he may not long endure,
ffor he is passyng seke I yow ensure.'   1295

When Auferius the kyng herd that he saide,   1296
All sodenly he waxhid bothe pale and wanne ;
ffurth on his waye to ride he hym purvayde
Vnto the kyng As fast as euer he canne,   1299
And wete ye will he was an hevy man :
ffor by the tyme he came vnto that place,

The kyng was dede, whiche was a hevy case.   1302

For hym was made grete ordenaunce I yow ensure ;
The peopill wept, ther hertys were full sore,
And for to purvaye for his sepulture
They besyed them echon, bothe lesse and more,   1306
Thanne was ther made an ordenaunce therfore,
ffull rially with all maner seruice ;
As fell to his estate in euery wise.   1309

W[i]thynne a while after all this was do,   1310
A non ther was callid a parlement,
By Auferius and other lordis moo,
ffully concludid All by on Assent,   1313

Be cause the kyng left non of his disente,
Nor of his blode of that land to be kyng^t,
To chese them on And lefe all other thing^t.   1316

And whanne they were Assemelyd euerychone,   1317
And them Avised them wele in euery thing^t ;
They were fully Accordid all in one,

That Auferius suerly shuld be ther kyng¹ :   1320   chose Auferius
he was to them) so trew And so loving,   to succeed him.
And so rightwise in euery Iugement,   [leaf 7, back]
That so able was now to ther entent.   1323

And shortly to procede in this mater,   1324
They chase hym) kyng¹ by voice of the land,
The lordes and the Ientilles aH in feere,
To hym) dede homage as I vnderstonde,   1327
With fuH promes ther feithes in his hand,
Atte aH seasones to hym) to owe ther seruice,
And hym) obeyed in eny maner wise.   1330

Whanne this was do he sent for quene Sereyne,   1331
And in as goodly hast as it myght be,
The mariage was made be twix them) twayn),   The marriage
With grete honour and grete solempnite,   1334 was made
So grete a gaderyng¹ was neuer in that contre ;   Queen Sereyne,
ffor to that fest he bedde his lordes euerychone,
Theder thei came and ladys many on).   1337

And whanne the fest was aH to geder don),   1338
Not long after withynne a liteH space,
The quene Sereyne was with child fuH sone
And whanne tyme came, as god wiH geve hir grace,   and in due
She bare a sonne, a threfte child he was ;   time she bare a
And whanne that he was growe to mannys age,   son,
he was callid IsmaeH the Savage :   1344 Ismael the
                                       Savage.

For he was wild in aH his demening¹,   1345
Vnto the tyme he drew to more sadnesse,
Thanne afterward he was withoute feyning¹
A nobyH knyght, the story doth witnesse :   1348
Now late vs thenne speke of Generydes,   Now let us
What payn) he hadde for fayre clarionas,   speak of
By grete envy of cursid malichias.   1351 Generydes.

One morning he went to speak with his lady.

In a mornyng⸱ arose Generydes,   1352
To his lady he toke the way fuꝉ rigꝏt,
To speke witꝫ hir as for his hartys ease ;
This Malichias of hym⸱ he had a sigꝏt,   1355
And after hym⸱, as fast as euer he mygꝏt,
ffuꝉ secretly he gotꝫ hym⸱ to aspye,
hym⸱ for to do sum shame and velanye.   1358

Malichias hid in a tree to hear what they said,

And to perfourme aꝉ his purpose in dede,   1359
Vppe in a tree he stode fuꝉ secretly,
That what they seid therof he toke good heede,

and told the Sultan all that he could say to

And to the Sowdon⸱ told it by and by :   1362
And where as he dede noo thyng⸱ ellys trewly,
But spake witꝫ hir to telle hir꞉ his entente,
he hym⸱ reportid wers thanne euer he ment,   1365

her dishonour.

To hir dishonour aꝉ that he cowde say.   1366

The Sultan sware they should die,

Whanne the Sowdon⸱ had knowlage of this case,
he sware his othe ther was non⸱ other waye,
Butt bothe they shuld be dede be goddes grace.   1369
To hym⸱ anon⸱ thanne sayde Malichias,
‘ Of your꞉ dougꝏter ye may not avenge yow soo,
But as for hym⸱ ye wote what is to do.’   1372

Yet in his wraugth this thougꝏt he euer among⸱,   1373

but could not kill Generydes for fear of the people.

If he shuld avenge hym⸱ sodenly,
Aꝉ his pepiꝉ wold say he did hym⸱ wrong⸱,
Withoute Iustice to cause hym⸱ so to dye ;   1376
And to eschew the Rumber and the crye,
his purpose thanne he chaungyd aꝉ in feere :
And Malichias was wrotꝫ in his maner,   1379

And thougꝏt he was mystr[est]ed vtterly,   1380
Be cause the Sowdon⸱ dede not as he ment ;
ffor he was fayn⸱ to think that he shuld dye,

Butt for aƚƚ he myst of his entent,   1383   Malichias did not leave his malice
Yet in his malice he was so fervent
he wold not leve, butt stille alway opece[1]
Dede aƚƚ that he cowde to hurt Generydes.   1386   against Generydes.

So oꝛ) a tyme fuƚƚ streyght he toke the waye   1387
To the Sowdoꝛ), and seid in this mane*r* ;
'My lord,' q*uo*d he, 'ye leve not that I saye,
And if it please yow my counceƚƚ for to here,   1390
Ye shaƚƚ haue knowlache of this mater clere.'
'Wele thanne,' q*uo*d he, 'if I may fynd it soo,
Ye shaƚƚ sone wete what I shaƚƚ do therto.'   1393

'In a mornyng', if it please yow to rise,'   1394   He took the Sultan one morning
Q*uo*d Malichias, 'I canne say yow nomore,
But[2] ye shaƚƚ se you*r* self in eue*r*y wise
The very trougth, as I haue seid before ;   1397
And wete ye wiƚƚ it grevith me fuƚƚ soore,
That ye shuld me mystrest by eny waye,
I wold not that for more thanne I wold saye.'   1400

The[3] Sowdoꝛ) sayde, 'as towchyng this mater,   1401
I wolle gladly be after you*r* avise.'
Soo oꝛ) a day the wedder was fuƚƚ clere,
In a mornyng' the Sowdoꝛ) ganne to rise,   1404
As erly as he cowde in eny wise ;
ffurth on he goth, and with hyꝛ) Malichias,
Streight to the chaunbo*ur* of Clarionas.   1407   to the chamber of Clarionas,

Save Malichias with hyꝛ) ther was noo moo,   1408
Atte A wyndow they stode hyꝛ) to Aspye.   where they watched the lovers from a window.
Generydes, as he was wont to do,
ffuƚƚ sone after he came fuƚƚ secretly,   1411
As oft tyme As he came, yet trewly
he mystrestid neue*r* erthely maꝛ) be fore,   Generydes was sad
Yet As he Stode he Seighed wonder soore.   1414

---

[1] MS. *opoce*. Perhaps we should read *alway stille opece*.
[2] MS. *Be*.   [3] MS. *She*.

To hym anoñ thanne seid Clarionas,   1415
' Ye seigħ gretly, I prae yow telle me why.'
' Madame,' quod he, ' for certayn it was,

for a dream he
had dreamt of
Malichias.

This nygħt I hadde a wonder dreme trewly   1418
Of Malichias ; noo mo but[1] he And I
Were in A place, this is the certeyn[te],
And of my clothez ther he robbid me.   1421

I drew my swerd to reskewe hym ageyn,   1422
Butt in that case I mygħt not haue my wiħ,

[leaf 8]

The Sowdon came and cast me downe, I wene,
In a depe pitte, whiche grevid me fuħ iħ :   1425
With that my swerd owt of myn hand it feħ
On Malichias and gave hym suche a wounde
Vppon the hede that downe he felle to the grownde.

Yet cowde I not eskape owt of the pitte,   1429
ffor aħ the craft that I cowde wele devise ;
Butt atte last, as god wold fortune it,
Ye aħ only, and by your interprise,   1432
Owt of daunger ye causid me to rise.'
To hym anone thanne seid clarionas,
' I am a ferde,' quod she, ' of Malichias ;   1435

Clarionas also
had had a
dream.

For I dremyd that he wold haue me slayn,   1436
Save it lay not in his powere to do,
ffor he purposiħ by some maner trayn,
Whanne he may see a tyme to shew vs woo.'   1439

When they had
spoken

And whanne thei had to geder spokeñ soo,
Supposyng wele that aħ had ben in pece,

the Sultan took
Generydes

The Sowdon came and toke Generydes,   1442

In grete anger rebukyng hym fuħ soore,   1443
And chargid Malichias in aħ the hast
To bynd hym fast, and also ferthermore

[1] MS. be.

That he in prison depe he shuld be cast,   1446
Ther to abide while that his lyff may last ;
Or ellys he shuld by[1] Malichias avise
Be putte to deth in a right shamefull wise.   1449

and ordered him to be put in prison.

For his doughter he sent full hastely,   1450
And in his hete gave hir a grete repreff,
And callid hir, god wote, right shamefully
All other wise thanne he cowde make the preff :   1453
And in his hert it was an vtter greff,
ffor he demyd on hir that she ne sought,[2]
Whiche afterward full gretely hym for thought.   1456

His daughter he called by a shameful name.

Now Generydes goth with Malichias,   1457
his handes bounden as a prisonere,
Streyght to a towre wherein the prison was ;
And hym delyueryd onto Anasore,   1460
A gentill knyght keping the prison ther,
To kepe hym hard and strayte in his office,
Withoute favour in eny maner wise.   1463

Generydes was put in a tower,

under the charge of Anasore,

And for to shew his malys vtterly,   1464
With strong yrons this cursed Malichias
he feteryd hym, and that soo grevously
The blode sprange owt in many dyuerse places ;[3]   1467
And whith an hevy hammer that ther was,
On his leggys so sore he lette hym falle,
Att euery tyme he brake the skynne with all.   1470

and fettered grievously by Malichias.

Thanne Anasar was wrothe in his maner,   1471
And in this wise seid to Malichias,
' Ye do me wrong, sithe I am keper here,
To do that is myn office in this case ;   1474
ffor his offence[4] or how that [euer] it was,
It is agayn all reson in certayne,
To do [to] hym this importabill payn.'   1477

---

[1] MS. *be by.*   [2] So MS. ; perhaps for *that he ne ought.*
[3] So MS. ; perhaps for *place.*   [4] MS. *office.*

For noo prayer yet wold he neuer sece,   1478
But trewely did as he did before :
Longer suffer myght not Generydes,

At length
Generydes smote
him that he died.

Nor nought he wold thow he shuld die¹ therfore, 1481
And with his fist he smote hym wonder soore,
That bothe his eyne owt of his hede ganne falle,
And sodenly he died furth withall.   1484

The keeper
gave out

And whanne the keper sawe that he was dede,   1485
Thanne was he sory for Generydes ;
If it were knowen that he were don to ded,
The Sowdon wold be wroth withouten lese,   1488
Owt of reason that noman cowde hym sese :
Wherefore he founde a meane to his entente,
By there avise that were with hym present.   1491

How² Malichias whanne he came fro the towre,   1492
And don that the Sowdon bad hym do,

that he fell down-
stairs and brake
his neck.

his fete fayled in vnhappy oure,
And down he felle and brake his nek in ij ;   1495
And for to make a preff that it was soo,
They toke hym vppe and layde hym soft and fayr',
Down Atte lowest foote of all the stayre.   1498

Thus were they all accordyd euerychone,   1499
Generydes to quyte all vtterly ;
Among' them all ther was on,

A knight Darell

A knyght that alway was in companye   1502
With anasor, and lovyd hym trewly ;
And as he wold the toder wold the same
In euery thing', and darell was his name.   1505

was chief of the
council in this
matter,

In this mater' he was chef of councell   1506
With anasor to helpe Generydes :
he bad hym goo and in no wise to fayle

¹ MS. did.   ² MS. Now.

To the Sowdoṅ, and telle hyṁ the processe,   1509
And he wold be[1] oṅ of his cheff witnesse.
Thanne anosor' ther as the Sowdoṅ was
ffull sone he went, and told hyṁ all the case.   1512

Yet or [that] he departyd was and gone,   ·1513
ffull streyte he went vnto Generydes,
And of his bandis losed hyṁ anoṅ,
That he somewhat myght be att his hartes ease.   1516
ffor though[2] ther were a noyse among the prese,
Yet wist he wele as for fayre Clarionas,
That he was no thing' gilty in that case.   1519

first having
loosed Generydes.

Furth in his waye goth now the Chastelyṅ,   1520
And to the Sowdoṅ saide in this maner :
'I shall yow telle of a ventur' certeyṅ,
And that a strange, if it please yow to here,   1523
hough Malichias, withynne my office here,
Toke vppoṅ hyṁ as for Generydes
All that ye bad me do withoute lease.   1526

He tells his tale,

And ouer that he dede full trewely,   1527
With strong Irons and feteryd hyṁ full sore,[3]
The blode ranne owt and that full petevously ;
Whanne he had doṅ, to seye yow ferthermore,   1530
Downne of the greses he felle the hede before,
And brake his nek, it myght noṅ other be,
ffor this he died in very certeynte.'   1533

[leaf 8, back]

Whanne the Sowdoṅ hard this, I yow be hight   1534
Ther myght no maṅ be wrother thanne was he,
'What, serys !' he seith, 'this goth not All a right :
Thow Chastelyṅ, in what wise may this be ?   1537
All this is done but for a sotilte,
To hide your' falshede vnder a coverture,
But he shall dye to morow be ye sure.'   1540

and the Sultan
was wroth and
suspicious.

[1] MS. *he*.   [2] MS. *thought*.   [3] MS *fast*.
GENERYDES.   4

To hym anon answered the Chastelyn ;   1541
' Ser, if it please your lordshepe for to here,
ffor your wurchippe yow most your self reteyne,
And take a good avise in this mater,   1544
See that your grounde be very good and clere,
To your entente accordeng to the same,
Or ellys it is but slaunder to your name.'   1547

The more he spak the more he lost his payn ;   1548
Whanne Anasar saw that he went his wey :
The Sowden callid fourth his chaumberleyn,
'Goo,' quod he, ' as fast as euer ye may,   1551

and ordered Malichias to be buried.

And see that Malichias in good arraye
Be caryed thens, ther as his body is,
To the temple in honorabill wise.'   1554

Now goth the chaumberlayn furth on his way,   1555
With all the hoole howse att his comaundment,

His body was found torn to pieces by hounds.

And whanne they came ther as the body lay,
It for to bery after ther entent,   1558
Ther they founde it with hundes alto rent,
Some rede, some blak, and some of dyuerse hude,
Ther cowde no man nownber the multitude.   1561

Eche of them bare a pece away,   1562
Of flessh ne boon ther was no thyng behynd ;
The chammberleyn whanne he sawe that arraye,
he went furth sore musyng in his mynde,   1565
And told the Sowdon as he shuld it fynde ;
In euery thyng thanne was he grevid soore,

The Sultan was more wroth,

And more wrother thanne he was before.   1568

Thanne for his lordes [1] furth with all he sent,   1569
That they [2] shuld come withoute eny fayle :
Whanne they were come anon incontynent,

---

[1] MS. *lordes thanne.*   [2] MS. *he.*

Generydes was brougħt owt of the Iayle,   1572   and sent for
ffuħ sore aferd as it was noo mervaħ ;   Generydes,
And ther he stode before them euerychone,
Rigħt in this wise the Sowdon sayde anon :   1575

'This felaw her, this yong man that ye see,   1576   whom he accused
Generydes,' he saide, ' that is his name ;   before his lords
he was suerly the man that plesid me,
Wenyng¹ to me that he hadde be the same ;   1579
Butte now he hatħ don me an vtter shame,
ffor he hatħ done my dougħter villanye,   of seducing his
And layne be hir I sey yow certenly.   1582   daughter.

I saw hym speke witħ hir in secrete wise,   1583
Wherefore I wote it may non other be ;
And I shaħ wele aquyte hym his seruice,
ffor he shaħ dye therfore, now trostith me ;   1586
That other may ensampyħ take and see,
To be ware how they in suche case
here afterward offende in eny place.'   1589

Witħ that anon answerd Generides :   1590
' My lord,' quod he, 'if ye cause me to dye,   Generydes offered
Ye do me wrong, I take god to my witnesse ;   to prove this
And wele I wote ther is no reasone whye,   1593   false,
ffor in this poynt I am no thyng gilty,
And that I shaħ make good, I yow ensure,
On knygħt or Squyer whiħ my lyff endure.'   1596

Whanne the Sowdon had hard aħ that he seid ; 1597
' Trowist thu to fygħt,' quod he, ' as in this case ?
Nay think it not, thy bost shaħ sone be layde,
ffor thu shalt [dye] to morow withoute grace,   1600
And what that euer be withynne this place,   but the Sultan
That wolle for the entrete in eny wise,   urged his lords
he shaħ not spede I yow promysse.   1603

to condemn him
to death.

Wherefore I wold ye gave your' full assent   1604
Among yow all this processe to fulfille,
Accordeng' plenly to that Iugement.'

All were silent
but Anasore

And ther withall the lordes were ful stille,   1607
And seid noo word neyther good nee ill,
Thanne Atte last the Chastelyn) alone,
like as a knyght spake afore them) euerychone :   1610

'My lordes All,' he seid, 'hough may this be ?   1611
This is a thyng whiche I neuer sawe,
The Sowdon) doth vs wrong, As thinkith me,
To make vs deme a man) withoute lawe ;   1614
And for my part, for favour or for awe,
I shall neuer assent to this mater,
Consideryng what he hath proferyd her.'   1617

Thanne was the Sowdon) owt of pacience   1618
With Anasor', And spake full hastely ;
'Ye are,' quod he, 'to bold in my presence,
Ayenst my will to speke so vtterly,   1621
It is noo sygne of very loue trewly,
Not withstondeng I wote wele what ye mene,
But troste me wele it goo not as ye wene.'   1624

and Darell, who
took the part of
Generydes.

Thanne came Darell and putt hym) self in prese,   1625
Where here be fore rehersid is by name,
Of nobyll kynne he was withouten) lese,
The more bolder he was to take a blame   1628
In this mater accordyng' to the same ;
And in this wise he seid be fore them) all,
And to the Sowdon) in especiall :   1631

'As for my felawe her, the Chastelayn),   1632
I haue mervell that he rebukith hym) soo ;

[leaf 9]

And wele I wote that he hath don) his payn),

ffor your' pleasur' in aH that he cowde doo,   1635
And vtterly this wiH I saye also,
he that wiH do Generydes a shame,
I yow ensure he shaH do me the same.'   1638

Thanne to the Sowdon furth with aH they went, 1639   The lords then
The lordes and the knyghtes euerychone,   prayed the
And prayed hym) to respite the Iugement,   Sultan to
ffor certenly his wurchippe laye ther on);   1642   respite the
And wele they wist that reson was ther [n]on),   judgment.
A man) to deme, in eny maner case,
Withoute lawe and in so litiH space.   1645

The Sowdon) was as wrothe as he myght be,   1646   The Sultan
That in noo wise he wist not what to saye ;   was wroth,
Thanne was ther on), the Story tellith me,
A knyght whiche hadde be with hym) many a day,
And wele cheryshed with hym) he was Alway,   but was pre-
like as he wold the Sowdon) wold the same   vailed upon by
In euery thyng', and Lucas was his name.   1652   Lucas,

Vnto the Sowdon) he seid thus anon) :   1653
' Me think, ser, as ferre as I canne fele,
These lordes and these knyghtes euerychone
In this mater they haue not seyde but wele,   1656
hasty processe wiH shende it euery dele,
Avise yow wele and do be good councell,
And that shaH gretly yow honour and provaile.' 1659

Whanne the Sowdon) had hard hym) euery dele, 1660
Withynne a while he was right temperate,
Of aH his wordes he remembryd wele,
And with hym) self he was half atte debate ;   1663
he thought he wold noo more be obstenate,
And gaue them) respite be fore them euerychon),   and gave a
TiH one and xx^{ti} dayes were come and goon).   1666   respite of xxi
                                                           days.

Therof was aH the felashepe fuH fayn),   1667
And wele content that he hadde suche [grace]

Generydes went
back to prison,

Generydes to prisone went ayeyn),
Atte hartes ease meche better thanne he was ;   1670
ffor Anasore hadde graunt hym) aH the place
ffor his Disporte, to take it as hym) list,
In hym) he hadde no maner of mystrest.   1673

Whille he was stille in prisone a bideng',   1674

and thought of
Clarionas.

his thougĥt was aH on) Clarionas ;
And euer in his mynd remembryng',
how fayre [1] of hewe and womanly she was ;   1677
And if he mygĥt stonde in so good a case,
hir to reioyse and haue hir atte his wissĥ,
Of aH his payne he wold not sett a rissh.   1680

She was vppe on) A chaunbyr stiH opece,   1681
And euery man) that passid to and fro
She askyd fast aftur Generydes,
In very trougtĥ if he were dede or noo ;   1684
They seid he was ageyn) to prisone goo,
And was a lyue they knewe it for certayn),
The whiche some what conforte[d] hir Ayeyn).   1687

On the day
fixed

The Sowdon) charge[d] them to kepe the day,   1688
In eny wise what thing that euer faH :
And so they dede his pleasure to obeye,
Theder they came ichon) in generaH ;   1691
Thanne was the place to litiH for them) aH,
Wherefore the Sowdon) anon) dede ordeyne
A larger place aH owt vppon) the playn).   1694

And for to determytte this mater,   1695

Generydes was
brought out
of prison,

Generydes was brougĥt owt of the gaile ;
The Sowdon) thanne rehersid thanne in fere

---

[1] MS. *good fayre.*

his displeasur' withoute eny fayle,   1698 and the Sultan
hougħ he mygħt best to his entente prevaile ;   related his
And sodenly, among them euerychone,   displeasure,
ffurth witħ ther came a massanger anon,   1701

In hast[y] wise as fast as he cowde ride,   1702
And to the Sowdon he scid, rigħt in this wise :
' I am not come my massage for to hide,   when a mes-
    senger came
But boldly for to telle you myn avise.   1705 from the King
Ther is a kyng not ferre from thise partise,
In aħ contres ther as men riden and goon,
Vnder hevyn so grete ther levitħ non.   1708

Kyng' of Egipte he is, the sotħ to saye,   1709 of Egypt,
And haue merveħ, sithe ye be hold soo wise,
That ye so long haue putte it in delaye,
And come not furtħ to offer your' seruice ;   1712
Wherefore he wiħ that ye in eny wise
Yeld vppe your' land att his comaund[e]ment,   demanding the
    Sultan's land.
And vtterly obey to his entent: 1715

And for to take avise in this mater,   1716
he grauntitħ yow a monetħ day of space,
And by that day to geve a playn answere,
As ye wiħ be demeanyd in this case ;   1719
And your' dougħter also clarionas,
I counceħ yow to send hir to the kyng,   and his daughter.
ffor your' ease and welefare in tyme comyng.'   1722

Whanne he hadde seid his massage aħ in feere,   1723
The Sowdon was displeasid for certayn ;
And furtħ witħ aħ he chargid Anasar',
To take with hym Generydes ayeyn,   1726
And ther to kepe hym suerly on A payn,
ffor he mygħt not procede furmabely,
Because the tidyngez came so hastely.   1729

'Now telle what man*er* a man) is he,'   1730
Seid the Sowdon), 'that is of suche powre ;

[leaf 9, back]

And sey me now the very certente.'
To hym) anon) thanne seid the Masseng*er*,   1733
'If it please yow to wete, that ye shaH here:

Belen the Bold is
the King of
Egypt's name.

Belen the bold his name is ou*er* aH,
And kyng of kyngges now men) do hym) calle ;   1736

His loggyng is vppon) a fayre Ryu*er*,   1737
Callid teger, not ferre owt of this cost ;
And there he litĥ witĥ rigĥt a grete powre,
his owne p*er*sone and also aH his oste ;   1740
he wiH that it be knowen) to litiH [1] And most,
That fro that grownde he wiH nott part Away,
TiH he haue redy word what ye [2] wiH saye.'   1743

The Sultan
refused his
daughter,

The Sowdon) thanne gave Answere furtĥ w*it*ĥ aH,   1744
And in this wise seid to the massanger ;
'Of my dougĥter, as for the principaH,
I lete yow wete, for pleasur' nee for fere   1747
Think not ther on), for she shaH not come ther',
Nother in no nother place I yow ensure,
The whiche mygĥt sownne onto here dishono*ur*.   1750

and for the
rest of the
message,

As for the Remen*au*nte of your' message,   1751
Be cause I wiH not lette yow of your' waye,
Whanne eu*er* ye wiH ye may take your' viage,
ffor your' Answere I wiH that ye shaH sey,   1754

he would answer
it in a month.

I wiH send word withynne a moneth day
Vnto your' prince, where eu*er* he be present,
AH vtterly the fyne of myn) entent.'   1757

The messenger
left, and the
Sultan consulted
his lords,

The massanger anon) he toke his leve,   1758
And furtĥ he went whanne he hadde his answer'.
The Sowdon) anon) he ganne his counceH to meve

[1] MS. *likill.*   [2] MS. *he.*

Of that mater that towchid hym soo nere,   1761
And Askid ther avise in this mater,
Not on nor twayne, but all in generall,
Thanne spake ser Darell, and Answerd furth with All :

'These lordes here, that ben of your councell   1765
And my falow, and I be on Assent
In that mater to se what may prevaile,
As we seme ¹ best we shall shewe our entent.'   1768
Thanne spake lucas anon encontinent,
'Ser, dought ye not,' quod he, 'in this case
It shall be purvayde fore with goddes grace;   1771

Sithe tyme of mend this land ded neuer soo,   1772   who advised
                                                                him to resist
And as for vs we will not [now] begynne.'   Belen,
his lordes all Assentid wele therto,
And thought that lucas seid right wele therin.   1775
'We trost,' quod they, 'the victory for to wynne,
Vppon that prince so myghti in his strength,
Or ij monethys be fully drawe o length.   1778

But this we will require yow euerychone,   1779
To shew your grace on to Generydes ;   and to release
                                                                  Generydes.
ffor wele we wote offence he hath do non,
Vs thynk he shuld the soner haue his pece ;   1782
We yow beseche your rancour for to sese,²
ffor att this tyme he may do good seruice,
And suche as shall please yow in euery wise.   1785

And in this wise, yf it please yow to here,   1786
Be myn avise ye shall send³ for your ost :
And these lordes that ben with yow here,
lett them send for ther men in euery cost,   1789
In all ther best array both lesse and most ;
And so shall yow, with all your baronage,
Defende your lande that it pay noo trewage.'   1792

¹ So MS. ? deme.   ² MS. sesee.   ³ MS. sent.

The Sultan
The Sowdon markyd wele ther wordes all,   1793
And thought it was but reason that they seide.
' Now, seris,' quod he, ' sithe yow in generall
ffor this young man so specially hath prayed,   1796
agrees to free
Generydes,
That ye desire of me shall nott be nayed ;
Ye may telle hym he shall stonde in my grace,
like as he dede before in eny place.'   1799

They were right glad and thankyd hym icheon,   1800
That they for hym had sped so wele that day;
and Anasor
and Darell
Thanne Anasor and Darell went anon
Vnto the towre where he in prison laye.   1803
' What tydinges now,' quod he, ' I praye yow saye.'
' Be of good chere,' quod they, ' dought ye no dele,
Your pece is made, and all shall be right wele.'   1806

set him free.
They toke his feters of incontenent   1807
ffrom his leggis, and whan they had so do,
Thanne was he glad Inow, and furth he went
To the Sowdon as fast as he cowde goo,   1810
With Darell and ser Anasor Also ;
And whanne that he come to his presens,
ffull vmbely he did his Reuerence,   1813

Generydes begs
for the Sultan's
favour,
And to the Sowdon seid right in this wise ;   1814
' I wold beseche yow, ser, graunte me your grace,
I neuer offendid yow in my seruice,
Nother to yow nor to Clarionas.   1817
But hir to wurchippe as my dute was
In that that I cowde do, I yow ensure,
As long as I in seruice dede indure.   1820

And more ouer, as for the massanger,   1821
It grevid me full ill to here hym speke :
he sett his wordes in soo grete maner,

That I wold̶ fayn̶ on̶ hym̶ haue ben̶ wreke ;　1824
With̶ your' licence his purpose shaH I breke,
And if I may your' pleasure vnderstonde,
With that prowde kyng¹ I wiH fig̶h̶t hand be hand.　1827

and offers to fight the king of Egypt hand to hand.

He shaH not do your' dought̶er dishono*ur*,　1828
As long as god wiH send me lyff and space ;
Nor of his pride shaH neuer come that our'
That ye shaH paye trebute, be goddis grace,　1831
This land shaH neuer' stande in suche case ;
And if ye geve me leve, without̶e fayle
ffor aH his strength I wiH hym̶ onys assayle.'　1834

[leaf 10]

Whanne the Sowdon̶ had hard hym̶ sey so wiH,　1835
' Generydes,' q*uo*d he, ' I geue yow grace,
AH myn̶ eviH wiH I for geve eu*er*y deele,
And ye to stonde in soo good a case　1838
As euer ye dede withynne eny place ;
ffor now I know that ye, in eu*er*y wise,
haue contynued fuH trew in your' ser*u*ice.　1841

The Sultan restored Generydes to favour,

And ferthermore, withoute more dalay,　1842
To morow suerly I wiH make yow a knyg̶h̶t ;
And for your' sake an hundred more that day
Ther shaH be made, and then̶ with goddes myg̶h̶t　1845
I shaH purvay as for the landes rig̶h̶t,
It to defende, and that it may be clere
ffrom̶ aH ser*u*age and clene owt of daunger.'　1848

and promised on the morrow: to make him a knight.

Thanne was his thoug̶h̶t vppon̶ Clarionas,　1849
Sithe he hir saughe hym̶ thought passing long ;
That she myg̶h̶t stonde in his favour' and grace ¹
like as she dede, for he had don̶ hir wrong¹ ;　1852
And that he cowde remembre euer among¹ :
Wherefore he thoug̶h̶t hir to recompence,
he sendit̶h̶ for hir to come to his presence.　1855

He then sent for Clarionas,

¹ MS. *his grace.*

Thanne Anasore was chargid for to goo   1856
Vnto the chaunbyr of fayre Clarionas,
To bryng her furth the Sowdon) bad hym) soo,
That euery man) myght see withynne the place,   1859
hough wele she stode with hym) in euery case :
And whanne she came befoore hym), for certayn),

and took her
in his arms.
The Sowdon) toke hir in his armys twayn).   1862

'Doughter,' he seid, 'for yow I am to blame,   1863
ffull wrongfully to me ye were accusid,
And not gilty I will recorde the same,
To say the soth it may not be refusid ;   1866
So hold I yow all vtterly excusid
In euery thing[1]; and here, or where ye be,
Att All tymes right wele come on) to me.'   1869

Clarionas was fayn) whanne this was doo,   1870
Of hym) she toke hir leve full curtesly ;
Thanne was Generydes full glad also,
Be cause hir pece was made so trewly :   1873
And as she went he cast on) hir his lee,
So as he durst, to saue hym) self fro blame,
And she ayenward Aquyte hym) with the same.   1876

Thanne was ther sone Assigned knyghtez twayn) 1877
To bryng hir to hir chaumber furth with All,

Next day
he assembled
his knights,
And on) the morow the Sowdon) for certayn)
With his lordes he come in to the hall,   1880
And ther anone [among] his knyghtez all,
And, soth to say, the first of eny man)

Generydes the
first of any.
Generides the order ther beganne.   1883

They took
their leave,
and went to
make ready.
The lordes toke ther leve on) be on),   1884
To make them) redy atte ther owyn) devise ;
The ffelischepe departid euerychon)

[1] MS. *think.*

To goo and come ageyn̄ to ther seruice,   1887
And euery man̄ in defensable wise,
hors and harnes withoute eny more delay,
To muster withynne a monetħ day.   1890

Furst the Sowdon̄ sent his letters owt,   1891   The Sultan sent
With massengers as fast as they cowde ride,   letters to the
                                                                    kings and
To kynges and to princes aħ abougħt,   princes
The nexst that were marching on̄ euery side,   1894
Desireng them̄ armour to provide
And in aħ goodly hast for them̄ he sende [1]
To come to hym̄ his contre to defende.   1897   to help him.

These lettres came on̄ to these princez aħ,   1898
hym̄ for to helpe they grauntid euerychone,
Whanne they were come, furst in especiaħ   There came
                                                                    Croves, king
Croves the kyng of Arabye was on̄ ;   1901   of Arabia,
.ij. thousand knygħtes came witħ hym̄ alone,
Be side archers a nowmbyr fuħ notabyħ,
Whiche for werre Were rigħt good men̄ and able. 1904

The kyng¹ was wele in age I yow ensur²,   1905
And anasor³ his sone was for certeyn̄   father of Anasor,
A goodly prince and comly of stature ;
Of his comeng¹ the Sowdon was fayn̄ ;   1908
Notwitħstondyng it was to hym̄ a payn̄
So ferre owt of his contre to travaħ,
But his promesse was suche he wold not fayle.   1911

Nexst after hym̄ ther came owt of turkey   1912   a prince of
                                                                    Turkey, and
A myghti prince, and witħ hym people grete,   his two sons,
A thousand helmys witħ hym̄ in companye,
O[f] his contre the best that he cowde gete,   1915
his sonnes bothe witħ hym̄ were not [2] for yete,
And for to sey yow sotħ, and not to feyn̄,
Trewly they were fuħ semely knygthez twayn̄ ;   1918

        [1] MS. sent.   [2] MS. not ferre.

Off grete wurchippe and of rigħt nobiħ fame,   1919

David and Abell,   The eldest higħt *ser* Dauid, as I rede,

The yonger sone *ser* Abeħ was his name,

Whiche of his enmys [1] had but litiħ drede ;   1922

The kyng hym self was a lest man in dede,

Also he louyd wele fayre Clarionas,

Butt she hadde sette hir hert in other place.   1925

the king of   Thanne came the prince of Cesare sone vppon),   1926
Cæsarea,
                    With vij hundred knygħtes of his own lande ;

[leaf 10, back]   The Story seitħ his name was Cherydone,
Cherydone,
the father of   And *ser* Dareħ his sonne was, I vnderstonde :   1929
Darell,
                    This prince was hold fuħ manly of his hande,

his archers and his foote men wele arrayed,

The Sowdon of hym was rigħt wele apayd.   1932

Obeth, king   Thanne came the fortħt, whiche was of Sesiħ kyng,
of Sicily,
                    A wurthy prince, And Obetħ was his name ;

.v. honderyd knygħtes he dede witħ hym bring',

And men a foote accordeng' to the same ;   1936

The prince hym self of good and noble fame,

Theder to come he was rigħt wele content,

As sone as he his lettres to hym sent.   1939

the king of   Nexst after come the kyng of Nicomede,   1940
Nicomedia,
Esaunce,   iij. thousand men he brougħt on to the Citee ;
(with 3000 men as
black as coal,)   As blak as cole icheon thei [2] were in dede,

Save only ther tethe ther was noo white to see,   1943

Strong men they were the story tellitħ it me :

Esaunce he higħt, the story dotħ witnesse,

A curtese knygħt and fuħ of gentilnes.   1946

the king of   From Ethiope ther came another kyng,   1947
Ethiopia,
                    ij thowsand knygħtes att his gou*er*naunce,

With [3] meche pepiħ on foote Att his leding :

[1] MS. *elmys.*   [2] MS. *ther.*   [3] MS. *Whiche.*

Thanne after came A riaH ordenaunce,   1950
Too mygħty princes witħ a grete pusaunce,
ffro Masedeyn and owt of Arkadye,   and the princes
                                                         of Macedon
Ther cowde no man the nowmber specifie.   1953   and Arcadia,

Thanne came Moab, of Capadoor the kyng,   1954   Moab, the king
                                                         of Cappadocia,
To the Sowdon as fast as he cowde hye
Witħ ij knyghtes in felashepe rideng,
Balam the tone And yeferus trewly,   1957
The kyng of Damask and of Ermonye,   the kings of
                                                         Damascus and
Of knygħtes wel Arrayed witħ spere and Shelde,   of Ermonye,
xv. thowsand they brougħt in to the feld.   1960

Sone after come the kyng of orkenay,   1961   the king of
                                                         Orkney, and
In his companye ther came also   after him two
                                                         kings more,
Another kyng in good riche Arraye;
And after hym ther came ij kynggez moo,   1964
O thirde CesaH the kyng was on of thoo;
And what peopyH they brougħt among them three,   and a third Cesall,
Mynne Auctour seitħ it is a wonder to see.   1967

Now haue I here rehersid in substaunce   1968
xv kynges, As shortly as I mygħt,   15 kings in all,
Witħ ther powre and AH ther hoole puysaunce,
Whiche was so grete, to sey yow very rigħt,   1971
The Cite mygħt resseyue them day ne nygħt;   and met in a
                                                         wood without
Butt vnder nethe a woode withoute the town,   the town.
Ther was sette vppe the Sowdones pavilyon   1974   The Sultan's
                                                         pavilion

Vppon A playn, and made of silk and gold   1975   was set up on a
                                                         plain,
As richely as thei cowde wele ordeyne,
Witħ many moo fuH goodly to beholde,   with many more.
And tentys large, fuH riche and wele besen,   1978
And who so had be thence a myle or twayn,
Vppon the feld to loke or cast his Ie,
It shuld hym seme a town or A Citee.   1981

Upon a time the Sultan went

Vppon a tyme the seasone was fayre,　　1982
With his lordes the Sowdon) toke the waye,
Owt of the Cite to take the ayre,
In the feld vppon) a Somerys day,　　1985

to see the host,

And for to see the Ost in ther arraye ;
Beholdyng them) with countenaunce right stabill,
hym) semyd they were pepill innumerable.　　1988

and told them of the king of Egypt's demand

Thanne seid he thus vnto them) euerychon),　　1989
That were princes and other lordes all,
' In this contre,' quod he, ' ther is come on),
And kyng of kyngges thus he doth hym) calle,　　1992
Whiche thing may neuer in my reasone falle ;
ffor ther may non) be suche in dede ne thought,
Butt he that fourmed all this world of nought.　　1995

for tribute.

Also he askid tr[i]bute of this land,　　1996
Whiche may not be, what case that euer fall.'
The formest ganne to speke, I vnderstonde,
The kyngges sonne of turkey furth with All ;　　1999

Sir Abell said,

A semely prince, ser abell they do hym) calle,
Vnto the Sowdon) sone he gaue[1] answer',
As these wordes he seid as ye shall here :　　2002

the land of Persia should pay no tribute.

' As for the land of perse, this will I saye,　　2003
It ought to paye noo tribute in noo wise ;
Ne our' enmys shall neuer see the day,
ffor we are strongge I now I yow promys　　2006
Too kepe it from) All suche maner seruice ;

We will meet the Egyptians in the field.

And for to make it good with spere and Sheld,
Goo we to morow and mete them) in the feld.　　2009

Do as ye leke, for this is my councell ;　　2010
Besechyng yow to be remembryd here,
That whanne the lande of perse hath gevyn) batell,

[1] MS. *gaue an.*

Of tyme passid before in many yere,   2013
My lord and fader hath ben) Banyere,
And in the formest batell for to be
he and his ayeris claymeth it of dewte.   2016

Also to be made constabill of your' ost,   2017   Let me be the
And the voward' to haue in gouernaunce,   constable of
                                                           your host,
ffor to Turkey of right it longith most ;
Beseching yow with vmble obeysaunce,   2020
Of your' lordshipe ye list so it Avaunce,
That I may [bere] withoute envy or blame
The formest baner in my faders name.'   2023   and standard-
                                                          bearer.'

Anon) with all the Sowdon) gaue answere ;   2024   [leaf 11]
'All your' desire I graunt, it is but right.'   The Sultan
                                                          granted his
The kyng hym) thankid in full curtes maner,   desire.
Thanne to ther tentys sone they ganne them) dight,
And dressid all ther harnes ouer nyght,
That they myght on) the morow withoute fayle
All maner men) be redy to Batell.   2030

Whanne it was day, forward they ganne them) dresse   At daybreak
In bright harnes these princes euerychone,   they made them
                                                          ready for batt'e,
With other dyuerce lordes more and lesse,
Of Dukes and Erles and Barons anon),   2034
Ther helmes garnysshed that they had vppon),
With perlys and dyamauntez of price,
Ther course[r]s trappid in the fressest wise.   2037

In the Citee through owt in euery strete   2038
Ther was grete noyse of pepill all abought,
To dresse them) fourth ther enmys for to mete,
And sone vppon) withoute eny dought   2041
ffro the Citee the Sowdon) passid owt,   and went out
And rideth streyte to his pavilion),   of the city,
With lordes abought hym) in euery rome.   2044

GENERYDES.   5

And whanne that they were redy to goo,   2045

And Aꝅ assemelid in a companye,

60,000 strong.   iij skore thowsand they were withoute moo.

Thanne were ordeyned the wardes by and by ;   2048

The foremost ward the king of Turkey had with   The formest warde Aꝅ redy for to gye

The kyngꞌ of Turkey had in gouernaunce,

Be very rigꞅt of his enheritaunce.   2051

3000 knights ;   Thre thowsand knygꞅtes att his demeningꞌ,   2052

Be side Archers and foote me�^ that were *ther*,

And As his graunt was atte begynnengꞌ,

his sonne *ser* Abeꝅ he was baneer.   2055

The secunde ward, to certifie yow here,

the king of Arabia had the second, with 2000 ;   Was putte oꝏ to the kyngꞌ of Araby,

ij thowsand knygꞅtez in his companye.   2058

the third, Sir Anasore and Generydes,   The iij^{de} warꝺ ther in was ser Anasore,   2059

And witꞅ hyꝏ was Generydes also,

And Aꝅ the new made knygꞅtez they were thore,[1]

with 1500 ;   And xv hundred meꝏ withoute moo,   2062

Of choseꝏ meꝏ what eu*er* they shuld do,

Aꝅ vnder nethe bothe the rule of more[2] and lesse,

Of Anasore and [of] Generydes.   2065

Cherydone was fourth,   The prince of Cesare, callid cherydone,   2066

he was the iiij^{th}, aꝅ in Another ward,

his felisshepe wele be sene echoꝏ,

with 1000 knights waiting on him ; next came the king of Sicily and 3000 knights ;   A thowsand knygꞅt[ez] waytengꞌ oꝏ his garꝺ.   2069

Thanne came the kyng of Ceseꝅ afterwarꝺ,

iij thowsand knygꞅtez in his companye,

Witꞅ Archers and foote meꝏ by and by.   2072

the king of Nicomedia   Nexst after·hyꝏ came the kyng of Nycomede,   2073

V thowsand knygꞅtes, wonder to behold,

ffuꝅ begely shapeꝏ bothe in lengetꞅ Anꝺ brede,

---

[1] MS. *y^{er}*.   [2] So MS.   *? the rule bothe more.*

As blak as coole, as I befoore haue tolð,   2076
The vj^{te} bateH to rule it as he wolð,   *ruled the sixth battle;*
And as in writeng in fynde¹ remembraunce,
Was putte hooly on to his gouernaunce.   2079

The kyng of Ethiope, witħ pepiH grete,   2080 *the king of Ethiopia had the seventh;*
The vij^{te} warð he hadd in gouernaunce,
ffuH wele purveid his enmys for to mete ;
And in the viij^{te} warð, to saye yow the substaunce,   *the king of Macedon and two others the eighth;*
iij kyng[ez] moo, witħ aH ther ordenaunce,
Of Masedoyne and other kyngez twayne,
Witħ moche peopiH to sey yow the certaynð.   2086

The ix^{te} ward the kyng of Capadoce,   2087 *the ninth, the king of Cappadocia;*
Witħ the nowmber of knygħtez iij thowsand,
ffuH wele wellyd to werre vppoŋ ther foys ;
The x^{te} batayH kyng Balam toke oŋ hond,   2090 *the tenth, king Balam;*
Witħ iij thowsand knygħtez I vnderstonde ;
The xj^{te} ward² therin was zepherus,   *the eleventh, Zephyrus;*
A myghti prince in armys corageus.   2093

The xij^{te} warð the kyng of Orkenaye,   2094 *the king of Orkney twelfth;*
Witħ grete peopiH I say yow sekerly ;
The xiij^{te}, the southly³ for to say,   *the thirteenth, King Phares;*
Kyngꞌ phares witħ a nobiH companye ;   2097
The last saue oŋ the kyng of Barbary.   *the last but one the king of Barbary.*
These iij princes hadde after ther entente
vj thowsand knygħtez in ther poyntement.   2100

The last bateH therin the Sowdoŋ was,   2101 *The Sultan was last of all,*
iij thowsand knygħtez witħ hyɱ ther were,
Some of his lande and some of dyuerce place,
And euery maŋ wele dressid in his geere ;   2104
In that bateH DareH was Baner,   *and Darell his standard-bearer.*
And as the story seitħ in euery wise
he was a likely knygħt for that Office.   2107

¹ So MS. *? I fynde.*   ² MS. *was.*   ³ So MS. *? southe.*

Anon with all ther Baneres were displayed,　　2108

It was a royal sight to see them arrayed.

A riall sight it was to behold,

Eche of them wele horsid and arrayed,

And in ther harnes dressid as they wold,　　2111

Ther cote Armers of siluer and of gold;

And so forward they partid all in feere,

The trompettys blew, it was A Ioye to here.　　2114

Now let us turn again to the [leaf 11, back] mighty king.

Now late vs leue them rideng on the way,　　2115

And to this myghti kyng turne we agayn,

Hough he purveith in all that euer he may,

And in what wise that he may best ordeyne,　　2118

Of euery ward to make a capteyn,

ffirst he appoynted in especiall,

He was in the foremost ward.

hym self was in the formest of them all.　　2121

Three kings were with him,

Three kynggez were with hym in companye,　　2122

Also he hadde of[1] knyghtes vj. thowsand,

And in nowmber as many by and by,

In euery warde was poynted afore hand,　　2125

And by writeng as I vnderstonde;

and Gwynan his son, standard-bearer.

Gwynan his sonne, whiche was full dere,

Of his batell he made hym Banere.　　2128

Then came Sir Amelok, king of India,

Thanne came ser Amelok, the kyng of ynd,　　2129

Whiche lande, god wote, full traytoru[s]ly he wanne,

And vntrewly, the story makith mynde,

who betrayed king Auferius.

Betrayed his prince whiche was a nobill man.　　2132

The secunde ward ser Amelok beganne

With meche pepill, to say yow certenly,

ij kynges mo were in his companye.　　2135

Sanyk,

So forthermore thanne came the kyng Sanyk　　2136

Nexst afterward, and with hym kynggez twayn;

king of Africa,

A myghti prince, and kyng[2] of Auferyk,[3]

[1] MS. *haddes f.*　　　[2] MS. *kyng he was.*　　　[3] MS. *Anseryk.*

And fader to the quene of ynde certayn,   2139
The whiche forsoke hir husbond be a trayn :
This prince hadde in his rewle and gou*er*naunce
The iij^de bateH with aH the orden*a*unce.   2142 had the third battle;

The iiij^te bateH to rule and to ordeyne   2143 the king of Thrace the fourth;
Madane[1] hadde it, whiche was kyng of Trace ;
And as myn Auct*our* specifieth certayn
Right yong And fressh a lest man he was.   2146
And in the v^te ther came Barachias,   the fifth, Barachias, king of Europe;
Kyng of Europe, and suche a companye
As eu*er*y ward was poynted by and by.   2149

Nexst after hym came Ermones the kyng,   2150 the sixth, king Ermones,
The vj^te BateH to gou*er*ne as he wold,
ffuH boustous folk and iH faryng,   with men
With visages fowle, fuH gresely to beholde,   2153
AH of on sorte they were both yong and old,
Ther bakkes and ther belly were soo large,   so big that horses could not carry them,
Ther was noo hors of them wold bere the charge ; 2156

Wherefore they rode on camelys eu*er*ychon,   2157 so they rode on camels,
Think wele it was a vounderfuH array,
ffor as for spere or swerd they handelid non,
Ther wepons were more stronger, I yow say,   2160 and had weapons (see p. 80) like mattocks, with long helves;
lyke as mattokez Shapyn so were they,
Ther helvys long, that whanne they shuld fight
Ther strokes shuld come with grete wight.   2163

Two kyngez moo were in his company,   2164
Of suche makyng and of on man*er* kynd.
The vij^te ward the kyng of Assirye,   the seventh, Galad, king of Assyria;
Galad he hight in story, as I fynde,   2167
A prince worthy for to [be] had in mynd ;
The viij^te BateH therin was manassen,   the eighth, Manassen;
And vnder hym was his sone ruben.   2170

[1] MS. *Madame.*

the ninth,
Lamadone,
king of Libya;

the tenth,
Auferius,

king of India,

The kyng of lybie, callid lamadone,   2171
The ix^{te} warde hadde att his leding¹;
And the x^{te}, the last of eu*er*ychone,
Was auferius, the welebelouyd kyng   2174
That was of ynd, and ther had his dwellyng
Till he was putte [from] his enheritaunce,
Wherof be fore was made remembraunce.   2177

Two kynges mo were in his poyntement,   2178
With the nowmber of knyghtes accordeng,
Owt of the Reme of Trace with hym) ther were,
To wayte on) hym) ther were [they] well willyng¹, 2181

who knew not
that he had to
fight against his
son Generydes.

But of on) thing he had no knowlaching¹,
That his fortune was suche withoute lese
To fight ayenst his sone Generydes :   2184

The last batell was putt on) to his gard,   2185
And for this cawse it was apoyntid so,
Ser Amelok he hadde the secunde ward,
That noo debate shuld be bytwix them) twoo,   2188
Thanne after this ther was no more a doo ;
The men) of armys bothe with spere and sheld,
With grete corage dressid them) in to the feld.   2191

And on) the toder part forward they went ;   2192
Among his men) the Sowdon) came rideng¹,

The Sultan sent
out 3 knights
to reconnoitre.

And prevely iij knyghtez owt he sent,
Of his enmys to knowe ther demeanyng¹,   2195
They brought hym) word ayenward *th*ei were comyng¹,
And so they rode ye space of half a nyght,
That eu*er*ychone of other hadde a sight.   2198

Thanne afterward thei made noo taryeng¹,   2199
But furth they goo withoute eny lett,
Wete ye wele ther was a sorowfull encount*er*yng¹,

Whanne the batels to geder were mett, 2202 The battles met.
Euerychone on) other ferly they sette
With grete corage, and trewly for to speke
It was a world to here the sperys breke. 2205

The kyng of kynggez rode on euery side, 2206 The king of
                                                  kings
ffull clene armyd formest of euerychone,
There were butt fewe his strokes wold abide,   [leaf 12]
So many he on) horsid one be one ; 2209 unhorsed many a
                                            one.
A comly prince he was to loke vppon),
And therwith [all] right good and honorable,
And in the feld a knyght right confortable. 2212

Ser abell was of perse the Banere, 2213 Sir Abell met
                                            him,
Avaunsid hym) and to a kyng ganne ride,
And thorough owt the body he hym) bare,
That on) his hors he myght not longe abide, 2216
Butt to the grownde he felle and ther he dyed ;
And thanne ser Abell, in a hasty brayde,
Vnto the kyng of kyngges thanne he seide : 2219

' Good ser,' quod he, ' how likith yow this game ? '
With tho wordes the kyng liked full ill,
he thought full wele to quyte hym) with ye same,
And ranne to hym) with a full eger will, 2223
That from ser Abell downe the baner fell,   but lost his
                                                  banner in the
And suche a stroke he hadde, to say yow trew,   fight,
That from) his hors almost he ther ouer threw. 2226

The kyng his fader sawe the baner down), 2227 which his father
                                                  rescued.
he hastyd hym) as fast as euer he myght,
And with an hundered knyghtes of renown)
The baner sone they reisid it vppe right ; 2230
Thanne was the batell sore, I yow be hight,
And many slayn) ; but or the day was past
The men of perse with drew them) atte last. 2233 The men of
                                                    Persia withdrew,

The nexst bateﬂ, whanne thei wist how it was,   2234

but Generydes
came up and
won the ground
again,

Generydes and Anasore in certayn),

They brougﬅt ther felishepe bothe more and lesse,

And in a while they wanne the grownd ayen) ;   2237

Generydes sawe Guynan on) the playn),

The kyngges sone, rideng' with spere and sheld ;

he taryd not, butt mette hym) in the feld.   2240

fought with
Gwynan,

Gwaynan on) to Generides he ranne,   2241

And with [his] spere he brake his sheld on) twayne ;

Generides ayenward like a man)

With stode his stroke, and smote hym) so ageyn), 2244

That from) his hors he felle vppon) the playn),

And who that euer that was wele payde or wroth,

unhorsed him,

he toke his hors with hym and furth he goth.   2247

Thanne was ther on) not ferre owt of ye prese,   2248

lyke a harowed he semyd for to be,

To hym) Anon) thanne seid Generydes,

' Good ser,' quod he, ' doo now sum what for me ;' 2251

' What is your' wiﬂ and pleasure ?' quod he.

' My lorde,' he seid, ' that ye wiﬂ in this nede

Chaunge my Sadyﬂ and sett it on) this stede.   2254

Whanne ye haue do, take ye my stede therfore.' 2255

Sygrem hym did as Generides hym) badde,

he hight so, and to sey yow more

In his demeanyng he was wise and sadde ;   2258

Of bothe partys right grete favour' he hadde,

To gentilmen) he was right servisable,

And ther withaﬂ fuﬂ good and companable.   2261

and took his
horse,

Generydes leppe vppe vppon) his stede,   2262

A better was not onder nethe the sonne ;

ﬀor grete suerte in story as I rede,

The kyng of kyngges gave it to his sonne,   2265
Or the bateᚻ was eny thing begonne ;
Sygrem was glad of chaungyng⁴ of his hors,   giving his own to Sygrem.
ffor of his owne he gave butt litiᚻ fors.   2268

To hym̃ ɋnon̄ thanne seid Generydes,   2269 He asks Sygrem where Sir Amelok is.
' Sygrem,' q*uo*d he, ' do me to vnderstonde
Ser Amelok, if he be in the preese,
Whiche trayturly hath wonne my faders lande.   2272
ffayne wold I wete if he were here nye hande.'
' Trewly,' he seid, ' now I remembyr me,
Suche one ther is in very certente.   2275

Butt as for yow, I wote not what ye be,   2276
hym̃ knowe I wele trewly, that is noo nay ;   'I know him well; he is in the first battle save one.
The first bateᚻ saue on̄ ther in is he,
This is the very trougtᚻ that I yow saye,   2279
And what ye be, I beseche and praye
To lete me wete the truthe in eu*er*y wise,   Tell me who you are.'
And I shaᚻ trewly owe yow my ser*u*ice.'   2282

Generydes thanne gaue hym̃ this answere ;   2283 Generydes said,
' Sygrem,' he seid, ' to yow I wiᚻ not leyne,
I shaᚻ yow telle the trouth of this mater,
kyng auferius is my fader in certeyn̄,   2286 'Auferius is my father.'
Whiche was of ynd bothe lord and sou*er*eyn̄,
And now is kyng of Trace, as I yow say,
Butt lete this go noo ferther, I yow praye.'   2289

' Kyng⁴ auferius,' q*uo*d he, ' I knowe hym̃ wele,   2290 'I know him well,' replied Sygrem,
The last bateᚻ of aᚻ ther in he is,
As ferre as I canne vnderstonde and fele,
Ser Amelok is not his frende I wis,   2293 'and Sir Amelok is not his friend.'
And by what reason̄ I wiᚻ teᚻ yow this ;
The kyng of kynggez partyd them̃ twayn̄,
Be cause they shuld noo debate begynne certeyn̄.' 2296

'How shaíl I doo,' thanne seid Generydes,   2297
'Of Amelok to haue sum knowlachyng ?
ffor hyɱ that I may knowe amongꞇ the preese,
But if I haue sum redy tokyni[n]g̓.'   2300
'I shaíl yow telle,' quod he, ' withoute feyneng,

his stede is gray withoute layeɳ,
The hede is whiġĥt, to say yow for certayɳ.   2303

For more knowelage to telle yow which is he,   2304

his harmes are, who so list to be holde,
The felde of Goulys in very certeynte,
Ther witĥ also iij bandes aíl of gold.'   2307
And whanne that he Generydes had told
Of Amelok, and hougĥ he shuld hyɱ fynde,
Wete ye wele he was the gladder in hys mynde. 2310

Furtĥ oɳ his stede ridetĥ Generydes,   2311
To fynd ser Amelok if that he may,
Witĥ hyɱ ridetĥ Sygrem stiíl opeese,
And as they twayne rode spekyngꞇ be the waye, 2314

Segrem was ware wher in a valay
Ser Amelok came oɳ rideng A pace,
hyɱ for to rest as for a litiíl space :   2317

'Loo yender is ser Amelok,' he seid,   2318
' And savingꞇ oɳ witĥ hyɱ ther is no moo.'
And witĥ that word Generydes abrayde,
'Now is,' quod he, 'good tyme for me to goo ;' 2321
So furth he riditĥ tiíl that he came hyɱ too :
The toder sawe hyɱ come witĥ spere and sheld,

And furtĥ he gothe and mette hyɱ in the feld. 2324

And atte first he stroke Generydes,   2325
And witĥ that stroke he brast his sheld in twayɳ,
Anone witĥ aíl he quyte hyɱ dowteles,

And smote his sheld quyte on) the playn).　　　2328
Thanne seid Generides, 'now am I fayn),
Thow shalt not laughe atte me in mokkery,
ffor thow hast lost thy sheld as wele as I.　　2331

And as for on) thyng¹ I shall the wele ensure,　2332
As for thy sheld thu shalt haue it no more,
ffor myn) is broke it may noo more endure,
Be thow right sure I will haue thynne therfore :' 2335
And thanne beganne the batell passing sore,
Ther was non) of them) shewid favour³ to a no*ther*,
ffor right dedely the tone hatid the toder.　　2338

Syr Amelok was wrothe as he myght be,　　　2339
And to Generydes right thus he sayde ;
'I shall yow quyte that thu hast doo to me,'
And smote hym) on) the hide with suche a brayde, 2342
That in hym) self he was some what dismayed :
Quod Amelok, ' thu hast I now this day,
Reche me my¹ sheld and thu goo thy waye.'　　2345

'Thow getist it not, fals traytour [that] thu art, 2346
Or thu goo ferther thu shalt haue myschaunse,
ffor thu hast with thy fals envyous hert
Putte my fader from) his enheritaunce,　　　2349
Whiche was his Ioye, his lyfe, and his pleasur³,
And in my faders presence thu me smote,²
Whiche I haue not forgete yet, god it wote.　　2352

And thanne I myght not ease my hert in dede,　2353
But now thu shalt repent it or thu goo :'
And with his swerd he smette hym) on) the hede,
The helme to brast anon) in peces two ;　　　2356
his lippys and his noose he smote away also,
Clene from) his face, and ther with all full sone,
he bledde so fast that he felle in A swonne.　　2359

¹ MS. *thy*.　　　　² MS. *smette*.

Side notes:
Generydes cuts away Amelok's shield.

They fight on.

Generydes reproaches Amelok for his treachery.

Sir Amelok is wounded

and unhorsed,

To hym̄ thanne seide Generides anon̄,   2360
'Whih̄ ere thu bad I shuld reche the thy sheld,
And now me think thu hast nede of on̄,
ffor neyther spere ne sheld that thu may weld:' 2363

but rescued   And with̄ that word vppeward his hede [he] helde,
Risyng with̄ ah̄ to helpe hym̄ self righ̄t fayne;
Generydes thanne smote hym̄ down̄ ageyn̄,   2366

Hym for to slee was fully his entente.   2367

by his knights.   With̄ that anon̄ his knygh̄tes came hym̄ to,
And sette hym̄ on̄ his hors and furth̄ they went,
As soft a pace as y^ei̱ mygh̄t with̄ hym̄ goo,   2370
Too se hym̄ in that pligh̄t they were fuh̄ woo;

Generydes took the horse he had won of Amelok,   his stede anon̄ thanne toke Generydes,
And led hym̄ furth̄ with̄ hym̄ in to the prese.   2373

And whanne that he was eskepyd trewly,   2374
Sygrem he found anon̄ in continent,
'My frende,' quod [he], 'I prae yow feth̄fully
To do my massage after myn̄ entent,   2377

and sent it to Auferius by Sygrem.   That ye wih̄ take this stede, and hym̄ present
To auferius my lord and fader dere,
And say to hym̄ that I haue wonne hym̄ here   2380

Off Amalok, the traytour most vntrewe;   2381
And if he aske as for more witnesse,
Who sent to hym̄ and how that I hym knewe,
Telle hym̄ it is his sone Generydes,   2384
And hough̄ that Amelok in ah̄ the prese,
Withynne his howse and in his high̄ presence,
ffuh̄ cruely smote hym̄ with violence;   2387

And he ayenward smete hym̄ with̄ his knyff   2388
Thorough̄ the Arme in very certente.'
Sygrem Ayenward seid, 'ser, be my liff,

I shaH do that ye haue comaundyd me,   2391
And take hym this present where euer he be.'
Now goo Sygrem, as fast as ye may spede,
To Auferius to present hym this stede.   2394

And whanne this stede to Auferius was brought, 2395
And wist fro whense he came, thanne was he fayn;
'Now, good Sygrem, as euer I may do ougHt
ffor thy pleasur,' quod auferius ayen),   2398
'Of my sonne telle me somme token playn),
hougH I may best knowe hym among them aH;'
'Ser,' quod Sygrem, 'witH rigHt good wiH I shaH.' 2401

Auferius asked Sygrem some token by which he might know [leaf 13] his son.

Sygrem hym told tokynnes moo thanne on),   2402
his sonne to knowe be rigHt of his office,
What colour was his hors he rode vppon),
And what harmys he bare, and what devise,   2405
AH this he told hym in fuH redy wise;
kyng auferius ther witH he was contente,
And hym rewardid weH for his presente.[1]   2408

He told him the colour of his horse and his arms.

As now putte we this mater in respite,   2409
And to Generydes turne we ageyn),
Whiche founde his felawes aH most discomfete,
ffor they had fougHt aH the day certeyn);   2412
Yet whanne they hȳm sawe thenne were *th*ei fayn),
And ganne reioyse whanne they to geder mette,
With knygHtly corage frely on) they sette.   2415

Generydes found his fellows almost discomfited.

When they saw him they were glad.

And thanne beganne the bateH passing sore;   2416
They fougHt alway to geder stiH opece,
The men) of perse were hartid more and more,
AH be counfort of Generides: 2419
he styntid not, nor neuer wold he sese,
And witH his swerd where that his stroke glynt,
Owt of ther sadiH fuH redely they went.   2422

Every one went down before the stroke of Generydes.

[1] MS. *presence.*

The king of kings
asked Sygrem,

The kyng of kyngges toke good hede [   ],   2423
To hym he callid Sygrem furth with all anon,

'What knight is
yonder on my
son's horse?

'What knyghte is yender,' quod he, 'canne ye me saye?
That in the feld outrayth euerychone ;   2426
So good a knyght as he me semyth now
In all the world, but on thyng I mervell,
My sonnys stede hath he, withoute fayle ;   2429

Where with trewly I am not wele apayed,   2430
Notwithstondeng a nobyll knyght is he,
And that ye knowe right wele, Sygrem,' he sayd,

I would he were
dwelling with
me.'

'Wherefore I wold he were dwellyng with me ;   2433
Of gold and siluer he shall haue plente,
Townys and castelys at his obyseaunce,
And other thinges moo to his plesaunce.'   2436

'Sir,' quoth
Sygrem, 'he is of
a high lineage,

'Ser,' quod Sygrem, 'trewly it will not be,   2437
he is descendid of an high lenage,
And as fer[1] furth as I canne fele and see,
he waytith after right grete heritage,   2440
ffor with the Sowdon he will take no wage,

and his trust
is to have
Clarionas.'

And for to telle yow trouthe as in this case,
his trost is to haue fayre Clarionas.'   2443

'Nay,' said the
king, 'I take her
for my own,

'Clarionas,' quod he, 'nay, Iete be that ;   2444
I take hir for my owen, ser, be the rode,

and will make it
good on his
body.'

Whether he will or noo, for wote ye what,
Vppon his body I will make it good :'   2447
And whanne Sygrem these wordes vnderstode,
ffull sone he went to Generydes,
And told hym what he seid more or lesse.   2450

Belen now
seeks Generydes,

Now kyng Belleyn secheith Generydes   2451
Thorough the ost, to fynde hym if he maye,
And as he rode a side hand of the prece,

[1] MS. *for*.

he sawe where that he rode in [a] valaye ;   2454   and finds him in
                                                              a valley.
To hym anon full streyght he toke the waye,
And on a high he beganne to crye,
'Turne the,' he seid, 'for tyme it is trewly :   2457

Vppon my stede blanchard thu ridest here,   2458
Butt on my list thu shalt hym sone for goo.'
That word anon Generides ganne here,
he turnyd hym withoute wordes moo.   2461
They toke ther coursis and ranne to geder soo,   They ran
                                                              together and were
Thanne iche atte other and bothe ther sperys helde,
But thei were clene onhorsid in the feld.   2464   both unhorsed,

Vppon ther stedis sone thei were ayeyn,   2465   but got up on
                                                              their steeds
And so they fought to geder hand to hand,   again, and
Ther was noo favour shewid be twix them twayn,   fought hand to
                                                              hand.
Butt strokes grete and sore, I vnderstonde ;   2468
ij better knyghtes were not in all the land,
ffor long' thei fought and neuer wold thei lette,
Ne yet departe to tyme the ostes mette.[1]   2471

Thanne wax the batell euer more and more,   2472   The battle waxed
                                                              sore.
As thei resortid on euery side ;
lordes and knyghtez were hurt right soore,
And many ligging dede with woundes wide ;   2475
lucas ffull sone Manessen had aspied,   Lucas rode at
                                                              Manassen,
With sheld and spere he dressid hym full right,
And ranne to hym in all that euer he myght.   2478

The stede[2] was good that lucas rode vppon,   2479
And suche a stroke he gave hym with a spere,
That thorough the harnes and the shulder bon,
Thorough owt his bak and slew hym ther ;   2482   and slew him,
Thanne to the kyng he seid in this maner :
'Take yow here this present or ye goo,
And I shall do my part to send yow moo.'   2485

            [1] MS. *mettez*.   [2] MS. *stode*.

Tho wordes toke the kyng in Mokkery,   2486
And made hym redy with spere and sheld,
To *ser* lucas he ranne full egerly

but was unhorsed
by the king,
and rescued by
Generydes,
[leaf 13, back]

And stroke hym fro his hors in to the feld ;   2489
With that anon Generydes beheld
how lucas was owttrayed among[1] his foys,
And in he came and rescuyd hym att onys.   2492

Streyght to the kyng he rideth for certayn,   2493
And with his swerd he smote hym on the hede,
The helme to brast anon in pecys twayn,
And with that stroke he slewe his hors in dede,   2496

who slew the
king's horse.

And so the stede fell vnder nethe hym dede,
hym self also ther with was astoinyd sore,

The king blew
his horn,

And blew his horne, to saye yow forthermore.   2499

and a thousand
knights came up

Thanne came a thowsaund knyghtez of his ost,   2500
And vppe thei sette hym on a nother stede,
And glad they were, wenyng[1] they had hym lost,

and carried him
off.
Then came in the
men of higher
India,
(see p. 69)

And furth owt of the prese with hym they yede.[1]   2503
Thanne came ther in as fast as thei myght spede,
The buscommest folk, the men of higher ynd,
Of whom before the story makith mend.   2506

Whanne they come in they made rome Alabought,

with weapons
out of all
measure.

Ther wepons were made owt of all mesur,
ffull ill shapyn with pekys in and owt,
Ther strokes myght no man endure ;   2510

The men of
Persia were
discomfited,

The men of Perse were att discomfeture,
And whanne the Sowdon hard of that tiding[1],
he came anon and made no taryng[1] ;   2513

Conforting[1] them in full good maner,   2514
And for ther *ser*uice thankyd them Also :
The prince of Cesare gave hym this answere,

[1] MS. *yode.*

'Now truly, ser,' quod he, 'if it were so   2517
That they were men) with whom) we haue a do,
We wold not dowte to mete them) on) be on),
But suerly they be fendez euerychone.   2520

Ther wepons be suche ther may no man) abide,   2521
Wherefore this is now myn) avise,' quod[1] he,
'Vs to with drawe a litell owt aside,   *and withdrew*
That our enmys perseyue not that we fle.'   2524   *towards the city, Mountenor.*
The Sowdon) saw it wold non) other be,
Butt nedis he must geve his assent ther to,
And yet he was full loth so for to do.   2527

They drewe softely to the Citee Warđ,   2523
The Sowdon) blow his horn) that thei mygħt here,
The lordes and the knygħtez of his garde,
Whanne thei it harđ anon) thei drew hym) nyere,   2531
As as they rode to geder all in feer',
Ther enmys made on) them) a newe afraye,
That vnnethe mygħt the Sowdon) skape a waye.   2534 *The Sultan barely escaped,*

V. hunderyd of his men) he lost also,   2535 *and lost 500 men and 1000 horses.*
And of horsis a thowsand atte lest
Among them) All thei lost withoute moo,
And some lordes and knygħtez of the best ;   2538
The day passid, the sonne drewe to the rest,
And be that tyme his felisshepe and he
Were come to Mountoner the riche Citee.   2541

And of all this wist not Generides,   2542 *Generydes and Anasore wist not of this, but fought Galad, the king of Assyria,*
Nor anasor', to say yow certeynly,
ffor thei were allway fightyng still opece
Ayenst Galad the kyng of Asirye ;   2545
And whanne they had knowlage vtterly,
Of the Sowdon) and of his distresse,
Thanne were they bothe in rigħt grete hevynesse. 2548

          [1] MS. *now q^d.*
GENERYDES.   6

Yer[1] fought thei still and reskew was *ther* non,   2549
Nor non comyng' as ferre as they myght see,
Ther men almost distressid euerychone,

And many slayne, thenne of necessite   2552
They them withdrewe, and towarde the Citee
They toke the way, and in conclusion
Thanne was the oste be twene them and y[e] town ;   2555

That in no wise they wist not hough to pas,   2556
Ne hough to do they knowe noo sertente,
Thanne Anasor' remembred that ther was
A postrene yssuyng' owt of the Citee,   2559
And thederward they drewe to haue entree,
But or they myght in suerte come and goo
Be twix them bothe they had I noughe to do.   2562

Now to the Sowdon lete us turne ageyn,   2563
ffor here peopill what mone that he do make ;
Of euery man he enqueryd the certente,
Whiche of his men were ded and which were take ;
The Citee made grete sorow for ther sake,
And specially thei made grete hevynes
ffor Anasore and for Generides ;   2569

And thought suerly it myght non other be,   2570
Butte thei were bothe [putte] to discomforture.
Thanne sayde Darell, 'it were full grete pite
Suche ij knyghtez to lese, I yow ensure ;'   2573
And furth he goth vppon his aventure,
Beseching' god to councell hym and rede,
ffor he wold fynd hym[2] eyther quyk or dede.   2576

Thanne was a noyse the Citee all along'   2577
That they were slayn, and woo thei were *ther*fore ;
Clarionas herd how the tydingez sprong',

¹ MS. *Yey.*   ² MS. *hyn.*

here chere was doɴ, she wept passing sore :   2580   it and wept sore,
Myrabeℍ sawe she wept more and more,
'Madame,' qu*o*d she, 'these tydengez that be now,   but Mirabell did
A wager dare I ley they are not trew :   2583   not believe the
                                                   news.

And if it please yow, for youᴿ disporte,   2584
To walk vppe to the towre[1] ther shaℍ ye see
P*a*raventurᴿ that may be youᴿ coumfort.'
'I wiℍ,' she sayde, 'do as as ye counceℍ me :   2587
Comforte or no, or hougℏ that eu*er* it be.'   [leaf 14]
So furtℏ she went vppe to the towre oɴ hye,   Clarionas went
Butt nougℏt she sawe, she wept so wtterly.   2590   to the top of
                                                   the tower,
                                                   but saw nothing
                                                   for weeping.
Thanne was DareH come to Generides,   2591   Sir Darell made
And glad thei were, bothe he and Anasorᴿ,   his way to
ffor thei had longꞌ endured counfortles :   Generydes.
Whanne he was come amendid was ther cherᴿ,   2594
And att that tyme owt of the prese thei were,
To rest theɴ self a seasoɴ to endure,
Ther eche to other told his aventurᴿ.   2597

Clarionas was oɴ the towre oɴ hye,   2598   Clarionas on the
Of here wepyngꞌ she ded hir self refrayɴ,   tower
And owt vppoɴ the feld she ganne aspye,
Where Anasore came rideng vppoɴ the playɴ ;   2601   saw Anasore,
By his Armys she knewe hyɴ for certayɴ
That it was he, and ther withaℍ anoɴ
A grete part of hir hevynesse was gooɴ.   2604

Generides was also in the feld,   2605   but did not know
Butt whiche was he she had noo knowlachingꞌ,   Generydes because
ffor he had oɴ s*er* Amelokkez sheld,   he had Sir
Witℏ his devise, in very tokenyngꞌ   2608   Amelok's shield.
That he it wanne att ther encount*er*yngꞌ,
And so they rode oyther witℏ spere and sheld,
Toward towɴ clarionas theɴ beheld.   2611

            [1] MS. *town*.

Auferius with 500 knights rode And as thei rode anon) thei were Aspied   2612
By on) that was with Auferius the kyng',
And in noo wise thanne wold he not abide,
And told his lord withoute more taryeng';   2615
And he anon), leving' Aħ other thing',
Sent furth knyghtez v. C. in aray,
to meet them.   hym) self also to mete them) on) the waye.   2618

And aħ was to withstonde ther passage,   2619
With these knyghtes he rode on) stiħ opece ;
The foremost was Ismael the Savage,   The formest was Ismael the Savage,
Kyng' Auferius sonne withoute leese,   2622
And very brother onto Generides ;
who encountered Generydes.   Be fore them) aħ he came hym) self alone,
Generides was ware therof anon).   2625

He toke his spere And mette hym) in the feld,   2626
They toke ther course and ranne to rownde :
he stroke Generydes vppon) the sheld,
That hors and man) Almost were att grownde,   2629
But vppe he rose anon) both hoole and sounde,
And with his swerd he smote hym) so ageyn),
That with that stroke he brake his sheld on) twayn).

They fought till Generydes smote   So fought y^ei stiħ withoute eny drede,   2633
And neyther of them) wold to other yeld ;
Generydes hym) sette so vppon) the hede,
off Ismael's helm,   That his helme flew quyte in to the feld,   2636
With that anon) Generydes beheld
and saw his features.   The fetures wele that was in his visage,
Demyng' that they were aħ of on) lenage.   2639

And for to haue ther of very knowlaching,   2640
To Ismael he said, in very certente,
'Good *ser*,' qu*o*d he, 'for loue of hevyn) kyng',

TeH me for trougth what man*er* a maɳ ye be, 2643 He asked him who he was.
And whense ye came, and owt of what contre ?'
'What maɳ I am,' q*u*od Ismael ayeyɳ,
'And of what kynne I wiH not layɳ. 2646

Kyng⟩ auferius trewly my fader is, 2647 'Auferius is my father,' quoth Ismael.
To say yow sothe, and for to bere noo blame,
And of the Reme of Trace is kyng I wis,
Ther was I borɳ and brougħt vppe iɳ the same, 2650
And Ismael the Savage is myɳ name ;
Now I haue told yow aH withoute leese.'
'Gramercy, frende,' thanne sayd Generydes, 2653 'Gramercy, friend,' said Generydes,

'For we haue fougħt to long I yow ensure.' 2654
With that he toke hym in his armys twoo,
'We are brodereɳ,' q*u*od he, ' of oɳ nature, 'we are brethren.
kyng⟩ auferius my fader is also ; 2657
I may nott tary now, for I must goo,
My felawes hatħ merveH to see me heer,
Butt here after I shaH make yow better chere.' 2660

Thanne ther was aɳ hevy departeng⟩, 2661 There was a heavy parting between them.
hougħ iche of them made to other mone.
Generydes sawe where was thanne comyng⟩
his faders meɳ, wele horsid eue*r*ychone, 2664
And he fuH hevy butt hym self alone,
And they to many as to his entente,
So furth oɳ was he to his felawes went.[1] 2667 Generydes went on to his fellows,

Whanne he was come ther as his felawes were, 2668
They sawe comyng along in a valay and in a valley saw a great people coming to hinder them with a knight at their head.
A grete peopiH, wele dressed in ther geere,
To lette hym and his felawes oɳ the waye, 2671
Thanne was ther oɳ a knygħt in good aray,
Be fore them aH avaunsid hym to ride,
Generydes hym had rigħt sone aspyed ; 2674

[1] MS. *was to his felawes he went.*

Generydes rode
at him, and slew
him.

And furth with all he mette on) the playn), 2675
In sight of all the pepill that were ther,
And Atte first he brast his sheld in twayn),
That thorough owt the body ranne the spere ; 2678

Clarionas saw
this, and recog-
nized her lover.

Clarionas demyd that he was ther,
And to hir mayde she sayde full sobyrly,
'What knyght is that that doth so worthyly ?' 2681

[leaf 14, back]

'It is your loue,' quod she, 'withoute moo.' 2682
'Now good Mirabell, what is your avise ?'
'Trewly,' quod she, 'I trow that it be soo,
Me think it shuld ben) he in) eny wise ; 2685
The rede pensell I see att his devise,
The whiche in sothe ye dede for hym) ordeyn),
Gwynot brought it hym) your Cha[m]berleyn).' 2688

'O trouth,' quod she, 'Madame,[1] that is trew ; 2689
Now am I wele remembryd ther vppon),
Butt euermore my sorow doth renewe,
Withoute reskewe to se hym) so alone, 2692
Thus shall they be distressid euerychone,
Namely my love, whiche is so good a knyght,
ffor hym) is all my mone I yow be hight. 2695

For wele I wote, ther is noo knyght a lyve 2696
That better doith here and in euery place,
And this to say my reson) doith me dryve,
ffor I am his while I haue lyffe and space.' 2699
And while she remembryd all this case

Ismael and
Darell meet,

Come Ismael rideng' with spere and sheld,
And to Darell he ridith in to the feld. 2702

Bothe to the grounde he bare hors and man), 2703
ffurth with came the ost vppon) the playn),
And as ser Darell wold haue Res[k]eu thanne,

[1] ? *Mirabell.*

Ther came a knyght and held hym down Ayeyn, 2706
And with his swerd wold haue Darell slayn,
Butt in the most and in the thikest prese
hym to reskew thanne came Generides. 2709

and Darell would
have been slain,
but was saved
by Generydes,

Streight as he cowde to that knyght he rode, 2710
he brake his helme and stróke hym on the heede,
That on his hors no lengger he a bode,
But downe he fell and fast beganne to blede; 2713
Generydes with hym he toke his stede,
And furth fro them he rode a litill aside,
And toke it Darell theron for to ride. 2716

and they rode
forth together.

Clarionas beheld this euery dele; 2717
Quod she ayeyn to Mirabell here mayde,
'The same is he, the whiche I love so well;
'Madame,' quod she, 'so haue I alway sayde, 2720
ye nede noo thyng for hym to be dismayde,
Nor let no mo suche thoughtez yow assayle,
ffor it is he withoute eny fayle.' 2723

Now rideth Darell with Generides, 2724
As full of thought for his fortune that day,
And as they rode a litill fro the prese,
kyng¹ Auferius came crossyng¹ them the way, 2727
ffull clene armyd in riche and good Aray.
Darell anon dressid hym full right,
And ranne to hym in all that euer he myght. 2730

Auferius crossed
their path,

and Darell rode
at him,

And one the hede smote Auferius the kyng¹; 2731
The helme was sure, or ellys he had hym slayn,
kyng¹ auferius withoute more tarieng¹
he gave ser Darell another for certayn 2734
Vppon the helme, the fyre thanne sprang¹ owt ayeyn,
And ther withall, with a full soden brayde,
To ser Darell right in this wise he saide: 2737

and smote him
on the head.

Auferius gave
him a blow in
return.

'Old men can smite,' quoth he.

'The [1] yong knyghtez,' quod he, 'that ben so prowde,
Old men canne smyte, wete wele it is trew.'

Generydes heard his voice, and knew it was his father.

Generides hard hough he spake so lowde,
And by the voyce his fader thanne he knewe,   2741
Toward them both anon he drewe ;
Whanne he was come in full vmble wise
To his fader, he said right in this wise :   2744

' I praye yow, ser, your hand fro me refrayn,   2745
To the tyme ye knowe my purpose vtterly,

He parted them,

here am I come to departe yow twayn,
ffor I must loue yow bothe and reason whye ;   2748
And namely yow alone most specially,
As for this knyght while my life [2] maye endure,
I shall hym neuer fayle I yow ensure.'   2751

' What maner a man be ye thanne,' saide the kyng,
' That putte your self soo fer [3] furth in the prese ?'
' I shall yow telle,' quod he, ' withoute feyneng ;
Of Surre am I born withoute leese,   2755

told his name,

As for my name I hight Generides.'
And ther with all he tared not certayn,

and joined his fellows.

Butt to [4] his felawes furth he goth ayeyn.   2758

Auferius was dismayed.

Kyng Auferius thanne was sumwhat dismayed,   2759
Be cause that he departid so ayeyn ;
ffor be the wordes whiche he to hym saide,
he was his sonne, he knew it for certayn ;   2762
Yet of the sight of hym he was full fayn,
As nature wold, and in especiall
That he was wexen soo goodly a knyght with all.   2765

Now was the batell dureng still o'pece,   2766
The kynggez ost encresid more and more ;

Said Darell unto Generydes,

Thanne sayd Darell on to Generides,

[1] ? Ye.   [2] MS. list.   [3] MS. for.   [4] MS. he to.

'ffor your' pleasure we shaℍ repente it sore.'   2769   'For your
pleasure we
shall repent
it sore :
'ffor hym)[1],' quod he, ' now good teℍ me wherefore.'
'yes yes,' quod he, ' this is the case,
your' Iee is euer stedfast in on) place.'   2772   your eye is ever

' What place is that ?' [quod he] ' I prae yow saye ;
As for the kyng', I see hym nott I wise.'
'I mene not that,' quod Dareℍ, ' be this daye,
It is another thing', so haue I blis.   2776   [leaf 15]
On yender towre on) highe I see where is   on yonder tower.'
That causiℏ yow these mastereys for to shewe,
Now haue I told yow aℍ wiℏ wordes fewe.'   2779

' In sothe,' quod he, ' ye bere me wrong' in hand,   2780   'In sooth,' quoth
Generydes, 'I saw
her not till now.'
ffor certenly I saugℏ hir not to nowe ;
Sithe she is ther, as now I vnderstonde,
If I do wele she woℍ me more allowe.   2783
Now be not wroth, for by licence of yow
Yet onys I wiℍ assaye what I canne do.'
' I graunt,' quod Dareℍ, ' late vs goo thertoo.'   2786

Generides, and wiℏ hym) ser Dareℍ,   2787
Bothe on) thei rode to knowe what was ther vre ;   They rode on,
And wiℏ Generides was Nataneℍ,
Beryng' a spere of tymber good and sure ;   2790
Generides ther mette att a venture   and Generydes
The kyng' Ruben, Redy with spere and sheld,   met Ruben,
And ther they strake to geder in the feld.   2793

Vppon) the sheld he strake Generides,   2794
And ther with brake his sheld in pecis twayn) :
A mighty man) he was, butt neuer the lesse
Atte same course he smote hym) so ayeyn),   2797   and smote him
from his horse,
That of his hors he felle vppon) the playn),
With that Generides boℏ fair' and wele
his hors he delyuered on) to Nataneℍ.   2800

[1] ? myn.

which he sent

'I pray yow, s*er*,' he saide, ' haue here this stede,   2801
And take ye hym) on to my lady der' ;
Me recomaunding' on to hir' goodly hede,
And say to hir that I haue wonne hym) here.'   2804
'Well s*er*,' q*u*od he, ' as towching' this mater,
late me alone now that I knowe yo*u*r entente,
In all the hast I wull hym) to hir p*r*esent.'   2807

Furth with the steede he went owt of ye prese,   2808

to Clarionas by Natanell.

And streyght he goth on) to Clarionas ;
'Madame,' q*u*od he, ' my lord Generides
hym) reco*m*maundith lowly to your' grace,   2811
And sent yow here a stede of his purchase
And where that he hadde it to tell yow very playn),
Of kyng' Ruben he wanne hym) for c*er*tayn).'   2814

She was right glad.

'Ye be right welcome, Natanell,' q*u*od she,   2815
' Of this I am right gladde and wele content,
And moche gladder to knowe the certente
Of his welefare that hath yow heder sent.'   2818
'Madame,' q*u*od he, ' right now encontynent
I wold that he hym) self were with yow here.'
' With me,' q*u*od she, ' so wold I that he were.'   2821

Natanell returned to Generydes,

Thanne Natanell departid furth w*ith* all,   2822
And had a token) onto Generides ;
In to the feld he goth amòng' them all,
And founde hym) ther aside hand of the prese,   2825

and told him all.

And furth with all told hym the [1] hoole processe,
In eu*er*y thing' that he hadde done and saide,
Tho was Generides full wele apayed ;   2828

He took courage,

And ther with all he toke anon) corage,   2829
And to the feld he dressid hym) to ride ;
Of yong' and old and eu*er*y man) of age

[1] MS. *all the.*

Ther wer butt few his strokes wold abide. 2832 and few could
abide his stroke.
The kyngges ost drew to the Citez side,
Generides was thanne vppon the playn,
A while ther to rest hym *ther* in certayn. 2835

The kyng¹ of kynggez thanne was in his tente, 2836 The king of
kings
And of aH this he hard no man*er* thing¹ ;
he harde a noyse and wist not what it ment,
But furth he goth leving¹ AH other thing¹, 2839
And toke his hors withoute taryeng¹,
he blew his horn that aH his men myght here, blew his horn,
and his men
With that thei come a¹ bought hym AH in feere. 2842 came about him.

Whanne DareH sawe the kyng¹ of kyngges ost, 2843 Darell prayed
Generydes to
Generydes anon full fayre [he] prayed ; retire into the
city.
'ffor love of god that is of myghtez most,
Goo we in to the Citee now,' he sayde ; 2846
'DareH,' q*uo*d he, 'wher of be ye dismayd ?
I see noo cause, for we shaH do right wele
And skape ther handes, doughte ye neu*er* a dele.' 2849

'I am contente,' q*uo*d he, 'that we do so ; 2850 'I am content,'
quoth he.
As for my part now late vs goo ther on.'
And with hym was ser Anosore Also ;
his horn thanne blew Generides anon, 2853
With that ther came A bowte hym eu*er*ychone,
his felasshepe and what that eu*er* he ment,
Thei were redy atte his co*m*maundment. 2856

And furth they dressid hym in his gere, 2857 He, Darell, and
Anasore have
Generydes, DareH, and Anasor', done bravely.
Might neu*er* men doo better on a day ther,
Thanne they dede ther so fewe pepill as thei were :
Eche of them iij so wele quiete them ther,
They slew iij knyghtez eu[*er*]ychone for on,
The remenaunt were putte to flight eu*er*ychon. 2863

    ¹ MS. *an.*

And while they fougħt to geder in the feld, 2864
The cite sent owt anonɔ in contenent
iij skore knygħtez, Armyd witħ spere And sheld ;
Ther witħ Generides was wele content : 2867
' lo serys !' quod hee, ' Aftur your ownɔ entent,
The felissheppe is yourez that yender ye see,
Now may I suerly entre the Citee.' 2870

They took the way to the city.
[leaf 15, back]

And whanne they were aħ to geder mett, 2871
To the Citee they toke the wey fuħ rigħt,
And in they went withoute eny lette :

Then was there joy.

Thanne was ther Ioy, I yow be higħt, 2874
In euery strete si[n]ggyngᵗ and fyres bright ;
And euery creature, botħ more and lesse,
Gaue a gret lawde onto Generides. 2877

The Sultan anon sent for him and thanked him.

Anonɔ withaħ the Sowdonɔ for hymɔ sent, 2878
And gaue hymɔ ther his thank in feythfuħ wise ;
ffor he perseyuyd wele in his entent,
he hadde hymɔ do rigħt wurchipfuħ seruice : 2881
And ther the Sowdonɔ made hymɔ fuħ promys,
Seyngᵗ his labour' and his grete traveħ,
That in noo wise he wold hymɔ neuer fayle. 2884

The king of kings sent for men of craft to

The kyngᵗ of kyngges erly vppe he rose, 2885
And sent for menɔ of craft in aħ the hast,
To make engenys after his purpose,

break the walls.

The waħis to breke, the Citee for to wast ; 2888
Whanne this was purveyd for thanne atte last,

Ermones said

Kyngᵗ Ermones stode vppe before themɔ Aħ,
And to the kyngᵗ he spake in especiaħ : 2891

' Me think, ser, as after mynɔ avise, 2892
It nedith not to make aħ this arraye,
To distroye the Cite it is noo grete entrepri[se],

It were better to saue it if ye may : 2895 it were better to save it.
ffor yow it were more wurchippe euery waye,
And in your fame the lenger to endur,
To wynne it in the feld I yow ensure.' 2898

' How may that be ? ' thanne saide the kyng Ayeyn,
' Your councell is right good, so mote I goo, 2900
Owt of the town they will nott in certeyn,
What think ye best thanne,' quod he, 'yᵗ we shall doo ? '
' Ser, on my life, ye shall not fynde it soo,
And if ye will enbatell vs euerychone, 'They will come anon out of the
Owt of the Citee thei will come anon ; 2905 city.

I wote my self as wele as eny wight, 2906
ffor ther is on that will be all ther gide ;
In all the world is nott A better knyght
Thanne he is on, and better dare Abide.' 2909
' Nay,' quod the kyng, 'All that shalbe denyed,
ffor in wurchippe and in knyghtoode sekerly
I knowe hym nott that is so good as I. 2912

Notwithstondeng After your good avise, 2913
late vs anon goo sett our feld ayeyn, Let us go set our field again.'
And wheder they or we shall bere the prise,
Ryght sone we shall haue knowlage in certayn.' 2916
Anon withall thei gaderid on the playn
The kyngez ost, and in conclusion
They hym enbatelid streyght as for the town. 2919

Thanne sayde madan, that was the kyng of Trase,
' Me think ye do right wele to sette this feld,
ffor ye shall see withynne a litill space,
They will come owt or ellys them yeld.' 2923 They of the city, came forth
And whanne thei of the Citee them beheld,
hough sone they were enbatelyd euerychone,
They tared not, butt furth they come Alone,¹ 2926

¹ ? anone.

A grete nowmber of men) in good arraye :   2927
Thanne they withoute anon to them) thei hyed,

*and made no
more delay.*
Right sone thei mette, And made no more delaye,
ffull fressh on) [them] thei sette on) euery side,   2930
Darell anon) kyng⸱ Sanyk had Aspyed,

*Darell ran at
King Sanyk,
and broke his
arm in two.*
And with his spere he ranne and smote hym) soo,
That with that stroke he brake his arme on) twoo. 2933

*Barachias, king
of Europe,*
Thanne came rideng⸱ the kyng⸱ barachias,   2934
Of Europe he was lord and Souereyn) ;
Whanne Anasore Aspyed where he was,

*was smitten down
by Anasore.*
To hym) he ranne and smote hym) for certeyn),   2937
That from) his hors he felle vppon) the playn),
And as he fell his legge was brokyn) soo,
That from) the grownde he myght noo ferther goo. 2940

Thanne the kyng⸱ of Trace putt hym) self in prese, 2941

*Madan, the king
of Thrace,
was slain by
Generydes.*
Madan he hight so as I vnderstounde,
To hym) anon) thanne ranne Generides,
Right wele armed, a good spere in his hande,   2944
Ther myght no maner harnesse hym) withstonde ;
ffor thoroughowt he strake hym) quyte And clene,
That atte bak the rede pensell was sene ;   2947

And with that stroke he fell and ther he dyed. 2948

*The king
of kings*
The kyng⸱ of kynggez harkenyd of that case,
he taryd not nor lenger wold⸱ Abide,
Butt rideth furth streyght in to the place   2951
Ther as Madan the kynggez body was,

*beheld it with
a heavy cheer.*
And it beheld with a full hevy chere,
Complayneng⸱ sore [1] A pitevous thing⸱ to here.   2954

He hadde hym) do right wurchipfull seruice,   2955
And harmones, the kyng⸱ of higher ynde,
That what so euer he dede in eny wise

[1] MS. *sone.*

Thoo ij princes wer' neu*er* owt of his mynde :   2958
And for be cause they wer' to hym) so kynd,
And sware his othe as he was rightwise kyng',
Ther deth he wold' avenge for eny thing'.   2961

And in this hast he rode in to the feld',   2962
Abell that was of perse the Ban*ere*,
To hym) he Ranne and smote hym) thorough ye sheld',
ffor thorough owt ye harnes persid ye spere,   2965
And afterward he bought that stroke full dere,
And with his swerd he smote hym) ayeyn),
And slew hym) or he passid owt of the playn).   2968

He rode to the field and slew Abell, the standard-bearer of Persia.

[leaf 16]

Grete hevynes made his felissheppe all,   2969
Whanne thei *per*seyued suerly how it was,
And first and formest in especiall,
The dede body they caryed from) the place   2972
To the Citee not half a myle of space,
And as the Costom was, after ther gise,
They beryed hym[1] in honorabill wise.   2975

The batell thanne enduryd passing sore,   2976
And many lordes slayn) on) eu*ery* side,
They of the town) had fought so long' afore,
That thei ne myght noo lenger ther abide,   2979
And to the Citeewarde furst ganne they ride ;
Yet or they were ent*er*ed eu*er*ychone,
Of them ther were distressid manye on).   2982

They of the town rode city-ward,

and many of them were distressed.

The Sowdon) was as woode as he myght be,   2983
To see his knyghtes stande in suche distresse,
All full of thought and counfortles was he ;
To hym) anon) thanne seid Generides,   2986
'Good s*er*,' q*uo*d he, ' take ye no man*er* of hevynesse,
Now shynneth the sonne and [now] god sendith showrez,
This day was therys, A nother[2] shalbe ourez.   2989

The Sultan was mad to see them.

Generydes said,

---

[1] MS. *them*   [2] MS. *And A noth*er*

'Let us rest
a day or two,

And late vs rest as for a daye or twayne,   2990
That your' pepiłł may haue refresshing',

and give them
battle again.'

Thanne we wolle geve them) batełł new ageyn),
Withoute delaye and lenger taryeng',   2993
And witħ the grace of god and good gideng' ;
And trust suerly, ye shałł wele vnderstonde,
That we shałł haue of them) the ouer hande.'   2996

Now they haue refresshid them) trewly,   2997
And are redy ther enmys to Assayle,[1]
A thowsand knyghtez in A companye,
And furtħ they went to geve them) new batełł,   3000
Witħ grete corage in knyghthode to prevayle ;
And whanne the toder meny them) behelđ,
Anon) they came and mette them) in the feld.   3003

And in a vały togederwarđ they went,   3004

The battle then
began anew.

The batełł thanne beganne new ayeyn),
No trewys was taken) ne noo poyntement,
Butt strong' feightyng' and many knyghtez slayn) ; 3007
Generides, for to sey yow certeyn,
Whom) that euer he mette vppon) the grene,
ffrom) his sadiłł he wente quyte And clene.   3010

Syr Anasore the knygħt, And ser Darełł,   3011
And Ałł the toder knyghtez euerychone,
Eche for his parte quyte hym) self fułł wele,

The king's
host fled.

And of the kynges ost slew many on) ;   3014
The remenaunte remevid bak anon),
And as thei fled, the writeng' makitħ mynd,

Ermones,

Come Ermones, the kyng' of higher ynd,   3017

with his mighty
men and their
foul weapons,
(see p. 60, p. 80,)

Witħ myghti men) of mervelous makyng',   3018
like as it is rehersid here before ;
Ther wepons fowle and iłł faryng',

[1] MS. *Assoyle.*

Wher with they layde on) stroke[s] grete And sore.
Kyng Ermones, to say yow ferthermore,
Ser Anosore right sone he had Aspied, rode at Sir
And furth with all to hym) he ganne ride : 3024 Anasore,

With his wepon) long and ill faryng, 3025
he slew his hors and smote hym) on) the hede, slew his horse,
And in the feld he left hym) liggeng, and left him
Demyng non) other butt that he was dede, 3028 lying in the field for dead.
With Anosore ther was non other rede,
Butte vppe he rose as god wold geve hym) *grace*,
And to his felawes furth he goth a pase. 3031

Hym to a venge his thought was and his mend, 3032
And sone he was vppon) another stede, Anasore got
Streyght he rideth to a knyght of ynde, another steed, and slew a
And with a swerd he cleue a ij his hede, 3035 knight of India.
That in the feld he felle ther and was dede :
Whanne Ermones wist of this Aventure, Ermones
A hevy man) he was I[1] yow ensur, 3038

And streyght he rideth onto Generides : 3039 rode at
Butt[2] he anon) was ware of his comyng, Generydes,
And with a naked swerd in to the prese
Ayenst hym) full fast he come rideng ; 3042
As sone as Ermones the kyng
Sawe that he was withynne his wepons length,
Anon) he smote Att hym) with all his strength. 3045 and smote at him,

His wepon) light vppon) Generides, 3046
And brast his sheld with all in pecys twayn), breaking
Also it ranne down) quyte thorough the harnes, his shield.
A grace of god that he had not ben) slayn) ; 3049
Ther with Generydes smote hym) ayeyn), Generydes clave
Thoroughowt the helme a hye vppon) the crest, his head to the breast.
And claue his hede streyte down) to the brest. 3052

[1] MS. *h.* [2] MS. *Be.*

And with that stroke kyngᵗ Ermones was ded ;   3053
ffor hym) his knyghtez made grete ordenaunce,

*His men
carried him off,*

They hym) with drew, ther was non) other rede,
And fast they hyed them) owt of ther distaunce,   3056
Thinkyngᵗ them) self owt of good gouernaunce,

[leaf 16, back]

And as they rode togeder complaynengᵗ,

*and met King
Belen,*

Vppon) the way they mette Boleyn) the kyngᵗ ;   3059

*who would have
had them turn,*

And fayn) he wold haue them) turne ayeyn),   3060
Comfortid them) in all that euer he myght,
Butt All that euer he spak it was in vayn) ;
With that anon) ther answerd hym) a knyght,   3063
And as the story seith Otran he hight,
'Of our fortune in euery thyngᵗ,' quod he,
'I shall suerly telle yow the certente.   3066

*but they said,
'In yonder host
is a knight who
is a very fiend,*

In yender ost,' quod he, 'ther is a knyght,   3067
he is noo very man), what euer he be,
Butt rather a fende, and that I yow be hight,
Ther is no man) alyve that he wolle flee ;   3070

*and hath slain
our king.'*

Oure kyngᵗ is ded, whiche sore repentith me.
And suche a prince we canne not gete ayeyn),
And he it is suerly that hath hym) slayn).'   3073

*Belen seeks
Generydes,*

Whanne kyngᵗ Bolyn) had knowlage of yᵗ case,   3074
A hevy man) he was and comforteles,
And furth with all he rideth on a pace,
All in a rage sechingᵗ Generides,   3077
And ther they mette togeder in the prese,
Thanne was the batell all togeder doon),

*but they were
parted.*

So att that tyme thei were departid sone.   3080

*The men of
Persia won
the day.*

The men) of perce that day were fortenat,   3081
The toder fled as fast as euer thei might,
And in hym) self they stode soo desolate ;

Whanne kyng' Bolyn) saw they were putte to fligħt,
That in noo wise they wold no lenger fight,
With hym) ther was non) other poyntement,
Butt lost the feld and rideth to his tent.   3087

Too the Citee rideth Generides,   3088   Generydes rides
With knygħtes and with Sqyers many on),   to the city,
ffor hym) was made grete Ioy of more And lesse,   and is received
And festis made among' them eu[er]ychon).   3091   with great joy.
Thanne to the Sowdon) furth he went anon),
Of whom) he hadde his thank right specially,
And grete yeftys as he was wele worthy.   3094

The kyng' of kynggez still was in his tent,   3095   The King of
And yndly wroth that no man) cowde hym) plese,   kings was wroth,
And in hym) self he cowde not be content,   and would not
                                                            be content till
Till he had fougħt with Generides,   3098   he fought
They twayn) to geder owt of all the prese,   with Generydes.
And ther vppon) he callid his councell,
That his entent the souner mygħt prevayle.   3101

At his callyng' his lordes came anon),   3102   He called his
And this he sayde, that euery man mygħt here,   council.
'Now ye be here in present euerychon,   'We have been
This is,' quod he, 'the effecte of my mater,   3105   here now a
                                                            quarter of a
It is now a full quarter of a yere,   year,' said he,
Oure lyeng' her the Sowdon) for to wynne,
And att this day we are new to be gynne.   3108   'and have to
                                                            begin anew.

And yet I wote right wele it lithe in me,   3109
The Sowdon) to distroye and all his lande,
Of all maner vitayle I haue plente ;
Notwithstondyng', if he will take on) hand   3112   Let the Sultan
                                                            find a knight to
To fynde a knyght, that I may vnderstond   fight with me,
Be right wele born and of high lenage,
To fight with me for all this Eritage,   3115

And so to make an ende of all this werre   3116
Betwix vs twayne ; and if he wold not so,
I will distroye his land both nyghe and ferre,
his land and hym self where euer hee goo,   3119
And for the Accompleshment Also,
Be cause I wold that it shuld be endid sone,
Withynne iiij dayes I wold that it were done.'   3122

King lamadon gave answere in this case,   3123
And in his speche he was som what dismayed,
This cowardly his hert and his seruice
Was to the Sowdon, what so euer he sayde ;   3126
Yet not for thy his reasone furth he layde
All opynly ; 'my lordes,' quod he,
'The kyng hath seid right wele as semyth me.'   3129

For this cause he gaue sone his assentt,   3130
That in that space a trety myght be hadde ;
And as he seid all other were content,
Thanne was the kyng of kynggez passing glad,   3133
And vppon these iij lordes wise and sadde
A poyntid were to goo on this massage,
Onto the Sowdon and his Baronage.   3136

On of them iij of Corynth¹ was he born,   3137
Callid Sampsone, the story doth expresse ;
The secunde, and his ancetors be forn,
In Damask born, the writeng doth witnesse,   3140
A man of wurchippe and of grete sadnesse ;
The iijᵈᵉ was a man, to say yow right,
Of Ethiope, and Ionathas he hight.   3143

Anon these lordes went on ther message,   3144
Eche man A brawnche of Olyve in his hande,
In token of pece for ther viage,

¹ MS. *Cornyth.*

and make an end of this war.'

Three lords were appointed to go to the Sultan,

each with a branch of olive.

Too goo and come saff, as I vnderstonde, 3147
lyke as the custom) was in euery lande ;
So fourth they went withoute more[1] delay,
To the Sowdon) ther errand for to say. 3150 [leaf 17]

And whanne that thei were come to his presence, 3151 They came to
Of ther massage they kept noo thyng⟨ in store, the Sultan
 and told him
Butt in aff the hast they told hym) the sentence, the message,
like as it is rehersid here before, 3154
In euery maner thing⟨ and summe[2] what more,
So as the kyng⟨ gave them) in commaundment,
Accordeng⟨ sum what onto his entent ; 3157

The whiche was this, to say yow in substaunce, 3158 and that he
 should send
That he shuld send his doughter to the kyng⟨, his daughter to
And by that meane the striff and variaunce the King.
Be twix them) bothe myght the souner haue endyng.[3]
ffor an answere in ther ayeyn) goyng⟨,
Of ther massag⟨ they praed them) to say
In aff this mater playnly ye or nay. 3164

Whanne ther massag⟨ was aff to geder sayde, 3165
Ther was noo lord nee knyght that gave answer⟨, The lords were
 silent and the
Wher with trewly the Sowdon) was dismayde ; Sultan dismayed.
Generides sawe that, and drew hym) nere : 3168
' Ser, if it like your⟨ goodnes for to here,
I shaff for yow,' quod he, ' be in this place,
Be your⟨ licence geve answer in this case.' 3171

And thus he sayde be fore them) eu[er]ychon) : 3172
' Thez massangers they shaff wele vnderstonde,
Among⟨ your⟨ knyghtez aff that ther is on)
Shaff vnder take to Answer⟨ for this lande ; 3175 Generydes
 undertook to
ffor I my self wiff take it att ther hand, answer for the
 land.
And here is my glove, this mater to defende,
Withynne iiij dayes therof to make an ende. 3178

[1] MS. *wordes more.* [2] MS. *sunne.* [3] MS. *an end.*

Generydes
guaranteed that
no dishonour
should befall
Clarionas.

And your' doughter also, Clarionas,   3179
he shall do hir no maner of villanye,
Nother dishonour, whill I haue liff and space,
And ferthermore I vnderstonde trewly,   3182
By ther massage declaryd opynly,
Ther shall now take of hym this enterprise,
Butt he be wele born in eny wise.   3185

And to that ye shall wele knowe my councell,   3186
Was neuer man herd so moche of me ;
A kyngges sonne I am withoute fayle,
And my moder is a quene in certayn[te] :   3189
here afterward ye shall wele know and see,
All though he be a prince of nobyll fame,
To fight with me to hym shalbe noo shame.'   3192

Whanne the Sowdon perseivid his entent,   3193
And herd hym wele in all that euer he sayde,
T.e Sultan was
glad.
Thanne was he gladde and verily well content,
That he was of so good a knyght purveyd ;   3196
Yet with hym self he was nott wele apayde,
And in his mende repentid hym full sore,
That he so meche had wrongid hym before.   3199

Whanne these lordes had answere in this wise,   3200
One of the lords
said Generydes
should take
advice before
meddling with
a prince that
was peerless.
One of them sayde on to Generides ;
' It is well don that ye take a good avise,
Or that ye putt your' self so ferre in prese,   3203
To medyll with a prince that is perles ;
ffor he is knowen in contres ferre and nere.'
Generides anon gave hym answere,   3206

Generydes said,
' Your king is
a noble knight,
And this he sayde, in presence of them all ;   3207
' As for your' kyng', he is a nobill knyght
I canne wele think, and so men do hym calle ;

Butt my quareⱦ is growndid vppoꝺ rigⱦt,   3210
Whiche gevitⱨ me corage for to figⱨt,
And here my trowtⱨ I wolle ꝺot fayle my day,   *but I will not*
My self alone, and so I pr*ae* yow saye.'   3213   *fail my day.'*

They toke his glove, And to that prince thei went 3214
Witⱨ thcr answere in eu*er*y man*er* thing¹ :
And of Generides and his entent
ffuⱦ playnly thei told onto the kyng¹ :   3217
And whanne that he ther of had knowlaching,
The kyng¹ hyꝺ self, withoute eny more,   *The king*
Ayenst that day he purveyd hyꝺ therfore.   3220

Too aⱦ his ost he gave A speciaⱦ charge,   3221 *gave his host*
Ayenst that day that he shuld figⱨt alone,   *charge to remove*
They shuld remeve that place ij myle large,   *two miles away,*
And ther to geder abide eu*er*ychoꝺ   3224
What eu*er* faⱦ, for reskewe wolḋ he noꝺ ;   *for rescue would*
And ther vppoꝺ, to folow his entent,   *he none.*
To themꝺ he gave a streigⱨt commaundment.   3227

The Citesens thanne was not wele apayde,   3228 *The citizens were*
Be cause Generides to[ke] this in hand :   *not pleased,*
They love[d] hyꝺ so wele, and this they said,
' A better knygⱨt ther is in noo land.'   3231
And whanne Clarionas ded vnderstonde   *and Clarionas*
That he shuld take vppoꝺ hyꝺ this bateⱦ,   *was full of*
Thanne was she fuⱦ of thougⱨt and noo merveⱦ. 3234 *thought,*

' Now, good Mirabeⱦ, what is best ? ' q*uo*d she, 3235
' What shaⱦ I doo ? saye me your² good avise.'
And said, ' wold god he wold do Aftur me,
Thanne shuld he not take this interprise.'   3238
' Nay, late be that in eny man*er* wise,
Madame,' q*uo*d she, ' for sothe he hatⱨ it take,
ffor his wurchipp*e* he may it not for sake.   3241

Nether he wiłł, Madame, I telle yow playṇ.'   3242
'Now thanne,' quod she, 'me think this is to dooṇ;
I wiłł send hyṃ Gwynot my chaunberleyṇ,
This rede pensełł I wiłł send hyṃ anoṇ;   3245

[leaf 17, back]

And or that he oṇ the batełł gooṇ,
ffor esing⸍ of my hert I wiłł hyṃ praye,
To speke witħ me to morow or to day.'   3248

'That is wele doo,' quod she, 'withoute lese.'   3249

and sent for
Generydes

Thanne chargyd she hir chaumberleyṇ to goo:
'hye yow,' quod she, 'onto Generides;
This rede pensełł ye shałł bere hyṃ also,   3252
Whiche I myself enbrowdred and no moo:
Pray hyṃ also or he passe the Citee,

to come and
speak with her.

In eny wise that he wiłł speke with me.'   3255

On this massage now gotħ hir chaunberleyṇ,   3256
And to Generides he takitħ the waye,
Witħ hir tokyṇ and ałł hir errand playṇ,
In ałł the hast possible that he may;   3259
And he also for gate nott for to say,
On hir behalf afore his departeng⸍,
hir for to seè leving⸍ ałł other thing⸍.   3262

Generydes was
glad of this,

Off that massage Generides was fayṇ,   3263
And furtħ witħ ałł rewardid hyṃ rigħt wełł;
he sent a tokeṇ oṇ to hir ayeyṇ,
Bee cause that she shuldᵗ vnderstonde and fele,   3266
That he had doṇ his massage euery dele,
And ferthermore he chargid hyṃ to say,

and promised to
see her soon.

he woldᵗ see hir in ałł the hast he may.   3269

Now gotħ Gwynot[1] vnto Clarionas,   3270
And told hir what he had doṇ that day.
Generides, whanne he had tyme and space,

[1] MS. *Gwynan.*

To hir chaunber he toke the redy waye ;   3273   He came to her
                                                          chamber window.
And att a wyndow, sothely for to say,
he spake to hir, right as he wold devise,
Att good leysere in honorabill wise.   3276

Whanne he departid ther was grete hevynes,   3277
And as he toke his leve in his goyngᵗ
Thanne eche to other made to geder full promyse,   Each to other
                                                          made promise
To kepe hymᴅ trew aboue all other thingᵗ,   3280   to be true.
Now late vs thanne speke of Belenᴅ the kyng,
Whiche att his day thinkyth with spere and sheld
hymᴅ self alone to come into the feld.   3283

The iijᵈᵉ morow, as sone as it was day,   3284   On the third
                                                          day King Belen
kyngᵗ Belynᴅ rose and made hym all redy,
his stede morcll trappyd in good arraye,
With his harnes enbrowderyd by and by,   3287
hymᴅ self armyd full wele and full sure[ly],   armed himself,
his helme was wele ordeynyd for the nonys,
Right wele garnysshed with perle & precious stonys.

Kyngᵗ Bellynᴅ rideth in to the feld alone,   3291   and rode to
                                                          the field.
As it appoynted was betwix themᴅ twaynᴅ ;
his pepill were avoydid euerychone,
And ther he taryed still vpponᴅ the playnᴅ,   3294
Supposingᵗ well ther was no manᴅ certeynᴅ,
Consideryngᵗ his manhod and his myght,
Wold be so bold ayenst hymᴅ to fight.   3297

The tidynggez thorough owt the Cite sprongᵗ,   3298
hough kyngᵗ Bellynᴅ was armed in the mede,
Generides thought he was passingᵗ longᵗ,   Generydes
                                                          mounted his
And furth anonᴅ was brought Grissell his stede, 3301   horse Grisell,
A myghti hors and very sure atte nede ,
The Sowdonᴅ gave it hymᴅ in certente,
Whiche no manᴅ shuld haue saue only he.   3304

Hys trappo*ur* was made in the fressest wise,   3305
Wrougħt with peerlys of mervelus makyng͛,
hym͜ self armyd atte poynte devise,
his helme witħ stonys had his garnysshyng͛ ;   3308
ˑThe rede penseħ vppon͜ his spere hangyng͛,
hym͜ to behold and Iuge withoute dougħt,
A knygħt hym͜ semyd for to be rigħt stougħt.   3311

and all the
people prayed

Aħ the pepyħ that in the Citee were,   3312
Men͜ and women͜ to prayer they them͜ gave,
Besechyng͛ god, with devout man*er*,

God to speed
him.

To spede hym͜ weħ ther contre for to save :   3315
Clarionas, good tidenggez for to haue,
late nee erly she wold nott seese,
Butt nygħt And day prayed for Generides.   3318

The Sultan
brought him
to the gate,

The Sowdon͜ brougħt hym͜ streigħt on͜ to yᵉ gate, 3319
And in like wise the Citezens eu*er*ychon͜),
And whanne that they had brougħt hym͜ Aħ *yer* at,

and he rode
forth alone,

he toke his leve and furtħ he rode alone   3322
In to the mede, and ther he founde anon͜

and found the
King of kings.

The kyng͛ of kynggez vppe and down͜ rideng͛,
And he anon͜ to hym͜ com͜ waloping͛.   3325

Whanne kyng͛ Bellyn͜ saw he was comyng͛,   3326
To hym͜ he rode, and mette hym͜ on͜ the waye,

' Say me sooth,'
quoth Belen,
' whether thou
art a messenger
or nay.'
' I am,' said
Generydes,
' and this is my
message :

' Now say me sotħ,' q*uo*d he, ' withoute feyning͛,
Wheder art thu a massang*er* or nay ? '   3329
' I am,' q*uo*d he, ' a massanger I saye ;
This way I take for my rigħt viage
ffro the Sowdon͜, and this is my massage.   3332

To warre vppon͜ my lord thu dost hym͜ wrong͛,   3333
he sent the word now, whanne I cam͜ hym͜ fro,

Void my lord's
ground,

To voyde his grownde and tary not to long͛,

Vnto thy contre wher thu hast to do :   3336
This thinkith me best, and if thu wilt do so,
Ayeyn) I will goo as a massanger,
And full trewly declare hym) thynne answer'.   3339

And if thu will not follow myn) avise,   3340   [leaf 18]
Thu shallt wele knowe that I am not come on) massage,
Peraventur' thu may[1] repent it twyes,   *if not thou*
                                                                  mayst repent it.'
That thu hast askid of this lande trevage ;   3343
To kepe it fre and owt of all seruage
I shall my self, as for this landis right,
With goddes grace defende it as a knyght.'   3346

And kyng' Bellyn) whanne his purpose hard',   3347   King Belen
And wherefore that he came in to the feld',
Thanne wex he pale and chaungyd clene his mode,   waxed pale ;
hym) self anon) he closed in his sheld ;   3350
Generides his countenaunce behelde,
he tared not butt dressid hym) in his gere,
And in his hande anon) he toke his spere.   3353

Thanne was no more a do butt on they sett,   3354
Anon) they Ranne to geder in the feld,   they ran together,
The kyng' and he fresshly ther they mette,
And eche of them) smote other on the sheld,   3357   and smote each
                                                                  other with great
With strokez grete, and bothe ther sperys helde,   strokes.
So ther vppon) they tared not certayn),
Butte furth with all they toke ther course ayeyn).   3360

Ther stedys were both Inly good and weight ;   3361
Generides came rounde vppon) the grownde,   In another
                                                                  course Generydes
And brake the kynggez helme before his sight,   brake the King's
                                                                  helm,
The spere went to the vesage quyte and rownde,   3364
Duryng' his liff it myght be know that wound.
The kyng' ayenward strake Generides   and the King
                                                                  pierced his
Vppon) the side, and perisshed the harnes   3367   harness

                    [1] MS. *may it.*

so that the blood
ran down.

Vnto the skynne; the blode ranne down) therby, 3368
Butt, as god wold, he felt no harme in dede.

He said in
mockery,

Thanne saide the kyng sum what in mokkery,
'Maister,' quod he, 'thy side begynne for to blede,
Wherefore this is my councell and my rede,
ffor this mater noo lenger for to stryff,

'Go home again,
and escape alive.'

Go home ageyn) and thu shalt skape alyve.' 3374

'I know,' quod he, 'that on) lyve I may skape, 3375
And so I shall wheder thu wilt or noo,

'The bleeding,'
said Generydes,
'is but a jape;
think of the
wound on your
face.'

The bledingge of my side is butt a Iape,
It encreasith my corage to and too; 3378
In thi vesage think on) thy wounde also,
The whiche shall neuer a way I the ensure,
Whill that yⁿ art a lyvez creature.' 3381

The King was
wrother,
and they ran
another course;

Thanne was the kyng¹ wrother, I yow behight; 3382
They toke ther course and ranne to geder new,
And ther the stedis mette with suche a myght

horses and men
went down.

Ther hors foundred, and, for to say yow trew, 3385
Bothe hors and man) and all yer ouer threw;
They of the Citee sawe that encownteryng¹,
And hough it was befall euery thing¹. 3388

And ferd they were as for Generides, 3389

Clarionas
was heavy
for Generydes.

ffull hevy was Clarionas thanne also,
And euer more in prayours still opese,
Vnto the tyme she knew it shuld goo. 3392
of that fortune kyng Bellyn) was full woo,
So was Generides a bashed¹ also thore,

They rose up,

Butte vppe they rose, to say yow ferthermore, 3395

and without
knowing it
changed horses,
and went at
each other with
their swords.

And chaungyd horses onto them) bothe vnknowyng,²
Wherefore they were full wroth, I yow ensure;
To geder thanne they went with swordes drawe,

¹ MS. and bashed.   ² So MS. ? vnknowe.

And leyde on strokes owt of all mesure,   3399
Generides sward was passing sure,   *Generydes'*
And, as the story wele remember canne,   *sword had*
                                                         belonged to the
It was a princes callid Iulyan,   3402   *Emperor Julian.*

Wniche was sumtyme of Rome the Emp*erour* ;   3403
The Sowdon had it after his deceasse,
And as a tresour every day and owre
he kept that sward in grete tendernesse,   3406
And after gaue it on to generides ;
So ferthermore, as I this mater feele,
Whanne eche of them had beten other wele,   3409

The kyng of kynggez seid to hym ayeyn,   3410   The King of
' What aylith the to fight for this mater ?   kings said to him.
                                                         ' Why dost thou
A grete foly for the take the payne,   fight thus ? it
To the it towchith not in no man*er* ;   3413   toucheth thee
                                                         not.
I councell ther for, while *th*ow art here,
Be come my man, and thu wilt do so   Become my man,
The pese shall sone be twix vs twoo.   3416

I shall also in wurchipp*e* the avaunce,   3417   I will advance
And largely departe with the also ;   thee,
ffor meche better it lith in my puessence,
Thanne in the Sowdon powre so to do :   3420
And for Clarionas I say also,   and when
                                                         Clarionas is
Whanne she is myn, here what I say to the,   mine thou shalt
Att thy pleasure hir shalt thu haue of me.   3423   have her.

And thu wilt not do as I the saye,   3424
I late the now haue knowlage vterly,
That of my hand here shalt thu dye to daye ;   If not thou shalt
Troste noo lenger to my curtessy,   3427   die to-day.'
I haue entretyd the full Ientelly,
And how thu wilt be rewlid in this case,
Say ye or nay, or ye go owt of this place.'   3430

Thanne furth with all Answered Generides,   3431
'To thy seruice,' quod he, 'if I me bynde,
I se right wele I may sone haue my pece ;

But that was neuer enprentid in my mende,   3434

'I cannot be
untrew to my
promise ;

To be vntrew it come me neuer of kynde ;
That I haue said and take of my promys,
O trowth I will not breke it in noo wise.   3437

and as for
Clarionas, I will
never have her
of thee.'

And forthermore, as for Clarionas,   3438
I vnderstonde thu proferest hir to me,
Whiche is not thyne truly ne neuer was,
And suche a yeft is litill worth parde ;   3441
ffor one thing shall I say in certente,
If I hir shall reioyse, so god me save,
Of the playnly hir will I neuer haue.'   3444

The king was
more wroth
than ever,
and they went
together again.

Thanne was the kyng mech wrother than before, 3445
And on they went to geder now ayen ;
Thanne eyther other layde wonder sore,
Wherof the sownd rebowndid on the playn,   3448

The stede that was the kynggez for certayn
Vnder Generides beganne to fayle,
Whiche hym abasshed sore and noo mervell.   3451

The kynggez stede was alwey good and sure   3452
ffor all his labour, yet onnese he swett ;
he saw right wele ye toder myght not dure,
Wherefore on hym right fressly[1] he sett,   3455
The shulders of ther horsez to geder mett ;
Generides vppon the feyntid stede,

Streyght to the grownde hors a[nd] man yede.   3458

His sword fell
from his hand,
but he caught it
again,

His swerd ther with ou[t] of his hand it fell,   3459
Butt as god wold he had it sone ayeyn,
he lay not long but riseth fayre and still,

[1] ? fersly.

And furth he goth, to sey yow for certayn,   3462
To kyng' Bellyng', And toke hym be the reyne.   *and seized the king's bridle.*
he sporyd his hors and from hym wold haue goo ;[1]
'A bide,' quod he, 'thu shalt not skape me soo.   3465

This stede,' he seith, ' hath seruyd the full wele,   3466
The whiche trewly repentith me full soore,
Ayenst my will thu hast hym euerydele,
Butt now o trowth thu shalt haue hym no more,   3469
This stede is myn, thu wist it wele [be]fore ;   *'This steed is mine,*
A light anon withoute wordes moo,   *alight anon.'*
Or suerly I shall make the or I goo.'   3472

The kyng' presid fast away certayn,   3473   *The king pressed away,*
Generides helde still the reane alway ;   *but Generydes held the rein,*
And so be twix the striving' of them twayn,   *and between them the horse*
The horse reversid bak, and ther he lay.   3476   *fell backward.*
Generides anon to hym ganne say,
' Not long agoo thu haddist me in this plight,
And now I trost to god I shall the quyte.'   3479

Generides his swarde toke in his hande,   3480   *Generydes took his sword Claryet*
Claryet it hight, the store tellith me so,
A better swerd ther was neuer in noo land.
The kyng' arose and wold a gon hym froo,   3483
ffor of his fayling' ther he was full woo ;
Generides was noo thyng' evill apayde,
And with his swerd full fast on hym he layde.   3486   *and laid on the King full fast,*

The kynges sheld he made a quarter lesse,   3487   *cutting a piece off his shield,*
The swerd' is glansid down on his kne,   *and breaking the harness on*
And ther is[2] brake asonder the harnes,   *his knee.*
That all to geder bare a man myght see :   3490
The kyng' Bellyn was wrothe as he myght be,   *The King wounded him*
he strake att hym with a full eger will,   *in the teeth.*
And in the tethe he woundid hym full ill.   3493

       [1] MS. *goon*.   [2] *? it.*

'Now,' said he, 'I have quit you.'

Thanne seyde the kyng¹, 'now att aH aventur'   3494
I haue the quyte, and ther of am I fayn,
The nexst that I the geve I the ensure,
I wiH thu vndersto[n]de it for sertayn :   3497
Ne shaH thu quyte it me ayeyn.'
With thoo wordes wrothe was Generides,
And to the kyng¹ presid stiH opese.   3500

Generydes gave him such a stroke that he cut his ear off.

And thanne suche a stroke he gave hym *yer*   3501
Vppon the helme, the bare visage was sene ;
The swerd was sharpe and ranne down be his ere,
That from the hede he smote it quyte and clene,   3504
And from his swerd it felle vppon the grene :
Thanne ¹ was kyng Bellyn astownyd sore,

The King was abashed.

And in hym self abasshed more and more.   3507

Both were weary, but their hearts were strong.

They were fuH wery bothe, I yow be higħt,   3508
Notwithstondeng¹ ther hartys were fuH strong¹,
On them ther was no pece of harnys right,
Of plate ne mayle, but aH to geder wrong¹ ;   3511
And no wonder, for they foughten long¹,

The King struck again at Generydes,

Yet in his hert for anger and for payn,
The kyng¹ stroke to Generides ayeyn,   3514

and smote him on the head.

And with his swerd he smote [him] on the hede,   3515
That wher he was he wist not vterly ;
'If thu,' q*uo*d he, 'had done after my rede,
Thu shuldest not now haue ben in this parte.'   3518
Generides hym Answeryd trewelly,
'If I noo thyng¹ dede after thynne entent,
Trust me right wele yet did I not repent.'   3521

Generydes in return smote him on the same side where he was hurt before,

And with that worde he smote hym so ayeyn,   3522
And cleue his hede down and hurt hym² sore,
And by fortune it happid so certeyn,

¹ MS. *Thãme*.   ² MS. *hyn*.

Vppon that side that he was hurt before : 3525
he bled so meche he myght stond no more,
Butt to the grownde anon *yer* he felle down),   and he lay in
And sore for blode he lay still in swoune. 3528 a swoon.
                                                   [leaf 19]

Generides stode still and hym be [1] held, 3529
And of the kyng thanne had he grete pite,
he toke hym vppe and layde hym on his sheld ;
Thanne seid the kyng, softely as it wold be, 3532 The King said
' haue here my swerd, I yeld it vppe to the,   softly, ' Here
As to a knyght the wordes,' [2] he saide,   is my sword,
' In all my lyffe that eue*r* I assayde. 3535

Off all this land I geve vppe my quarell, 3536 I give up my
And so I do Clarionas also,   claim to this
ffor certayn butt if she loue yow wele   land and
                                                  Clarionas,
She do no thyng hir part as she shuld do, 3539
And this I wold require yow or ye goo,
That I myght goo ther as my pepill be,   and will pass
And so to passe furth in to my contre.' 3542   forth to my
                                                  country.'

To hym thanne sayde Generides ayeyn, 3543 'I grant this
' All this request I graunt it verely ;'   request,' said
And vppe he toke hym in his armys twayn,   Generydes,
And sett hym on his stede [3] full Ientely. 3546 and set him on
So furth he ridith fayre and soberly ;   his steed again.
Whanne his pepill sawe hym in that mane*r*,   His people met
They mett hym all with a hevy chere. 3549   him with a
                                                  heavy cheer.

Vppon the playn restid Generides, 3550 Generydes rested
Wery and feynte, it was noo synne to saye ;   on the plain,
And whanne he was sum what more att his ease
Toward the Citee streyght he toke the waye. 3553 and then went
They of the town knewe wele be his araye   back to the city
That it was he, and glad thei were eche on,
So furth he came rideng hym self alone, 3556

---

[1] MS. *he*.   [2] So MS. ? *worthiest*.   [3] MS. *stete*.
GENERYDES.   8

with his two swords.

The lords all met him, and all the people

Towarde the Citee girde witħ his swerdez twayɲ :   3557
The lordes aħ mett hyɲ withoute the towɲ,
And aħ the Citezens vppoɲ the playɲ,
Witħ mynstrellys of many A dyuerse sownd,   3560

with royal procession.

Preletys, prestys, witħ riaħ precessioɲ,
And Childryɲ syɲgengꞌ in the fressest wise,
Witħ merthis moo thanne I canne now device.   3563

Clarionas was nothing behind.

Clarionas she was noo thyngꞌ behynd,   3564
Aħ hir counfort was by hir self alone ;
In hir hart she was and in hir mende
As weħ content as aħ they euerychone.   3567

They brought him to the Sultan, who gave him great gifts and thanked him.

To the Sowdoɲ thanne was he brougħt anoɲ
Whiche gave hyɲ yeftez grete for his seruice,
And thankid hyɲ in fuħ specially wise.   3570

Anoɲ with aħ were brought fro dyuerse place,   3571

The best surgeons that could be found came to attend him.

Good sorgeons, the best that cowde be fownde,
And they fuħ sone withynne a litiħ space,
hyɲ vndertoke to make hyɲ hoole and sounde,   3574
Of euery hurt and eke of euery wounde,
Whiche that he had and so to hyɲ thei saide,
Where witħ the Sowdoɲ was fuħ wele apayde.   3577

Belen told his lords he had given up his claim to Persia and Clarionas,

Now kyng Belyɲ lithe in fuħ hevy case,   3578
And told his lordis stondyngꞌ hyɲ before,
Of perce lande and of Clarionas
he hatħ geve vppe his clayme for euermore :   3581
And ther witħ aħ his woundes blede so sore,
his liff cowde no maɲ vnder take certayɲ,

and died of his wounds in a day or two.

And so he dyed withynne a day or twayɲ.   3584

For hyɲ his pepiħ made grete hevynes,   3585
Amongꞌ theɲ self witħ peteuose complayngꞌ,
And in aħ goodly hast thei ganne hyɲ dresse,

In to Egipte his body for to bryng',   3588
With grete estate and honour like a kyng' ;
Whanne that was don) with grete solempnite,
The lordes aH went home in to ther contre.   3591

His people took
his body to
Egypt, and
the lords went
home to their
countries.

Now late vs leue them) in ther contres aH,   3592
In to the tyme thei were sent for ayeyn),
Whiche was not longe, and in especiaH
To make Gwynan¹ ther kyng and souereyn),   3595
Whiche was the kyng' of kyngges sone certayn),
And so thei were agreed on) hym) alone,
he for to Reigne vppon) them) euerychone.   3598

Gwynan, the
King's son,
succeeded him,

And to sey yow in short conclusion),   3599
Be aH the hoole agrement of the lande,
Of Egipte he was kyng' and bare the crown),
Thanne to them) aH seid he, as I wnderstonde,   3602
' Suche maters as my fader toke in hande,
Towchyng' the Sowdon) and Clarionas,
Ye shaH sone wete my plesure in this case.   3605

and told his
people that he
did not give
up his claim
to Persia
and Clarionas.

As for the land of Perce aH maner wayis,   3606
I wiH pleynly declare yow myn) entent,
My lord and fader quyte it in his dayes
Yet for aH that I was not of assentt,   3609
Nor noo wise I canne not be content ;
And in like wise as for clarionas,
I wiH not be agreyd, nor neuer was.'   3612

Thanne was ther a man) of grete powre,   3613
A knyght that was wele cherisshed with yᵉ kyng',
he was right weel betrost both ferr' and neere,
What euer he saide or dede in eny thyng',   3616
A witty man), And subtiH in werkyng',
Ser YueH the Barn), the story seith he hight,
This was his name to say the very right.   3619

There was a
subtil knight,

Sir Yvell the
Barn,

¹ MS. Swynan.

[leaf 19, back]
to whom the
King in secret
told his love for
Clarionas.

In secrete wise the kyng⟨ saide to the knyght,   3620
'I shall yow telle my fortune as it was:
It happyd me,' quod he, 'I had a sight
Vppon the towre of faire Clarionas,   3623
And here I loue ; play[n]ly this is the case :
here to reioyse I wold haue sought the wayes,
Butt I for bare it in my faders dayes.   3626

'How can I
best obtain
her?'

The knight said,

And now I prae yow telle me your⟨ avise,   3627
hough I myght best to my purpose Attayne.'
The knyght anon gave answere in this wise :
'To folow your⟨ entent, I wold be fayn   3630
To putt ther to my diligence and payn,
And in this case I hope to do so wele,
That ye shall haue your⟨ pleasure euery dele.   3633

'I must have
a swift ship
prepared for
seven years,

and in that time
I shall convey
her to this
country.'

Butt I must haue A shippe bothe good and wight,   3634
And that it be right swiff vnder a saile ;
ffor vij yere it must be redy dight,
With men I now and plente of vitalle,   3637
And in that tyme withoute eny fayle,
I shall conveeye hir in to this contree,
And peraventur⟨ souner so may it be.'   3640

A ship was
provided,

and the wind
was ready.

With his promys the kyng⟨ was wele content,   3641
And thankyd hym right hertely therfore :
A Shippe was purveyd after his entent,
With all that is rehersid here before,   3644
And as fortune kepith here thanke in store,
And Shewith favour⟨ to suche as ben full ill,
Come was the wynde full redy att his will.   3647

He sailed to
the land of
Persia,
and found a
haven

So long⟨ he sayleth as I vnderstonde,   3648
That of the lande of Perse he hadde a sight ;
Whanne he came nere a havyn ther he fownde,

And thederwarð he toke the way fuH right :   3651
Whanne thei were in, as fast as euer thei myght,
Ther ancers owt thei cast on euery side,   *where he cast anchor,*
ffor ther awhile they cast them to Abide.   3654

Vppon that havyn ther was a faire Citee,   3655
Whiche stode fuH fayre vppon the Ryvers side ;
This knyght anon owt of the shippe goth he,
Butt twayn with hym and on to be his gide,   3658   *and landed with two others, and a guide.*
The remenaunt shuld in the shippe a bide   *The rest he ordered*
A day or twayne, and thanne, in craft[r][y] wise,
Go to the town be waye of merchaundise,   3661

To bye and seH as thei see other doo,   3662   *to buy and sell till they heard of him again.*
Vnto the tyme they hard of hym ayeyn.
So gothe he furth withoute wordes moo,
And as he went, he mette vppon the playn   3665   *As he went he met an old man, a palmer,*
A man that was right ferr in age certayn,
And aH for growe, a pilgrim as he were,
Thanne to hym saide the knyght in this maner :   3668

'Fader,' quod he, 'what tyme is of the day?'   3669   *of whom he asked the time of day,*
'ffor certayn, ser,' he saide, 'ij after none.'
Thanne seid the knyght, 'I purpose, if I maye,
This town to se, and whanne I haue don   3672
In to the shippe to come ayeyn right sone.'
Ayen thanne seid the palmer to the knyght,
'That may ye do long er[1] it be nyght.'   3675

'What do yow calle this town?' quod he ayeyn.   3676   *the name of the town, Clarionat,*
'Ser,' quod the palmer, 'Clarionat it hight.'
'Now, good fader, yet wold I wete fuH fayn,
Wher is the Sowdon, teH me very right :   3679   *and where the Sultan lay.*
Of his estate fayne wold I haue a sight.'
'The Sowdon,' he saide, 'ser, belevith me,
he lith att Mountoner the riche Citee.   3682   *'At Mountoner,' said the palmer*

¹ MS. *longer.*

'I was there but lately, and he made a feast for a knight Generydes,

Therin I was but late withoute lese,   3683
And thanne he made a fest I vnderstonde ;
Ther is a knyght callid Generides,
he hath made hym Stiward of all his land ;   3686

who fought King Bellyn, and kept this land from danger.

With kyng Bellyn he fought hand to hand,
And wanne hym in the feld as ye shall here,
And kept this lande from thraldom[1] and dangere.

He loves also Clarionas, the Sultan's daughter,

That knyght also lovith Clarionas,   3690
The Sowdon is hir fader in certayn,
And suche he dede first seruice in the place,
The love hath lastid still betwix them twayn,   3693

and she loves him again.'

ffor in like wise she lovith [hym] ayeyn :
And sekerly this is the comon voyse,
In all the courte that he shall hir reioyse.'   3696

Then said the knight,

Thanne saide the knyght, 'now, fader, I yow prae,
Be cause ye knowe so will this contre,

'Set me in the way to this city.'

To do so moche as sette me in the way
Whiche were most redyest to the Citee :   3700
And dowte ye not ye shall rewardid be.'
'Wele, ser,' he saide, 'I shall yow tell soo wele,
That of your waye ye shall fayle neuer a dele.   3703

Said the palmer, 'Go by yonder forest, the way will bring you to a plain,

Take hede of yender forest, I yow saye,   3704
ffor ther by must ye goo for eny thing ;
Withouten fayle ther lithe the redy way.
Vnto a goodly playn it[2] will yow bryng,   3707

over which you must travel four days, and then come to the city'

Whiche shall endure yow iiij dayes traveling,
And thanne anon, withoute eny more,
The fayre Citee ye shall see yow before.'   3710

[leaf 20]
The knight came to the end of his journey

This knyght furth with rewardid hym right wele, 3711
And furth he gothe [full] streight vppon ye way
As he was taught, and faylid neuer a dele,

---

¹ MS. *thraldon.*   ² MS. *in.*

Tiłł he come to the ende of his Iurnay,   3714
Whiche was atte after none the iiijth day :
And as it was abougħt the oure of three,
Ser Iuełł the knygħt came in to the Citee.   3717

To the Sowdoɯ fułł Streigħt he toke the way ;   3718
Whanne he hyɯ sawe he spake att his device,
'Ser, please it yow,' quod he, 'that I may saye
Wherefore that I am come and [in] what wise ;   3721
The trougħ is this to offre my seruice :
Gwynaɯ the kyng hath bannysshed me his lande,
And for what cause ye shałł wele vnderstonde.   3724

His fader made a clayme to y^{is} contre,   3725
And I was euer ayenst hyɯ in that case,
Wherefore the kyng^t his sonne now ha[ti]tħ me,
And vtterly hathe putte me froɯ his grace.   3728
here in this lande his fader slayɯ was,
Thanne was I trobolid sore oɯ euery side,
In Egipte durst I not lenger abide.'   3731

Ther with the Sowdoɯ answeryd hyɯ ayeyɯ :   3732
'To my presence ye are wiłł come,' quod he ;
'I must of reasone tender yow certayɯ,
Sithe ye haue be thus wrongyd for love of me,   3735
In my seruice now dayly shałł ye be ;
And if ye haue be trobelyd her before,
Of your^t pleasure now shałł ye haue the more.'   3738

So stiłł opece he was ther abideng^t,   3739
In his seruice purposyng^t to endure,
Passyng^t Ientiłł he was in euery thing^t,
And fułł pleasaunt to euery creature ;   3742
And ałł that was doɯ vnder a coverture,
That what he thougħt ther shuld no maɯ vnderstonde,
Of his tresone that he had take in hand.   3745

on the fourth
day,

and went straight
to the Sultan,
whom he told
his story,

how that Gwynan
had banished him

for opposing his
father's claim
to Persia.

The Sultan
answered,

'Since you have
been wronged
for my sake
you shall be in
my service.'

He abode in his
service,

and was gentle
and pleasant to
every one, to
cover his treason.

One day the
Sultan was alone
in his garden.
Sir Yvell was
aware,

Vppon a tyme the Sowdon was alone,　　　3746
In a garden was walkyng⸗ to and fro,
Ser Iuell Was ware therof anon,
To hym he goth withoute wordes moo.　　3749

and told him
that Generydes

'I must say yow,' quod he, 'a word or twoo ;
Beseching⸗ yow to kepe my councell,
Whiche shalbe to your honour and [a]vayle.　3752

Ther is a knyght callid Generides,　　　3753
here in your howse, and thus standith y⁰ case ;

plotted to carry
off Clarionas.

Bothe day and nyght he laboryth still opece,
ffrom hense to haue away Clarionas,　　3756
he restith not, butt wayteth tyme and space
To bryng⸗ abought his purpose if⸗ he maye,
This is the very trougth that I yow saye.'　3759

The Sowdon trostid all that euer he spake :　3760

The Sultan asked
his advice.

'Tell me,' he said, ' what is your best avise ? '
'Yes, ser,' quod he, ' this wolle I vndertake,
he shall not haue his purpose in noo wise,　3763
If ye will do as I shall yow device ;

'Go hunting
to-morrow,'
said he,

Go to morow on huntyng⸗ for the dere,
Thanne shall ye know the trowth of⸗ this mater. 3766

'and take
Generydes
with you.

But yow must take with yow Generides,　　3767
Not withstondeng⸗ he will be loth ther too ;

He will make
an excuse to
come home,

Whanne he is ther homeward he will hym dresse,
Thanne shall ye se anon what he will do.　　3770
Be myn avise me semyth best also,

but I will stay
and defeat his
purpose.'

That I abide atte home and kepe me close,
Thanne shall he not a tayne to his purpose.'　3773

The Sultan
assented.

The Sowdon gave his assent therto,　　　3774
And furth he goth on huntyng⸗ to the woode,
With hym he toke Generides also,

And suche moo knyȝtez as it semyd good ; 3777

And all sone as ser yuell vnderstode

The Sowdon was wele on warde on his way,

Vn to his shippe Iuell he sent withoute delay 3780

One of his men As fast as he cowde, 3781

Comaundyng them be redy euerychone ;

his ij. squyers he toke them owt Aside,

'helpe that I were Armyd anon, 3784

And in like wise cast your harnes vppon,

Secrely, that no man yow Aspye,

And that ye be on hors bak all redy. 3787

Withoute the Cite ther shall ye abide, 3788

And tary still as for a litill space.'

his hors was ther all redy for to ride,

And furth he went toward Clarionas, 3791

To hir chaunber ther as hir logging was :

' Madame,' he seyde, ' my lord, your fader dere,

To yow hath sent me on a massage her.' 3794

' What wold my fader ? I prae yow saye,' quod she.

' Madame,' quod he, ' he hath right happy game,

Wherefore in eny wise he wold that ye

Wer [1] ther with hym, that ye myght haue ye same.'

' Now may I goo,' quod she, ' withoute blame :'

And furth with all sche answeryd hym agayn,

' Att his pleasure to come I am right fayne.' 3801

Two palfreyes anone were brought owt of ye stable,

In all the goodly hast that myght be do,

One for hir, another for Mirabill,

Bothe were sadellyd redy for to goo, 3805

And furth they rode withoute wordes moo ;

And as ther couenaunde was in especiall,

his ij squyers mette hym withoute the wall. 3808

As soon as he
was gone hunting

Sir Yvell sent
one of his men
to his ship to

order it to be
ready,

and told his
two squires to
be armed

and wait
without the city.

He then went
and told Clarionas

that her father
had sent for her

to join the
hunting.
[leaf 20, back]

She and Mirabell
mounted their
palfreys and rode

forth on their
way.

[1] MS. *Wher*.

Thanne on) hir way rideth Clarionas,   3809
ffull Innocente was she of⸍ y^t in hir thought;

When they were two miles from the town, Mirabell suspected something,

Whanne thei were fro the town) ij myle of⸍ space,
Mirabell demyd sone that it was nought :   3812
ffro the forest a wayward he them) brought,
Thanne Myrabell, prevely as sche myght,

and made her lady alight.

Made hir lady from) hir palferay a light.   3815

Sir Yvell was wroth.

Where with ser yuell passing⸍ wroth he was,   3816
vn perseyuyd be countenaunce or sight :
Thanne said Mirabell onto Clarionas,

'Madam,' said Mirabell, 'we

'Madame,' quod she, 'this gothe not all aright,   3819
I wote my self⸍ as wele as eny wight ;

are betrayed.'

We are be trayde,' quod she, 'I dare well saye,
God wote,' quod she, 'this is noo thyng⸍ the way.'

As they sat, Natanell came up, chasing a hart.

And as thei sate to geder complayneng⸍,   3823
Came Natanell as fast as he myght ride,
Chasyng⸍ an hart as he come Reynyng⸍ ;
A none with all Mirabell had hym) aspied,   3826

Mirabell beckoned to him,

With hir kerche she bekenyd hym) aside,
And he full curtesly left all the chase,
And streight to hir he come ther as she was.   3829

'Natanell, for goddis loue, helpe,' quod she,   3830
'As for my lady here, Clarionas,

and told him that Sir Yvell had betrayed them.

Ser yuell hath betrayed bothe hir and me ;
Sayng⸍ suerly that he commaundyd was   3833
Be hir fader to bryng⸍ hir to the chase,
Whiche hym) thought shuld be hir grete counfort,
To see his huntyng⸍ And his disporte.   3836

But now I wote right wele it goth a mys ;   3837

'Go to your master and tell him this.'

Wherefore,' quod she, 'I prae you hertyly,
Go to your⸍ Maister now and tell hym) this,

for thanne he will nott tary sekerly,   3840
And that he come as fast as he may hye ;
Now, good Natanell, think wele her vppon.'
'It shall be do,' quod he, 'and that anone.'   3843

To the Cite streight he toke the waye,   3844   Natanell went
And brought his maister harnes ther he was,   straight to the
                                                                city, and fetched
And told hym ther, withoute more delaye,   his master's
Of ser yuell and of fayre Clarionas,   3847   armour, and
                                                                told him all
Of her messaventur and how it was,   about Clarionas.
And whanne Generides had hard hym wele,
A none he lefte his huntyng euery dele.   3850   Generides left
                                                                his hunting.

In this seasone was fayre Clarionas[1]   3851
ffull of sorow, god wote a wofull weight ;
Ser yuell sawe in what plight that she was,   Sir Yvell tried
                                                                to comfort
And her comfort in all that he myght :   3854   Clarionas by
'Madame,' quod he, 'this will I yow be hight,   telling her she
                                                                should be
Ye shall suerly be weddid to A kyng,   married to the
Vnder hevyn the migtiest lyvyng.   3857   mightiest king
                                                                under heaven.

Wherefore, madame, be ye noo thyng dismayde,   3858
All these thoughtez late them ouer slide !'
With that anon, as he these wordes sayde,
Generides come fro the forest side,   3861   Just then
                                                                Generydes
All clene armyd as fast as he cowde ride,   came out of
To ser Yuell streight vppon the felde,   the forest with
                                                                his sword drawn.
his swerd all nakyd in his hand he held.   3864

And whanne ser Iuell saw hym come rideng,   3865   When Sir Yvell
he made good countenaunce, but neuer the lesse   saw him he
                                                                made good
he was full sore adrede of his comyng,   countenance,
Purposing fully for to make his pece,   3868
And thus he seide on to Generides :   and said,
'Good ser,' quod he, 'be ye no thyng displesid,
ffor in this case your harte shall sone be easid.   3871

                    [1] MS. Clarianos.

This is trewly the mater in substance ;   3872

The kyng¹ of E[g]ipte, born) of higħe lenage,

Wold haue this lady here in gouernaunce,

Desiryng¹ hir be way of mariage ;   3875

And for this cause now I take this viage :

This is the trougtħ like now,¹ I yow devise,

Not to displese the Sowdon) in noo wise,   3878

Nor yow, and that ye shaħ vnderstonde,   3879

ffor that came neuer in my thougħt certayn) ;

This lady here ye shaħ in your' hande,

And to the Citee wiħ I turne ayeyn),   3882

Be cause no man) shaħ haue me in disdayn) ;

And forthermore, of that that I haue sayde

I yow beseche that I be not be wrayed.   3885

It is fuħ late for yow and here also   3886

As for this day to traveħ more And lesse,

Att youre pleasure to morow may ye goo.'

'I am content,' thanne seid Generides,   3889

ffuħ Innocente² of aħ his dobilnesse,

The whiche ser yueħ thougħt in his entente,

ffor to the Sowdon) hastely he went.   3892

Generides, withoute wordes moo,   3893

Made a logge as sone as euer he mygħt :

he made another for hym) self¹ also,

Thinkyng¹ noo harme ne malys to no weigħt ;   3896

And ther they restid stiħ as for that nygħt.

Thanne was ser yueħ fuħ bold in his maner

With the Sowdon), and saide as ye shaħ here :   3899

'Off your' doughter And of¹ Generides,   3900

ffuħ trewly shaħ ye fynde it as I say ;

ffor as this nygħt thei are, withoute lesse,

¹ MS. *now a.*   ² MS. *Innocence.*

Out of the town) wele onward on yer waye :   3903
And if ye wiłł goo ther anon), ye may
Se where they be and I shałł be your' gide.'   *I will be your guide.'*
'Yes,' quod the Sowdon), 'theder I wiłł ride,   3906

And that anon as fast as euer we[1] may,   3907
In secrete wise, no mo but ye and I.'
Now goth forward the Sowdon) on) his way,
And ser yuełł witħ hym) fułł secretly,   3910
he first be sougħt the Sowdon) feithfully,   *He besought him to slay Generydes.*
As for the cheve guerdon) of his seruice,
ffor to sle Generides in eny wise.   3913

The Sowdon) grauntyd hym) for so[2] to do ;   3914
And as he came owt of the forest side,
he sawe a logge, and in he went ther to ;   *They came to a lodge, and*
Ser yuełł stode withouten) hym) to abide,   3917
And furtħ witħ ałł the Sowdon) had aspyed
Withynne the logge wher lay Generides,   *the Sultan went in and saw Generydes sleeping*
In his harnes slepyng stiłł opece.   3920

Hys sward was drawyn), on)[3] the grownd it lay,   3921   *with his sword drawn by his side.*
To sle hym) the Sowdon) had grete pite,
Remembryng the seruice day by day,
Whiche he had don) in his necessite,   3924
And suche as no man) ded saue only he :
Wherefore he thougħt, be good and sad avise,   *The Sultan thought he would not slay him hastily,*
he wold not sle hym) in noo hasty wise.   3927

He toke Away the sward vppe from) ye ground,   3928   *but took away the sword and left his own.*
And leyde his owen) ther as the toder was ;
Butt litiłł thense another logge he founde,
Ther lay myrabełł and fayre Clarionas,   3931   *In the other lodge he found Clarionas and Mirabell,*
ffułł stedefastly he lokid on) hir face,
To knowe his doughter clerly be sigħt,
ffor bothe thei sleppe as fast as euer thei mygħt.   3934

[1] MS. *he.*   [2] MS. *to so.*   [3] MS. *on on.*

<table>
<tr><td>and took up
his daughter
fast asleep as
she was, and</td><td>He toke his doughter vppe as she laye,
And furth he bare hir in his armys twayn)
Owt of¹ the logge, she sleppe still alway,</td><td>3935</td></tr>
</table>

and took up
his daughter
fast asleep as
she was, and

He toke his doughter vppe as she laye,   3935
And furth he bare hir in his armys twayn)
Owt of¹ the logge, she sleppe still alway,

delivered her to
Sir Yvell

And to ser yuell delyueryd hir ayeyn,   3938
And told hym) that Generides was slayn).
Whanne ser Iuell herd¹ of that aventure,
Wote ye wele he was a ioyfull creature.   3941

The Sowdon) went ayeyn to his disporte ;   3942

to conduct her
to the city.

Ser Iuell hym) promysed for to goo,
With his doughter ayenward to resorte
Vn to the Citee, ther as she came froo,   3945

But he meant
nothing of
the kind.

Butt sekerly his thought was noo thyng¹ soo :
The Sowdon) wende she had gon) ther she was,
Butt alway he led fayre Clarionas.   3948

Clarionas awoke
and saw how
it was ;

Anone with all Clarionas awoke,   3949
And whanne that she perseivid how it was,

she took on sore
and swooned
twice.

ffull of sorow she was and sore on) toke,
That twyes she swounyd in a litill space ;   3952
God wote she stode in full petevous case,
More sorow had noo creature levyng¹,
for she had leuer a dᵛed than¹ eny thyng¹.   3955

He set her on
a palfrey and
led her to the
ship.

On a palfrey he sette Clarionas,   3956
And to the shippe he gideth hir full right ;
Generides, withynne a litill space,
he woke anon) thanne was it dayle light :   3959

When Generydes
awoke, he asked
Mirabell for
Clarionas.

Of Mirabell sone he had a sight,
And first of¹ all he sayde in this maner,
' Where is Clarionas, my lady dere ? '   3962

With thoo wordes Mirabell woke anon) ;   3963

'Alas said
she, ' my lady
is gone by false
treason.

' Alas,' quod she, ' what aventur¹ is this ?
By false tresone now is my lady goon),

¹ MS. thang.

And ser Iuell I wote it is :   3966 It is Sir Yvell,
Of hym) I dremyd all this nyght I wis,
I prae god geve hym) sorow now,' she saide,
'ffor this is twyes that he hath vs betrayde.'   3969 he hath betrayed
                                                           us twice.'

' Butt is she goon) ?' thanne saide Generides.   3970
' Yee,' quod Mirabell, ' and that me rewith sore.'
' ffare well,' quod he, ' my comfort and gladnes,   'Farewell,'
                                                           quoth he,
ffare well my ioye for now and euermore ;   3973 ' my comfort
What think¹ ye best that I shall doo yerfore ?'   and joy for
                                                           evermore.
'This is the best,' quod she, ' that I canne saye,   What think you
                                                           best to do ?'
Go after them) as fast as euer ye may,   3976 ' Go after them,'
                                                           said she,

And if it fortune that he may be take,   3977
ffor erthely good or eny fayre promes,   [leaf 21, back]
Do make hym) sure what couenaunte that he make.'
' Yes,' hardly thanne seid Generides.   3980
' To the Sowdon),' quod sche, ' I will me dresse,   'and I will go
                                                           to the Sultan,
And tell hym) trewly, as sone as euer I may,
ffor he will trost the wordes that I saye.'   3983 for he will trust
                                                           my words.'.

Generides thanne armyd hym) anon),   3984 Generydes then
                                                          armed himself,
Aftur ser Iuell to folow on the chase ;
he sought after his swerd and it was goon),
he founde another lying¹ in the place,   3987 and found the
                                                          Sultan's sword,
The Sowdons swerd he wist wele that it was :
To myrabell he seide in this maner,
' My lord the Sowdon) suerly hath ben) here :   3990

Where with I am comfortid verely,   3991 which comforted
                                                          him.
ffor of¹ my parte [he] demyd not amys,
And if he had, I say yow sekerly,
he wold haue slayn) me here, I wote wele this.'   3994
' Right as ye say,' quod she, ' me think¹ it is :
I will telle hym) [the] trougth whanne I hym) see,
ffor I will seche hym) wher' euer that he be.'   3997

Then quoth he,
'Tell Natanell to
come after me.'

'Thanne,' quod he, 'Mirabeꝉ, I yow prae,   3998
Byd Nataneꝉ anon) for eny thing¹
Come after me as fast as euer he may.'
'It shaꝉ be do,' quod she, 'withoute fey[n]ing¹ :   4001
he be your' spede that is our hevyn) kyng¹,
Whanne ye are goo I wiꝉ not long¹ abide,
ffor to my lord the Sowdon) I wiꝉ ryde.'   4004

Generydes
follows Yvell,

Generides is in his way rideng¹   4005
After Iueꝉ, to take hym) if he may.
Mirabeꝉ thanne made noo taryeng¹,

and Mirabell
goes to the
Sultan,

Butt to the Sowdon) she toke the waye,   4008
To teꝉ hym) aꝉ the trougth of here affraye,

but the Sultan
knew all before,

But or she came the Sowdon) knewe it wele,
ffor ther came on) and told¹ hym euery dele,   4011

Whiche mette ser yueꝉ and Clarionas :   4012

and was sore
astounded.
He rides to the
place where he
found Generydes,

Where with the Sowdon) was astownyd sore,
And furth with aꝉ he rideth in to the place,
Ther as he founde Generides before,   4015
Of¹ that fortune to harkyn) forthermore ;
This musyng¹ in his thought more and lesse,

and met Mirabell
on the way,

he mette Mirabeꝉ in grete hevynes.   4018

Be hir semlante he thought it shuld be she,   4019
And this to hir fuꝉ soberly he sayde ;
'Telle me, where is my doughter now?' seith he ;
And ther withaꝉ she was gretly dismayde,   4022

who told him
how Clarionas
was betrayed
at first,

'ffor certeyn), ser,' quod she, ' she is betrayed ;
Ser yueꝉ seid that ye had for hir sent,
And brought fro yow a streyt comaundment.   4025

And in this wise away with hir he rode,   4026
ffuꝉ vntrewly, and be a subtiꝉ trayne ;
Vppon) the way we hovyd and a boode.

Generides thanne reskewid hir ayeyn), 4029 and how
Generydes
rescued her,
Thanne was the day passid in certayn),
And nere nyght, wherefore he thought it best
Ther to abide as for oñ nyghtez rest. 4032

'As for Generides this dare I now saye, 4033
he was neuer that man), I yow ensure,
To dishonour your doughter be eny way,
Nor neuer while his liff may endure ; 4036
But whels he sleppe this cursyd creature and how,
while he slept,
Sir Yvell had
carried her off.
ffull trayturly with hir is goo ;
ffull wele I woote it is he and no moo.' 4039

To here answerd the Sowdon) in this wise ; 4040 The Sultan
answered,
'It is full true
'Ye say full trew, it may non) other be,
With his fayre wordes, full of flatrise,
he hath deseyuyd now bothe yow and me, 4043 he hath deceived
us both.
Butt where is now Generides ?' quod he ; But where is
Generydes ?'
'Trewly,' quod she, 'ser, he hath take the waye 'Truly,' said she,
Aftur this knyght, and thus he bad me say.' 4046 'he is gone
after this knight.'

'What think ye best,' quod he, 'that I shall doo ?'
'ffor sothe,' quod she, 'this is now myn) avise ;
Aftur ser yuell Generides is goo,
To take hym) if he canne in eny wise ; 4050
And as for yow to take the enterprise,
It shall nede if his liff may endure,
he will do moche ther to I yow ensure.' 4053

And as thei spake to geder he and she, 4054 As they spake
together
Natanell
rode up.
Came Natanell as fast as he cowde ride ;
Myrabell sone perseyuyd it was he,
ffull ertely she prayde hym) to abide : 4057
Anon) withall he reynyd his hors aside,
Thanne seid he this to Mirabell, 'I yow prae,
What is your' will now pleasit yow to say.' 4060

GENERYDES. 9

[leaf 22]
Mirabell gave
him Generydes'
message.

' [M]ynne owyɲ lady,' q*uo*d she, ' Clarionas,　　4061
Ser yueɫɫ now ayeyɲ witħ here is gone,
Whils we were bothe oɲ sleppe this is yᵉ case,
Generides is after aɫɫ alone,　　　　　　　　　4064
And wold that ye shuld follow hyɲ anone.'
' Maystres,' q*uo*d he, ' now trost me verily,
To hyɲ I wiɫɫ as fast as I canne higħe.'　　　4067

Natanell rides
after his master;

Now Nataneɫɫ, in aɫɫ the hast he may,　　　　4068
Is rideng⸍ after now Generides;

the Sultan and
Mirabell return
to the city,

Myrabeɫɫ witħ the Sowdoɲ take the way,
And to the Citee ward⸍ the Sowdoɲ ganne hyɲ dresse,
Complayneng⸍ sore in rigħt grete hevynes;

and Clarionas
by this time is
going on board
with Sir Yvell.

And by that tyme s*er* yueɫɫ redy was,
Takyng⸍ the shippe witħ fayre Clarionas.　　4074

When they were
under sail
Generydes
came up.

It was not long⸍ or thei were vnder sayle,　　4075
And by that tyme come was Generides;
Ser yueɫɫ knewe hyɲ wele withoute fayle,
By his stature and by his likenesse,　　　　4078
And these wordes he sayde to hyɲ expresse;

'It is too late,'
said Yvell.

' Generides,' q*uo*d he, ' I telle the playɲ,
Thou comyst to late to haue hir now ageyɲ.　4081

Thow slepist to long⸍, and I woke the while　4082
To spede this mater after my device,
My purpose was the fully to be gile,
Witħ the Sowdoɲ whanne I was in s*er*uice;　4085
I sette not be the thretyng⸍ in noo wise,

'Thou hast
lost her.'

And vterly this wolle I saye the more,
ffro this day furtħ thu hast lost her y*er*fore.'　4088

Generydes was
sore grieved,

Generides thanne was agrevid sore,　　　　　4089
ffor thoo wordes were saide in mokkery,
And in hyɲ self abasshed more and more,

Butt att that tyme ther was noo remedy :   4092   but there was
Clarionas be held hym verily,   no remedy.
his countenance was aH togeder doon,   Clarionas
Anone with aH ther she fylle down in swoune.   4095   saw him,
and fell down
in a swoon.

Syr yueH sawe she made suche hevynes,   4096
And with hir self she was not aH arigHt ;
ffor as the story dotH witnesse,
xv tymes she swounyd in his sigHt :   4099
he hir comfortid in aH that euer he mygHt ;   Sir Yvell tried
To turne hir hart he dede his besy payne,   to comfort her,
And aH for nougHt his labour was in vayne.   4102   but to no
purpose.

Generides the porte gotH aH a long,   4103   Generydes
To seke a shippe streight be the havyns side ;   went all along
Att last he saw a galy fayre and strong   the port to
lay atte rode, which was both large and wide,   4106   seek a ship,
And men I nowe therin for to gide ;   and found a
The maister of aH was ther present,   galley with
Generides anon to hym he went.   4109   master and men.

'Owt of what cost come ye, I prae yow say,   4110   He asked
Or what contre,' quod he, 'telle me the rigHt.'   them of what
The maister thougHt anon be his array,   coast they came.
Be cause he was armyd and like a knygHt,   4113
he was a man of powre and of mygHt,
Wherefore in sothe he was sumwhat dismayde,   The master
And to Generides rigHt thus he saide.   4116   was afraid,

'Sir, be not ye displeasid now,' quod he,   4117
'Be cause I haue of yow noo knowlachyng,
Owt of danger I wold be and in surete.'
'Surete,' quod he, 'drede yow no maner thyng ; 4120   but Generydes
On your part ther is non other desireng,   reassured him,
Butt I haue a mater now to begynne,
And I wold fayn haue your counceH therin.'   4123   and asked
his advice.

'My counsel, sir, is but simple,' he said.

'My councell is but symple, *ser*,' he seide ;　4124
'Butt as I canne I shall say myn) avice :
In this havyn) this galy now is layde,
I shall yow tell wherefore and in wha[t] wise ;　4127

'I come from Syria, where King Auferius lieth.

I come fro Surre and fro those partis,
Kyng¹ Auferius hath it in mariage,
And ther he lith with all his Baronage.　4130

I was with 100 ships on the way to India to win

A hunderyd shippes I lift ther Also,　4131
With them) I was in company certayn),
And toward¹ ynd they purpose them) to goo,

Auferius his right again.

To wynne kyng¹ auferius right ageyn),　4134
And of his sonnys, to say yow trew and playn),

To one of his sons, Ismaell the Savage,

A likely knyght on) And of mannys age,
The whiche is callid Ismaell the Savage.　4137

the king has given Thrace ;

The kyng¹ his fader hym) hath gevyn) fre　4138
The Reme of Trace, to rule it in his hand ;
And ferthermore, in very certente,
He hath a broder as I vnderstonde,　4141

the other, Generydes, a good knight,

As good a knyght as is in eny lande,
And as it is seide I telle yow very right,
And for certayn) Generides he hight.　4144

After deceasse of auferius the kyng¹,　4145

shall have Syria and India ;

He shall haue Surre in his owne demeyn,[1]
And all the Reme of ynd withoute feyning¹,
If fortune will that he it gete ayeyn) ;　4148

and my errand is to seek him.

In to this contre was myn) erande playn)
hym) for to seche, and as I vnderstonde
Withynne few dayes he was here in this land.　4151

Let me know where I may find him.'
[leaf 22, back]

And if ye knowe wher that I may hym) fynde,　4152
Now lete me wete, I *prae* yow hartely.'
Generides remembryd in his mynd

¹ MS. *demenyng.*

he was not wonte hym self to be wreye ; 4155
Yet this to hym he seid full soberly,
' My frend,' quod he, ' ye shall knowe my councell,
I am the same withoute eny fayle. 4158

Generydes said,
' I am the same,

Generides I hight, this is noo nay, 4159
kyng auferius my fader is certayn) ;
Butt I am a carefull man) this day,
By fortune suche before was neuer sene, 4162
By a subtill and false compassing trayn),
Clarionas, my lordis doughter dere,
Vntrewly is betrayed as ye shall here. 4165

my name is
Generydes,

but I am full of
care to-day, for

my lord's
daughter
Clarionas is
untruly
betrayed.

It is but late sithe she was vnder sayle, 4166
A knyght of Egipte, callid ser yuell,
With here is gone away withoute fayle.'
Thanne the maister seid, ' woll ye do well ? 4169
This galy lith not here to by ne selle ;
Do now be myn avice, and hardely
With goddes grace ye shall fynde remedy. 4172

A knight of
Egypt is gone
with her.'

The master said,
' Do now by my
advice ;

This galy shalbe redy for to goo, 4173
If ye will come ye shall hym ouer take.'
' Now,' quod Generides, ' late it be soo,
I prae yow hartly for cristis sake.' 4176
And furth with all he did it redy make,
In all the hast possible that [1] he may,
To shippe he goth withoute more delay. 4179

this galley shall
be ready to go,
and we will
overtake him.'
' Now,' quoth
Generydes,
' let it be so.'

And whanne they were all redy for to goo, 4180
Came Natanell onto the havyns side,
his Maisters hors he brought with hym Also ;
And whanne Generides hym had aspyed, 4183
he prayde the maister sumwhat to Abide,
ffull wele content he was of his comang',
Anone thei putt ther horses to shippyng'. 4186

When they were
ready to go,
Natanell came
with his master's

horse, and was
taken on board.

[1] MS. *that that.*

The master and
Generydes
sailed on,
Now is the Maister and Generides   4187
Vppon̄ the see, and sayle beganne to make,
And in here viage sailed stiłł opece,

and if the wind
had not begun
to slacken,
Sir Yvell would
have been taken,
but he landed
with Clarionas,
Tiłł atte last the wynde beganne to slake,   4190
And ellis in very trougth they had be take ;
Butt afterward, withynne a litiłł space,
Syr yuełł londyd with Clarionas.   4193

And thanne anon̄, as fast as euer he mygħt,   4194
and hasted on to
King Gwynan
Thei hastid them̄ forward of ther Iurnay ;
Ser yuełł gidyd hir the way fułł rigħt,
ffor he had knowen̄ the contre many Λ day ;   4197
To kyng¹ Guynan he toke the redy way,
To his palys ther as his abideng¹ was,
to a city called
Egidias.
In a Cite callid Egidias.   4200

Four hours after,
Generydes landed
with the others
Not long¹ after¹ the space of ourez fewe,   4201
The galy landyd witħ Generides ;
in the guise of
merchants.
In gise of mercaundez thei dede them̄ shewe,
ffułł craftely in Ałł ther besynes,   4204
Not like no men̄ of warre but ałł of pece,
So to gide them̄ thei wer' wełł apayde,
To harkyn̄ tidynges what these pepiłł saide.   4207

The king was
glad when
he heard of
Clarionas,
And whanne the tidynges came onto the kyng¹   4208
Of ser yuełł and fayre Clarionas,
A gladder man̄ was ther non̄ leving¹,
Nor migħt not be more ioyfułł thanne he was :   4211
The Citee made grete festis in euery place,
and his knights
went to meet
her, himself
following.
his knygħtes went to mete here on̄ the way,
hym̄ self come after in fułł good Arraye.   4214

He sent for his
lords to come
to his marriage,
And for his lordes furtħ witħ ałł he sent,   4215
They for to come onto the mariage,
And to folowe the effecte of his entente,

¹ MS. *after after.*

To the Citee came Aħ his Baronage :   4218
And as it is the custom) and vsage
Aħ way for princes shortly to device,
The ffest was made in rigħt solempne wise,   4221 and the feast
                                            was made,

And lastid long', my Auctour seitħ expresse ;   4222 and lasted long.
Another custome was in that contre   It was the
Of old vsage, the writeng' dotħ witnesse,   custom during
                                        the feast that
What tyme that eny kyng' weddid shuld be,   4225
Duryng' the tyme of that solempnite,
The kyng' and she shuld neuer togeder mete,   the king and
                                        his bride should
To tyme the fest were done And fuħ complete. 4228 not meet.

Thanne seid the Maister onto Generides,   4229 The master said
' Now it is wisdome to do be good avice,   to Generydes,
ffor by manhood[1] suerly or by prow[e]se
Yow shaħ spede your' mater in noo wise ;   4232
ffor your' entente I shaħ a craft devise   'I shall devise
Witħ goddes grace, and if it fortune wele,   a craft that you
                                        may gain your
That ye shaħ haue your' purpose euery dele. 4235 end.

I haue A thing' shaħ lye vppon) your' face, 4236 You shall put
That ye shaħ seme a meseħ [in] certayn),   something on
Butt dougħt ye not withynne a litiħ space,   your face which
Whanne euer ye list it shaħ a voyde ayeyn), 4239 shall make you
And your' visage to be as fayre And playn),   seem a leper,
As wele coloured and ther witħ also clene, '
Witħ onys wasshyng' as it had neuer ben).   4242

And forthermore ye must chaunge your Array 4243 and you
Witħ sum pore man), and take ye his clothing',   must change
And bere with yow sum tokyn) that she may   your clothes
                                        with some
Of your' persohe haue redy knowlaching';   4246 poor man.
                                        [leaf 23]
And from here pales as she is comyng',
Bothe to and froo ther must ye haue A place,   Take with you
                                        some token by
Now do as wele as god will geve you grace ; 4249 which she may
                                        know you,

[1] MS. mandhood.

and she will ordain some way to speak with you.	And, weł I woote, som way she wił ordeyn That she may speke you[1] atte your own device, And as ye canne accorde betwix you twayne, This wold I that ye did be myne avise ;	4250 4253
Bid Nataneł be ready to meet you with your horse.'	Bid Nataneł in eny maner wise, That he be redy and in especiał, To mete yow with your hors what euer faƚ.'	 4256
So Generydes did, and changed his clothes with a beggar,	Generides dede after his counceł, And with a begger he chaungyd his wede, The pore man thought it was for his availe, And glad he was, for he ther of had nede. Thanne seide Generides, 'so god yow spede, Whanne were ye atte court I pray yow saye.'	4257 4260
who told him he had been at court,	'Trewly,' quod he, 'I come fro thense to day ;	4263
and seen the queen,	And ther I sawe the quene in riche araye, But as me semyth by here countenance,	4264
but that she looked unhappy as she came from the temple.	And as she came from the tempiƚ by yᵉ waye, She likyd not that riał ordenaunce ; Me think ther was some cause of displesaunce, Butt me ought not to speke therof in dede.' 'Now goo, fader, and Ihu be thy spede.'	 2467 4270
Now Generydes goes to the court	Now goth Generides furth, I vnderstonde, Vn to the courte, his clothis ał to Rent ;	4271
with his cup and clapper in his hand,	holdyng his cuppe, his claper in his hande, And on his face he layde this oyntement, To bryng abought the effecte of his entent ;	 4274
and stood in a place near the temple where she should pass.	And ther anon he purveyd hym a place, Withoute the tempiƚ ther as she shuld pase.	 4277
He put a ring on his finger,	Whanne he had restid hym he putte a ryng On his fynger, be cause she shuld it see, And fro the tempiƚ as she is comyng,	4278

[1] MS. *yom.*

Thorougħ owt the prese anonɔ to hir comɔ he,   4281

And Askyd Almes for seynt charite,

The ryngᵗ vpponɔ his fynger sone she knewe ;

' I shaH,' thougħt she, ' here sum tidynggez newe.'   4284

and as she came from the temple he asked alms.

She knew the ring,

Thanne seid the quene, ' good manɔ, whense be ye ? '

' Madame,' quod he, ' o trougħ I shaH yow say ;

In ynd I was gotenɔ in very certente,

In surre I was bornɔ, this is no nay ;   4288

Now come I owt of perse the redy way,

And ther I was brougħt vppe, I telle yow playnɔ,

Sone¹ I was first att mannys age [certayn].   4291

and asked whence he was.
' Madam,' said he, ' I was gotten in India,

and born in Syria, and now I come from Persia, where I was brought up.'

Ye are a lady bornɔ of that contree,   4292

God hatħ me visite as his creature,

Besechyngᵗ yow yourʳ almes manɔ to be.'

The quene Answeryd witħ countenaunce demure,   4295

' Of mynɔ Almes,' quod she, ' ye shaH be sure.'

And furtħ with aH, withoute taryengᵗ,

She bad he shuld be brougħt to hir loggyng.   4298

She ordered him to be brought to her lodging.

To hir chaunbyr rigħt sone he was conueyed,   4299

And ther he spake with hir hymɔ self alone ;

' Madame,' quod he, ' be ye noo thingᵗ dismayde,

Thougħe my visage be lothe to loke vpponɔ,   4302

Witħ onys wasshyngᵗ it wiH away anone,

And trost that I say withoute othe,

I am yourʳ trew seruaunt Generides in sothe.'   4305

He was conveyed to her chamber, and spoke with her alone.
' Madam,' quoth he, ' be not dismayed,

I am your true servant Generydes,

' Generides !' quod she, ' nay that is not so,   4306

It is to me a wonder thing to here.'

' Madame,' he saide, ' ye shaH wete or ye goo,

Plese it yow to see a ryngᵗ that I haue here,   4309

The whiche I had of yow, my lady dere ;

And thougħ² I seme a meseH in yourʳ sigħt,

It is but counterfete,³ I yow be hight.'   4312

and though I seem a leper it is but counterfeit.'

¹ So MS. ? *Sene.*   ² MS. *thought.*   ³ MS. *coumterfete.*

'This ryng¹,' quod she, 'I know it veryly,   4313
Butt of your² persone yet I merveⱠ more.'

He had with him a water with which he washed his face, and he was as fair as ever. When she saw it she took him in her arms.

With hym⁾ he had a water ther redy,
And from his face he wessħ away it thore,   4316
he was as faire as euer he was be fore,
And whanne she sawe his vesage fayre and clene,
She toke hym⁾ in hir Armys as I wene ;   4319

She was soo glad, she had noo worde to saye.   4320

'Madam,' said he, 'appoint some ready place,

'Madame,' quod he, 'in sothe this is the case,
If ye wiⱠ now for sake aⱠ this arraye,
And that ye list apoynte some redy place,   4323

and Natanell and I will meet you.

Bothe NataneⱠ and I, be goddes grace,
With hors and harnes noo thing¹ shaⱠ be lette
To mete yow ther, what our² ye wiⱠ sett.   4326

Tnere is a ship ready to sail.'

Ther is a shippe AⱠ redy for to sayle,   4327
A bideng¹ stiⱠ opece of my comyng¹.'

'Generydes,' quoth she,

'Generides,' quod she, 'I haue merveⱠ
That ye putt dough* in eny thing¹   4330

'though he were king of ten realms,

As to meward, for thoughħ he were a kyng¹
Of reames x, And so fourtħ to endure,

I would go with you.

yet wold I goo witħ yow, I yow ensure.   4333

And for to spede this mater to purpose,   4334

You and Natanel must hide in my garden to-night early.'

In my garden⁾ Att nygħt sone must ye be,
Bothe NataneⱠ and ye, and kepe yow close,
Treis and busshes fuⱠ thikke yer shaⱠ yow se, 4337
To kepe yow secrete in, and as for me
I wiⱠ be ther, trost me in feithfuⱠ wise,

[leaf 23, back]

Betwix the day and nygħt, I yow promys.'   4340

Generydes joined Natanell in the forest, put off his rags,

Generides owt of the CasteⱠ went   4341
To NataneⱠ, whiche in the forest lay,
Ther he dede of his ragyd garment,

his disshe, his claper, and aH he cast awaye, 4344
And harnesid hym̄ aH now ayeyn̄ in his array:
To the garden̄ he toke the waye [att nyght],
And tared ther as he had hir be higħt. 4347

and armed himself again, and then waited in the garden.

Thanne Clarionas is now in grete musyng', 4348
And in this case be thinkitħ hir fuH strayte,
hir purpose craftely aboughť to bryng',
And vterly hir seasone for to wayte; 4351
Atte last she founde one of hir consaite
To whom̄ she told here counceH aH in fere,
And in certayne she was a lavendere. 4354

Clarionas found a laundress to whom she told her plan.

To here thanne sayde fayre Clarionas, 4355
'Ye are,' quod she, 'a woman̄ that is to trost
Of eny one that is withynne the place,
Of my counceH fayne wold I that ye wist.' 4358
'Att your' pleasure, Madame, what euer ye list.'
Quod she ageyn̄, 'withoute wordes moo,
That lith in me I wiH be glad to do.' 4361

'You are a woman to be trusted,' said she.

'Ye say rigħt wele, and as it semyth me,' 4362
Quod she onto the lavender thanne ayeyn̄,
'I am a straunger here in this contre,
This is my mater aH togeder playn̄; 4365
The kyng', whiche is my lord and souereyn̄,
On hym̄ my hert is sette, I yow be higħt,
That I for gete hym̄ not neyther day ne nygħt; 4368

'I am a stranger here,

and my heart is set on the king my lord.

And most I drede of eny maner thing', 4369
That I to hym̄ am noo thing' in this case,
Butt be the sterrys,' quod she, 'and be my connyng',
Where euer he goo or ride in eny place, 4372
I trost to god to stond so in his grace,
And in his favour' lengest to endure,
Of eny other levyng' creature. 4375

I wish by the stars to stand always in his favour.

<table>
<tr><td>

You and I must
go into my
garden when
the stars are up;

</td><td>

In to my gardeyn yow and I must goo,   4376
Whanne sterrys are vppe and whan it is very nygħt,
Butt I must surely be disgised soo
That I may goo vnknowen to eny wigħt,   4379

</td></tr>
<tr><td>

I will wear
your kirtle,
and each of us
must bear a
truss on our
heads.'

</td><td>

Your kirtiħ wiħ I were be cause of ligħt,
And iche of vs a trusse vppon oure hede,
This is trewly my counceħ and my rede.'   4382

</td></tr>
<tr><td>

The laundress
answered,
'I will keep
your counsel.'

</td><td>

Thanne Answeryd the lavender ayeyn,   4383
Seid [she], 'Madame, your seruaunt wiħ I be,
And aħ your counceħ kepe and layn,
I trost ther shaħ no fawte be founde in me,   4386
haue here my hande for a surete ;
And trostitħ wele that at I shaħ saye,
ffor erthely good I wiħ not yow bewraye.'   4389

</td></tr>
<tr><td>

She went to
her house and
brought a kirtle

</td><td>

And so fourtħ withoute wordis eny moo,   4390
And to hir house as fast as euer she mygħt
She went, and brougħt ayeyn with hir also
A kirtiħ, like as she be fore higħt.   4393
Whanne the day was passid and it was nygħt,

</td></tr>
<tr><td>

which the queen
put on, leaving
her rich array.

</td><td>

The quene dede on hir kirtiħ fayre and weħ,
here riche aray she left it euery dele ;   4396

</td></tr>
<tr><td>

Her clothes
were well
tucked up,

</td><td>

And tokkyd vppe she was weħ fro the grounde,   4397
Before hir eyne a kerche hanging side,
Ther trusses on ther hedes aħ redy bounde,

</td></tr>
<tr><td>

and forth
they went.
'Stop, stop,'
said the
laundress,
'your white
legs will
betray us.'

</td><td>

And furtħ thei went, them nede non other gide ;   4400
Thanne saide the lavender, 'abide, abide,
This white leggys,' quod she, 'I woote it wele,
They wolle shende oure purpose euery dele.'   4403

</td></tr>
<tr><td>

She washed
Clarionas's legs
with ashes and
water, and

</td><td>

'Ye, wote ye what,' quod she, 'that ye shaħ do ? 4404
Bryng me water, and thanne late me alone,
A Coppe of Aisshes ye must bryng Also,

</td></tr>
</table>

Where witħ my leggys shalbe wasshid anone,   4407
That Aħ the white I warant shalbe goɲ);'
Rigħt thus she dede in like wise as I saye,
And to the gardeyɲ rigħt thus she toke the waye.   4410

she and Clarionas
went on to the
garden.

Thorougħ owt the haħ bothe to geder gaɲ) goo,   4411
As no thyngᵗ were, fuħ sofft And demure,
Thorough out the courte they toke the way Also,
And atte gate thei mette att aventure   4414
Witħ ser yueħ, that cursid creature ;
She hard hyɲ) speke, and knewe hyɲ) be yᵉ voyse,
To me[te] hyɲ) ther was none other choyse.   4417

At the gate they
met Sir Yvell.

Whanne she perseivid weħ that it was he,   4418
A bak she drew and was fuħ iħ apayde.
Thanne came he hir nere to knowe the certente,
What that she was ; 'Whoɲ) haue yow here?' he seid.
'Me think,' quod he, 'it is a praty mayde ;
I cast here for to se what euer faħ :'
And vppe he lift here kerchewe furtħ witħ aħ.   4424

The queen was
afraid and
drew back.

'Whom have
you here?'
said he, and

lifted up her
kerchief.

She was so ferde hir truse was in fallingᵗ,   4425
Witħ that the lavender putt hyɲ) abak aye,
'Ye are to blame,' quod she, 'be hevyɲ) kyngᵗ ;
Now late my mayde alone, ser, I yow praye,   4428
We must hast bo[the] as moche as euer we maye,
These are the quenez clothes, I teħ you playɲ),
And she must haue theɲ) aħ to morow ayeyɲ).'   4431

The laundress
put him back,
saying

'Let my maid
alone, sir,
we must
make haste;
these are the
queen's clothes.'

'Yet woħ I wete,' quod he, 'withoute fayle,   4432
ffrom whense she came, and what she is,' quod he.
'Now, good ser,' quod she, 'what shaħ it availe
To make iche maɲ) to speke of yow and me?   4435
Yet and ye wiħ be rewlid weħ,' quod she,
'ffor your⁾ entente and after myɲ) avise,
Ye shaħ speke witħ hir att your⁾ owyɲ) device.   4438

'I will know,'
quoth he, 'from
whence she
came.'
[leaf 24]

This is the mater in short conclusioṅ,   4439
I am hir maystres and here gouernour ;

'Her father is a merchant of this town, and there is a knight who woos her for his paramour, so her friends put her with me for safety.

hir fader is a merchaunt of this towṅ.
Ther is a knyght hir wowith euery owre,   4442
Not for to wedde butt for his paramour ;
hir frendis wold haue hir in suerte,
And for that cause she is now here with me.   4445

Not withstondyng¹, withoute wordes moo,   4446

Go to my house, and wait there,

Go to myṅ house and tary ther,' quod she,
'Till I haue washt, and this moche woll I doo ;
Whanne I come home I shall bryng¹ hir with me,

and you shall see her at your pleasure.'

And att your pleasur ther shall ye hir see,
And speke with hir, ther shall nomaṅ sey nay.'
'I graunt,' quod he, 'will ye do as ye saye ?'   4452

He goes to her house,

He left theṁ ther, and oṅ he goth a pase   4453
Vnto hir howse as fast as euer he may :

and the laundress and Clarionas go into the garden,

The lavander with Clarionas
In to the gardeṅ all another way.   4456
Whanne thei were ther yer trussez dowṅ thei lay ;
'Now, faire Madame,' seide the lavender,
'Do now sum good for spede of this mater.'   4459

where they see Natanell,

Thanne in to the gardeyṅ came Natanell,   4460
Clarionas full sone had hyṁ aspied ;
'Where is your maister ?' quod she, 'will ye me tell ?'

who tells them Generydes is close at hand.

'Madame,' he saide, 'her be the gardeyṅ side,   4463
Att your comyng ther he will abide,
And euery thing¹ is redy to your entente.'
Thanne was Clarionas right wele content.   4466

The laundress wishes herself hence,

The lavender thanne was some what dismayde ;   4467
'I wold,' quod she, 'I hadde be hense this nyght,
ffor we do noo thyng¹ here as ye haue sayde,

Noyther in noo wise like as ye be highŧ;   4470
Madame,' quod she, ' this goth not aħ arighŧ;'
'Now be not wrothe,' thanne seid Clarionas,
'And I shaħ teħ yow trougth of aħ the case.'   4473

but Clarionas
tells her that

To hir' anoŋ thanne Answerd the lavender,   4474
'As for my part,' quod she, ' this shaħ I saye,
I wolle not here noo thyng¹ of this mater,
ffor me likiŧħ noo thyng¹ in this arraye,   4477
I wiħ calle after helpe some maner way!'
'Nay, god defende it,' quod Clarionas,
'That ye shaħ inpert me so in this case;   4480

I haue your' faythe and promys in my hand,   4481
That ye shaħ kepe my counceħ secretly;
If ye do this, ye shaħ wele vnderstonde,
Ye shaħ repente it sore as wele as I,   4484
Me think ye were moche better certaynly
To be rewlid as I shaħ yow counceħ,
And it shaħ suerly be to youre avayle: 4487

if she does not
keep faith she
will repent
it sore;

To knowe the very trougŧħ of this case,   4488
I shaħ declare it aħ [at] aventure;
Ther is a knygħt not ferre owt of this place,
I loue hyŋ best of eny creature,   4491
And of his loue ayenward I am sure;
Righŧ sone I wote he wiħ be here with me,
And streigħt wiŧħ hyŋ I will goo in to my contre.

that there is a
knight whom
she loves,

and who will
take her to her
own country.

Wherefore I counceħ yow leue aħ this fare,   4495
And come with me, it shaħ be for your best,
here shaħ ye leve in sorow and in care,
I canne not thynk that ye shaħ leve in rest,   4498
And I suerly wiħ make yow this behest,
If ye wiħ take the payŋ me for to plese,
I shaħ o trowgth make yow righŧ wele At ease.'   4501

She advises
her to come
with them.

The laundress thought that as she had deceived Sir Yuell this would be the best thing to do.

The lavender be thought hir in hir mynd,   4502
That she disseyuyd *ser* yueℋ be a trayn),
And if so[1] were that she abode be hynd,
She were vndone for eu*er* in certayn);   4505
Thanne seid she to Clarionas ayeyn),
'ffor your' plesure, madame, I am contente,
Witℋ you to go att your' commaundment.'   4508

Off hir Answere Clarionas was fayn),   4509
And ellys she had gon) all womanles,
Whiche had not ben) hir hon*our* in certayn),
And as thei went to geder stiℋ opese,   4512

Generydes came to the garden,

In to the garden) came Generides,
And atte first he wist not whiche was she :
'Where are ye now? fayre lady myn),' q*u*od he.   4515

Now what nedith long' *p*rocesse of y[is] mat*er*?   4516

and took up Clarionas behind him.
In like manner Natanell took the laundress.

She was sette vppe behynde Generides,
And Nataneℋ sette vppe the lavendere
vppon) his hors, and furth they ganne them) dresse.
Aℋ this while was *ser* yueℋ stiℋ opese,
Eu*er* wayteng' whanne the lavender shuld bryng'
That she *p*romysed att hir departeng'.   4522

Butt as it hatℋ be sayde full long' agoo,   4523
Some bete the busℋ and some the byrdes take,
And wheder that I be on) of thoo or noo,

[leaf 24, back]

I me reporte onto the letterys blake,   4526
And reasone wiℋ it may not be forsake,
he that entenditℋ villany of shame,
It is no synne to quyte hym) witℋ the same.   4529

Meanwhile Sir Yuell was waiting at the laundress's house till he thought something was wrong.

Syr Iue‖ thougℏt she taryed passyng' long',   4530
And vppe he rose and furth he goth alone,
In his conseite he demyd that it was wrong',

[1] MS. *sore.*

And to the quenys chaunber he is furth gon) ; 4533 He went to the queen's chamber
'Where is the quene?' quod he, 'telle me anon).'
'It is not long', they sayde, 'sithe she was here, and heard she had been with the
And with hir also spake the lavander.' 4536 laundress.

Whanne he hard that his hert was all away, 4537 Then he wist well it was not all right.
thanne wist he wele it was not all a right,
'This lavender,' quod he, 'this is noo naye,
hath don) all this, that most vnhappy wight. 4540
Butt I shall do my powre and my myght
hym) for to take, and if I happyn) wele
ffull sore thei shall repent it euery dele.' 4543

He armyd hym) and left all other thing', 4544 He armed himself
And furth he goth in all the hast he myght ;
he and his page, withoute more taryeng',
After Generides toke the way full right, 4547 and rode after Generydes.
And att the last, of hym) he had a sight,
Clarionas thanne cast hir yee a side, Clarionas saw him coming,
And ser yuell full sone she had Aspyde. 4550

Thanne to Generides full sone she saide, 4551 and said to Generydes,
'yender comyth your' mortall enmy,[1] 'Yonder is your mortal enemy.
The whiche full oft hath made me affrayde,
Now may ye wele ordeyne a remedy ; 4554
Wherefore,' quod she, 'I prae yow hartely,
That what some euer he say be his promys,
late hym) not skape your' handis in noo wise.' 4557 Let him not escape.'

To here answeryd Generides ayeyn), 4558 'Be not afraid,' said Generydes.
'Be ye noo thyng a ferde as in this case ;
Or we departe,' quod he, 'he shall be fayn)
his quarell vppe to yelde, be goddis grace.' 4561
With that anon) alight Clarionas ; Clarionas alighted.
Generides anon) hym) dressid in his gere,
And Natanell was redy with his spere. 4564

[1] MS. elmy.

GENERYDES. 10

Sir Yuell and
Generydes meet,

Syr yueⅡ ranne onto Generides,   4565
Thorougħ owt the sheld he smote hym) [in] certayn),
Butt for all that he skapid daungerles,
And furtħ with aⅡ ranne to hym) ayeyn),   4568
That witħ his spere he brast his sheld on twayn),

and Yuell is
wounded,

And in his body he woundid hym) so sore,
That down) he felle, endure mygħt he no more.   4571

and yields up
his horse to
Natanell.

Hys stede he delyueryd to NataneⅡ,   4572
A myghti hors and called passing' wigħt ;
'I wold,' q*u*od he, 'this hors were cherisshid wele,
ffor he is sure and good, I yow behigħt.'   4575
Generides adown) from) his hors aligħt,
Ser yueⅡ sawe it wold non) other be,
And vppe he rose and knelid on) his kne.   4578

He begs mercy
of Generydes,

Thanne seid he thus, ' mercy, Generides,   4579
I haue affendid yow, I wiⅡ no more ;'

but Clarionas
warned him not
to trust him
again.

Clarionas cryed alway stiⅡ opece,
' Though he speke fayre, trost hym) not therfore ; 4582
And if ye do ye shaⅡ repente[1] it sore :
Remembre wele he hatħ desseyuyd yow twyes,
ShaⅡ he neu*er* be trew, I yow promys.'   4585

Generides remembryd hym) ther one,   4586
She sayde hym) trew, he knewe it verily ;
Witħ that Clarionas aspyed anon),
Ser yueⅡ held a knyffe in his hande secretly ;   4589

'He will slay you,
he hath a knife in
his hand.'

' By ware,' q*u*od she, and ganne hym) to Aspye,
' he wiⅡ sle yow, ye may wele vnderstonde,
A knyff aⅡ way he kepitħ in his hande.'   4592

He stabbed
Generydes in
the thigh,

He smote generides in to the thye,   4593
And he was not gretly hurt, it was his vre ;
his purpose was to sle hym) vterly,

           [1] MS. *repentid.*

with fals tresone vnder a coverture :   4596
Thanne Generides thought on͛ hym͛ to be sure,
And with his swerd he clefe his hede on͛ twoo,   *and he in return*
That neuer after spake he wordes moo.   4599   *cleft his head in two.*

Thanne vppon͛ his stede lept generides,   4600
Be hynd hym͛ was sett Clarionas his lady dere,
And Nataneȴ aȴ redy ganne hym͛ dresse,
Vppon͛ an hors beforn͛ the lavendere,   4603   *So they all got on horseback again and rode on.*
And soo thei rode togeder aȴ in feer͛,
Owt of ther enmys handes they were sure,
Euerychone talkyng͛ of ther aventure.   4606

In this meane tyme the body of the knygħt   4607
his page anon͛ vppon͛ his hors it layde,
And to the courte[1] he went ayeyn͛ fuȴ rigħt.
Whanne it was knowen͛ the kyng͛ was sore dismayd,   *The king was sore dismayed when he heard*
'Now haue I lost my wor[l]dly Ioye,' he seid :
Grete thougħt he toke and way[led] more And more,
Wher with the courte[1] was trobelyd very sore.   4613

And how it was of aȴ that aventur͛,   4614   *of the adventure from the page of Sir Yuell.*
Thanne to the kyng͛ he told aȴ the hoole processe,
'Ther is,' quod he, 'no levyng creature
So dere to hir as is Generides ;   4617
Whiche in long͛ tyme hath dured stiȴ opese,
This is the trougtħ I say yow for certayn͛.   4619

. . . .

[*A leaf has been here cut out of the MS., containing* 187 *lines.*
  The catchwords of the next line are, 'And he it is suerly.']

. . . .

'And it obeye with humble reuerence,   4620   [leaf 25]
I[n] yow only is aȴ my feithfuȴ trest ;
I am your͛ child, demeane me as ye list.'   4622

                 [1] MS. *contre.*

She was glad
for Generydes,
but when she
thought of his
departure
her joy turned
to heaviness.

Rigĥt gladde she was as for Generides,   4623
But whanne she thougĥt of his departeng',
hir ioy was turnyd in to hevynes,
yet therof she made nonɔ opynɔ tokenning',   4626
By countenaunce or by other thing',
Butt alway kept it close in hir entente,
And to hir chaunber furtĥ witĥ she went.   4629

She lay on her
bed in despair,

Downɔ onɔ hir bed she felle[1] and ther she laye ;   4630
Mirabeℍ had merveℍ what it was,
' Madame,' she seid, ' what is this new affraye ?   4632
What mysfortune[2] ? and hougĥ be feℍ this case ?'
To here anonɔ Answerd Clarionas,
' This is,' quod she, ' come to me a late,
ye may wele saye I am vnfortunate.'   4636

' Vnfortunate,' quod she, ' that is not soo ;   4637
I canne wele think it is your' owynɔ conseite.'
' Nay,' quod Clarionas, ' so mote I goo,

and told Mirabell
that Generydes
had deceived her

I doo none other but mynɔ owenɔ detĥ Awayte,   4640
Generides hatĥ done me this disseite,
My fader hatĥ geve hymɔ half his eritage,
And me also ther witĥ in mariage.   4643

in saying that he
would go to
India and be
made king,
and then come
again.

In to the reame of ynd now wiℍ he goo,   4644
And ther he seitĥ that he shalbe a kyng',
Thanne wiℍ he come ayeynɔ whanne that is do,
And so make an ende of our weddyng' :   4647
But wele I wote aℍ this is butt feyning',
he is purveyd of some new Acquentaunce,
Whiche I canne think is more to his plesaunce.'   4650

' Leave these
fancies,' saith
Mirabell.

Thanne seid Mirabeℍ, ' Good Madame,' quod she, 4651
' ffor goddes loue leve aℍ these fantesies,
ffor this I knowe in very certente,

       [1] MS. *lay.*   [2] MS. *my fortune.*

ye shaH not fynde it thus, I yow promes ;   4654
Wene ye that he wiH departe from) your seruice
And vtterly refuse yow now euerydele ?
Nay, Madame, I know his trougtħ soo wele.'   4657   'I know his truth so well.'

To hir anon) thanne answerd Clarionas ;   4658
'Ye make yow sure of euery maner thing'.
I warante yow,' quod she, ' as in this case,
That I haue seid ye shaH fynde noo lesing' ;   4661
he will wedde me, he seitħ, whanne he is a kyng',
In grete estate and wurchippe many wayes,
And aH these are butt triffolys and delayes.'   4664

So lay she stiH in rigħt grete hevynes :   4665   Clarionas lay still in great heaviness,
MirabeH thanne owt of hir chaunber went ;
In hir goyng' she mette Generides,
And told hym) aH hir ladyes entent,   4668   and then Mirabell brought
' ye must come now,' quod she, ' or AH is shent,
ffor she canne think non) other sekerly,
Butt that ye haue for sake hir vtterly.'   4671

' For sake,' quod he, ' aye, benedicite,   4672   Generydes
Why wiH she me mystrost in eny wise ?
Trewly MirabeH,' quod he, ' As for me,
My hert his heris, my trowtħ and my ceruice,   4675   to her
It grevitħ me fuH sore suche fantesyce,
ffor be that lord that formyd me of nowgħt,
Other to wedde came neuer in my thougħt.'   4678

' AH that,' quod she, ' I haue told here fuH playn),
Yet takitħ she noo credence what I say,
Ther is noo bote butte ye must come certayn),
And that anon) as fast as euer ye may.'   4682
' I come,' quod he, ' withoute more delay ;'
So witħ MirabeH furth he went anon),
And to Clarionas streight he is goon).   4685

chamber.

In to hir chaunber furth he goth a pace,   4686
Of his comyng⟨ fu⟨ redely she knewe ;
'What do yow here ?' thanne seid Clarionas,

She taunted him
with his untruth.

'Of a⟨ knyghtes,' quod she, 'the most vntrew ;   4689
Your fayre behest a⟨ now may I rewe,
Your beyng⟨ here is to my grete displesaunce,
Goo now away onto your old Acqueyntaunce.   4692

' Sir Amelok hath
a fair daughter

Syr Amelok hath a doughter certayn⟩,   4693
Whiche is right fayre and lucidas she hight,

and the peace
will soon be made
between you.'

The pece is sone made betwix yow twayn⟩,
ffor to the chaunge your hert is wonder light ;   4696
I say for me, ther was no maner wight
That loved yow better thanne I dede before ;
A⟨ that is doo, for now I wi⟨ nomore.'   4699

Whanne she hadde sayde that pleasid hir to say, 4700

At this Generydes
fell down in a
swoon.

Thanne was Generides a wofu⟨ man⟩ :
Anone he felle in swouneng⟨ and ther he laye,
A⟨ discolored in vesage, pale and wanne,   4703
And furth with remembre she beganne
What man⟩ he was, and also what seruice,
That he hir fader dede in euery wise,   4706

With right good wi⟨ he was redy alway :   4707
Mirabe⟨ saide, ' what maner thing⟨ is this ?
Now certeynly ye are to blame, I saye ;
ffor wele I wote in hym⟩ ye demyd amys :   4710
yet atte last,'[1] quod she, ' ye shuld hym⟩ kysse.'

[leaf 25, back]

Thanne seid Clarionas, 'sith it is soo,
If that may do hym⟩ good, it shalbe doo   4713

With a⟨ myn⟩ hert,' quod she, ' what euer fa⟨ ;' 4714
To se hym⟩ soo she was right sore dismayde.

Clarionas kisses

Ther as he lay she kyst hym⟩ furth witha⟨,

[1] ? *lest.*

And he ther with all sodenly abrayde,　　　　　4717　him, and he recovers,
like as a man had ben sore affrayde ;
' Madame,' quod he, ' now please it yow to here
What I shall say as towchyng this mater.　　　4720

As for my parte ther is noo creature,　　　　　4721　and all was forgiven.
That will do more your honour to avaunce,
And o my trowth it was I neuer sure,
Vnto this our of now none Acqueyntance,　　　4724
In that ther is noo cause of displesaunce,
I haue ben alway trew in myn entent,
And of all this god wote I am full innocent.　　4727

Whanne he had seid so trewly and so playn,　　4728
In euerything as towchyng this mater :
' All is for geve,' quod she, ' betwix vs twayn,
And late vs still be frendis as we were.'　　　 4731
' Ther to I graunt,' quod he, ' with right good chere
To endure ; ' so with good contenuaunce
Iche to other made thei full assuraunce.　　　4734

Vppon this thanne he toke his leve for to goo,　4735　He took his leave of the Sultan, and of Clarionas,
Of the Sowdon and of fayre Clarionas ;
With hir he left a litill dogge also,　　　　　　and left with her a little dog.
Whiche went with hir a bought in euery place,　4738
In here conseite a grete Iewell it was ;
So toward ynd Generides is gon,
With hym the new made knyghtes euerychone.　4741

To Surre came Generides and his knyghtes a pace,
Ther was the ost of auferius ye kyng,　　　　　The army of Auferius was at Damas when Generydes came with his knights.
In a Cite whiche was callid Damas,
Theder thei came withoute more taryeng :　　　4745
Grete ioye made all the ost of ther comyng,
And of all other namyd in the prese,
They were most ioyfull of Generides.　　　　　4748

They took ship in all haste,

To the shippe they went in all the hast y⁽ᵉⁱ⁾ myght,
And as thei wold desire thei had the wynd ;
Vppon̄ the see thei toke ther course fuH right,
That sone thei were vppon̄ the cost of ynde,   4752
Right fayre havenys aH redy ganne thei fynd,

and soon landed.

And sone thei landyd, shortly for to say,
AH atte ther ease, was no man̄ seid nay.   4755

ffurth one thei went, and made noo taryeng⸱,   4756
The Cryes were made in euery good village,
AH thoo that wold obey the rightwise kyng
Shuld haue ther lyves and ther heritage ;   4759
And euery man̄ to haue his avauntage,
A moneth day to take avisement,
This was the kynggez own̄ poyntement.   4762

Furth with his ost kyng auferius is gon̄,   4763
And many lordes in his companye,

The king won the towns and castles,

The townys and the castelys euerychon̄
Euer as he went he wanne them̄ by and by,   4766

all except one

Save one, whiche was fuH stronge and myghty,
And as the story makith remembraunce,
Wold not be wonn̄e withoute grete ordenaunce : 4769

called Vice,

And Vice it hight, whiche is a fayre Cite ;   4770

near which Sir Amelok lay.

Ser Amelok fro thense a litiH he lay,
And of auferius comyng⸱ wist not he
No maner o thing, ne of aH that Arraye ;   4773
Thanne was ther on̄ that had hast in his way,
And ser Amelok Anon̄ he ganne hym̄ dresse,

He was playing chess.

Whiche with a knyght was playeng⸱ Att chesse. 4776

' This is no time for chess,' said one, ' it is check-mate to thee,

' What tyme is now to play Atte Chesse ? ' quod he,
' Thu byddest thy felaw chese, I vnderstonde ;
Butt for certeyn̄ I saye chek mate to the,

Kyng Auferius is here withynne the land,   4780

Townys and Castelys are yelde to his hand,

With hym) is come Generides also,

Take hede be tvme or aH is goo.'   4783

for Auferius and Generydes are here.'

Syr Amelok, whanne he the tydenges hard,   4784

A wrother man) yet saw he neuer non),

And as a man) beside hem) self he farde,

These tydengys came so hastely vppon) ;   4787

Ther with he sent his lettres owt anon),

AH men) to come and in hir best arraye,

Euery man) to make as many as they may   4790

Sir Amelok was beside himself for rage.

He sent out his letters

The townnys and the Castellys on) be on),   4791

he sett them) vnder rule and gouernaunce,

And made them) to be vitaylid euerychon)

With stuff of pepiH And of ordenaunce ;   4794

And specially in his remembraunce,

And in his mende the fayre Cite of Vice,

To make it strong' in eny maner awise.   4797

and victualled his towns and castles,

especially Vice.

And so he ded in AH that euer he myght ;   4798

Withynne ij myle thanne was the kyngges ost,

And ther was on) that gidid them) fuH right,

Whiche somtyme kept the forest in the cost,   4801

And brought tidengges whanne the Cite was lost,

The same forster suerly was ther gide,

ffuH wele he knew the wayes on) euery side.   4804

Auferius was two miles off,

[leaf 26]

led by the faithful forester.

Whanne the ost was come before ye town),   4805

he sett his felde and made no more delay ;

Whanne that was do, the kyng rode vppe and down),

Beholding' wele the grownde in euery way,   4808

And thanne he sette the pepiH in his arraye,

A xx. Rankys trewly for to accompt,

And iche of them A MH men) affronte.   4811

When he came before the town

he set his peop'e in array in 20 ranks, 1000 in each.

They of the town
were ware,
They of the towⁿ) were ware of yer comyng¹,   4812
And toke good hede hougħ they made ther feld ;
Among¹ themᵓ was noo lenger abideng¹,
But furtħ they dressid themᵓ witħ spere and sheld 4815
Owt of the towⁿ), that mygħt a weponᵓ weld,
And ther thei made a feld vpponᵓ the playⁿ),

and mustered
15,000 strong.
xv thowsand to say yow for certaynᵓ.   4818

The battles met,
It was not long¹ or bothe the battellez mett,   4819
And on that side of Auferius the kyng¹
Generides fuħ fresshly on they sett,
And was the first of that encounteryng¹,   4822
ffuħ wele horsyd att his likyng¹,

and Generydes
bore down
Ananyell,
And with a spere, the story canᵓ yow teħ,
he bare downᵓ a knygħt callid Ananyeħ,   4825

brother to Sir
Amelok.
And broder to ser Amelok he was ;   4826
A semely knyght, a manᵓ of grete powre,
Generides toke Nataneħ¹ his stede,
And hymᵓ he wold a takenᵓ prisoner,   4829
Thanne was ther of his felisshepe soo nere,
That saw thei hougħ his stede was goⁿ)
So furtħ witħ aħ they reskewe hymᵓ anoⁿ).   4832

He had a sworn
brother called
Sir Amysell,
He had a felaw that callid was ser Amyseħ,   4833
his swornᵓ broder he was in sothfastnes ;
Anone witħ aħ ranne to hymᵓ ser Dareħ,
And hymᵓ vnhorsyd ther in aħ the prese,   4836
And in like wise so ded Generides,
ffurtħ on he gotħ and yer as the prese was most,

whom Darell
unhorsed.
Syr Dareħ toke the stede and led hymᵓ to yᵉ ost. 4839

The other party
were wroth.
The toder part avaunce themᵓ anone   4840
And wrothe thei were yer menᵓ were so outrayed,

King Lamedon
was there,
kyng lamedonᵓ was ther, and formest of euerychonᵓ),

¹ So MS. for *Ananyell*.

And aH for love of lucidas the mayde,   4843   *and all for love of Lucidas*
The whiche was endly fayre, as it was sayde,
Of aH hir man*e*rys callid trew and p[l]ayne,
Ser Amelok hir fader was certayn :   4846   *the daughter of Amelok*

Serenides hir moder was Also,   4847   *and Serenydes;*
And aH she was of another dissposicio*n)*   *but she was of another disposition.*
As ye haue hard, withoute wordes moo,
VnWurchipfuH of hir condicio*n)*,   4850
like as the story makitħ mencio*n)*,
And so furtħ on, to say yow forther more,
Anone beganne the bateH passing' sore.   4853

Syr Amelok in the myddes of the play*n)*   4854   *Sir Amelok smote a knight with his spear,*
Ranne to A knygħt, and smote hy*m)* witħ his spere
Thorougħ owt the brest, and slew hy*m)* in certay*n)*.
Thanne he toke[1] the kyng' in this maner,   4857
'Be my counceH take ye this p*r*esent here,   *and sent to the king—'Take this and go.'*
And so departe and ellys I yow behigħt,
ye shaH haue more long' or it be nygħt.'   4860

Thanne who was wrothe but Auferius y*e* kyng?   4861   *Auferius was wroth,*
Witħ a spere he ranne in to the prese
ffuH egerly, and atte first metyng'
he slew the kyng Sanyk withoute lese,   4864   *and slew Sanyk king of Africa, the father of Serenydes.*
The whiche was fader onto Serenydes,
kyng of Auferyk, the story makitħ mynd,
As here before in writeng' may ye fynde.   4867

Hys sonne was ther and saw hy*m)* wher he laye,   4868   *His son, Sir Ysores, said to Sir Amelok,*
Ser ysores he higħt, to say yow fuH trew,
Thanne to s*er* Amelok this ganne he saye,
'Woo wortħ the tyme tha[t] eu*er* I the knewe !   4871   *'Wo worth the time that ever I knew thee!'*
Thy cursyd lyff,' q*u*od he, 'and most vntrew,
Thy hatefuH hart, and thy mysgou*er*naunce
hatħ browgtħ abowt this onhappy chaunse.'   4874

[1] ? told.

With 1000
knights he bore
his father to
town
Syr ysores, as sone as it myght be,   4875
Made certayn knyghtes bere his fader to town,
And with A Ml knyghtes in his company ;
And all they made grete lamentacion :   4878
The prestis mett hym with A procession,[1]
And of the Citee many a creature,
to his sepulture. Right so they brought hym to his sepulture.   4881

Serenydes
saw them,
Quod Serenydes, 'beholde them eu[er]ychon ;'   4882
And what it ment she wold a wist fayn :
And so among' all other was one,
'Madame,' quod he, 'the sothe I will not layn ;   4885
The kyng' your' fader ded is for certayn,
his knyghtes yender bere hym on his sheld,
kyng' Auferius hath slayn hym in the feld.'   4888

and when she
wist how it was
she was a woful
creature.
She took Lucidas
apart, and said,
And whanne Serenydes wist hough it was,   4889
wete ye wele she was a wofull creature ;
She toke aparte the mayden lucidas,
'Doughter,' quod she, 'now am I very sure,   4892
'My joy is gone. My Ioy is gon, And All good aventure ;
[leaf 26, back] I myght right wele A knowen All this before,
I haue deseruyd it if it were more.   4895

This is all come
for my untruth to
For myn on trowth all this come too [me],   4896
For more vntrew I trow ther was neuer non) ;
A better prince was neuer born,' quod she,
'In all this world thanne I was sure of on,   4899
And vtterly for euer he is now gone,
Vppon his grace it botith not to wayte,
ffor I shall neuer stonde in his conseite.   4902

Auferius.'
Kyng' auferius it is in certayn,   4903
To whom I weddid was be mariage,
I toke a new whiche sore repentith me,

[1] MS. precession.

It hath and will turne me to grete damage ; 4906
And doughter myn, now ye be yong' of age,
haue this in mynde, bothe now and euery owre,
late noo thyng' meve yow to your' dishonour.' 4909

In this meane tyme that she complayned soo, 4910
The batell lasted alway still opece,
Moche pepyll hurt and many slayn Also ;
ffull egerly thanne came rideng' ser ysores, 4913
And with a spere ranne to Generides,
And with grete corage all redy to fight,
To avenge his faders deth if that he myght. 4916

Generides full suerly hym beheld, 4917
hym for to mete anone he ganne hym dresse,
And ther they ranne to geder in the feld :
The toder knyght, callid ser ysores, 4920
vppon the shelde he smote Generides ;
And with [the] stroke his stede came on so rounde,
That hors and man were almost cast to grownd. 4923

Generides recoueryd vppe than ayeyn, 4924
Thinkyng suerly to quyte hym to for on,
And with his swerd he brast his sheld on twayn :
The swerde poynte ranne onto the shulder boon, 4927
Sore hurt he was, and reskewse was yer non,
Nor non comyng', wherefore ser ysores
Anon he yelded hym onto Generides, 4930

And furth with all delyueryd hym his swerd. 4931
To hym thanne seide Generides ayeyn,
'What man be ye that I haue here conquerred ?'[1]
'I am,' he seid, 'to say yow for certayn, 4934
The kynggez sone that here to day was slayn ;
And eyre to his landes withoute lese,
My suster is the quene Serenydes.' 4937

[1] MS. *conquerred here.*

The battle went
on meanwhile,

and Sir Ysores
ran at Generydes
to avenge his
father.

He struck him,
and nearly
brought him
down.

Generydes in
turn cut him
down with
his sword,

and took him
prisoner.

'What man be
ye ?' he asked.
'I am son to
the king who
was slain to-day,

and Serenydes is
my sister.'

'I know her well,'
quoth he,

'Serenydes,' quod he, 'I knowe here well ;   4938
This warre beganne noo creature but she,

'she is crop and
root of the war.

ffor she is croppe and rote and euery dele,
yet as for your persone ye shall goo fre,   4941

Tell her I am he
that she would
have destroyed.'

And say to Serenydes that I am he
Whiche she wold haue distroyed euer more ;
And now I trowe she wolle repent it sore.'   4944

Sir Ysores was
sore wounded,

Sore wondid Was ser ysores in dede,   4945
And sore for bled that vnnethe myght he stonde,

and Generydes
held him up
on his horse,

Might had he now to kepe hym on his stede,
Butt as Generides put to his hande ;   4948
Whereby a man myght knowe and vnderstonde

like a noble
knight.

A noble knyght and full of prow[es]se,
his enmy so to helpe in his distresse.   4951

To the Cite goth now ser ysores,   4952
Rideng alone soft and an easy pace ;

Serenydes saw
him from the
wall.

Vppon the wall stode Serenydes,
And saw hym come and callid lucidas ;   4955
'God wote,' quod she, 'I stonde in an hevy case,
I se my broder woundid passing sore,
My hevynes encreasith more and more.'   4958

Ther anon the mayde lucidas   4959
Comfortid hir in all that euer she myght ;

Sir Ysores
dismounted in
great pain,

Ser ysores be that tyme come was,
And with grete payne down of his hors light ;   4962

and told her
what Generydes
had said.

To his suster he toke the way full right,
Rehersyng euery word bothe more and lesse,
Whiche he shuld telle hir fro Generides.   4965

And whanne Serenydes wist hym so nere,   4966
God wote she was a wofull creature,
withoute eny comfort or eny maner chere,

Trostyng⸰ vppoɲ noo better aventure,   4969
ffor of his frendshippe cowde she not be sure.
And so furth on to telle yow ferthermore,
AH way the bateH lastid passing⸰ sore.   4972

Off euery side grete pepiH were slayɲ,   4973   Many people were
                                                                     slain on each side.
And moche grounde of ser Amelok [1] thei wanne ;
Ser DareH with a spere vppoɲ the playɲ   Sir Darell
                                                                     overthrew Ioatan,
Come rideng⸰ on, and to an erle he ranne,   4976
Borɲ in europe, his name was Ioatan,
And in serteyɲ, be writeng⸰ as I knowe,
Both hors with the Erle was ouer throwe.   4979

Syr DareH toke with hyɲ his stede ;   4980   and took his
                                                                     horse,
With that anoɲ his knyghtes were redy,
hyɲ to reskew thei made hasty spede ;
A long⸰ the Citee DareH rode by and by,   4983   and as he rode
                                                                     along the city
Vppon [2] A towre ther with he cast his yee,   he saw a maiden
                                                                     on a tower,
And [on] that towre he sawe a mayde sittyng⸰,
Right Inly fayre she was to his semyng⸰.   4986   right fair as he
                                                                     thought.

And thanne he callid Sygrem furth with aH,   4987   Then he called
                                                                     Sygrem,
'Segrem,' he saide, 'now for the loue of me,   [leaf 27]
Of oɲ thyng telle me in especiaH,
A gentilwomaɲ that I yonder see,   4990   and asked who
                                                                     she was.
What that she is, sey me the certente ;'   'To tell the truth
'Ser,' quod Sygrem, 'the soth I wiH not layɲ,   she is the
                                                                     daughter of Sir
Ser Amelok is hir fader in certayɲ ;   4993   Amelok.'

And she is callid good in euery place,   4994
Of hir maners soft and eke demure.'
Thanne saide DareH, 'trewly this is the case,   'She shall have
                                                                     my service,'
My seruice she shaH haue I yow ensure,   4997   quoth Darell,
ffor me thinkith hir a goodly creature ;
And yet I drede Generides therfore,   'but I fear
                                                                     Generydes.'
lest he ther with will be displeasid sore.'   5000

         [1] MS. *Amelek.*   [2] MS. *A vppon.*

'Doubt not,'
said Sygrem,
'Syr,' quod Sygrem, 'dougħt not in this case,   5001
If he loue not hir fader by noo maner waye,

'for he doth not
hate her.'
In trowtħ yet hate[t]h he not lucydas.
'Why, Who is that?' quod he, 'I prae yow say.' 5004
  It is the mayde,' quod he, 'ye sawe to day,
And if ye wiħ I shaħ a tokeɴ bere
To hir anoɴ, and bryng⸍ a trew answere.'   5007

'That I beseche yow hartely,' he saide;   5008
Darell then gave
him a ring to
carry to Lucidas,
And ther witħ aħ he delyueryd hyɴ a ryng⸍,
'Goo now,' quod he, 'to lucydas that mayde,
Witħ this tokyɴ and make noo taryeng⸍,   5011
And do your⸍ massage wele in euery thing⸍.'
Whanne he hadde tolď hyɴ aħ his erand playɴ,
and went back
to the field,
In to the feld he returnyd hyɴ ageyɴ,   5014

And in the thikkest prece of aħ the placo   5015
and unhorsed
Ananyell,
who was uncle
to Lucidas.
She saw it,
he bare dowɴ Ananyeħ, hors and aħ,
The whiche was vnkyħ onto lucydas;
She saw aħ that stondeng⸍ vpponɴ the waħ,   5018
Thanne thougħt she this, what thing⸍ y⸍ euer faħ
Shaħ nomaɴ think but that I do very rigħt,
Thougħ I besette my loue oɴ suche a knygħt.   5021

and asked her
mother,
'Which is
Generydes?
I think it is he
with the black
steed.
Thanne sayde she to hir moder in this wise;   5022
'wote ye whiche is generides?' quod she:
'As ferre furtħ as I canne device,
his stede is blak, me think the same is he;   5025
A noble knygħt is he, in very certente:
And o thing shaħ I telle yow that is trew,
Myɴ oweɴ vnkiħ now he ouer threw.   5028

But there is
another knight
on a white steed.'
Ther is,' quod she, 'another knygħt also,   5029
his stede is whigħt, this wote I for certayɴ,
In aħ the ost suerly ther is no moo,

That in knyghtwoode Are like to them twayn.'   5032
Thanne to hir answerd Serenydes ayeyn,
'Aɫ that is sothe,' she saide, 'and as for me,
Yett of them bothe I wote not whiche is he.   5035

'I know not which of the two he is,' said Serenydes.

But as for hym namyd first of aɫ,   5036
I shaɫ declare yow trewly myn entent,
With that ther myght be made a pece fenyaɫ,
And bothe partes beyng of on assent,   5039
Whiche in this case were fuɫ conuenient,
And if it myght be soo thanne wold I fayn
The mariage were made betwix yow twayn.'   5042

'But the first you named I would gladly see married to you when peace is made.'

In this mene while that she these wordes seid,   5043
Come Sygrem vppe and founde them sittyng;
Whanne she hym sawe thanne was she wele apayd:
'Sygrem,' she saide, 'canne ye teɫe me eny thing,
Whiche are the knyghtes of auferius the kyng?'
'Ye, ye, madame,' [quod he] 'soo mote I goo,
I know Generides and other moo.   5049

Meanwhile Sygrem came up,

and she asked him of the king's knights.

And if ye wiɫ haue knowlache whiche is he,   5050
he wiɫ come here anon be fore your sight,
his stede is white, this is the certente ;
With hym ther is also, I yow be hight,   5053
Another man whiche is a worthy knyght ;
his stede is blak, and therto Wight and good,
hym self also is come of right noble blode.   5056

'Generydes is he with the white steed,

but there is a knight on a black one,

Hys fader is a man of grete estate,   5057
And p[r]ince of Cesare by his enheritaunce,
A famose man, and alway fortenate
In euery thing his honour shuld Avaunce ;   5060
Now haue I told yow aɫ the circumstaunce.'
'What is the knyghtes name?' quod she ayeyn ;
'Ser Dareɫ he hight,' quod he, 'this is certayn.'   5063

son of the prince of Cesare,

Sir Darell.'

Lucidas blushed a little,	Whanne lucidas had hard hym euery dele,	5064
	Anon she wex a litiħ rede witħ aħ,	
and Serenydes pretended not to notice.	Serenydes perseyuyd it fuħ wele,	
	She let as though she knew noo thyng At Aħ,	5067
	And ther witħ aħ she rose vp fro the waħ ;	
As they were going, Sygrem whispered Lucydas,	And as thei [1] were remevyng fro the place,	
	ffuħ sustely [2] Sygrem callid lucydas,	5070
and gave her the ring.	And furtħ witħ aħ delyueryd hir the ryng,	5071
	Wherwitħ in sothe she was rigħt wele apayde,	
She hesitated about taking it	Yet made she danger in the reseyuyng,	
	Of his massage she was sumwhat dismayde,	5074
	And soberly to Sygrem thus she saide :	
	' Ryng ne Wríteng, as I remember canne,	
	I neuer yet reseyuyd of noo gentilman :	5077
[leaf 27, back]	Butt this I trost, in his grete gentilnes,	5078
	That his desire suerly and his entent	
	Is only me yn honour to encrease,	
	And in that wise this ryng that he me sent,	5081
	It to reseyue I am rigħt wele content.'	
but did so,	And so she toke the ryng in this maner,	
and gave him another,	And gave Segrym another for to bere.	5084
which Sygrem	Now is Sygrem departid on his way	5085
	ffrom lucidas, his erande for to do,	
	In to the feld as fast as euer he may,	
carried to Dareħ,	To ser Dareħ withoute wordes eny moo,	5088
	his tokyn ther he delyueryd to hym Also ;	
	Whanne he it had he was rigħt wele apayde,	
	And to Sygrem fuħ curtesly he sayde ;	5091
who thanked him,	' Ser,' quod he, ' I thank yow rigħt hertely	5092
	Of your good wiħ and trew seruice,	
	And one thyng I yow ensure verily,	

¹ MS. ther.   ² ? softely.

The first stede that I wynne in eny wise, 5095 and promised him the first horse he should win.
It shalbe your², and that I yow promes ;
So furth he gothe in to the feld anon),
And rode a course onto kyng⸱ lamedon). 5098 He rode at King Lamedon,

Anone thei mette to geder in the feld, 5099
Ther with ser Darell saw his lady fre,
he smote kyng⸱ lamedon) vppon) the sheld,
And suche a stroke he gave hym) with a spere, 5102 and brought horse and man to the ground.
That hors and man) bothe atte grownde were ;
And ther kyng⸱ lamedon) his stede he lost,
Ser Darell hym) toke and led hym) to his ost 5105

Callyng⸱ anon) to his remembraunce, 5106
What full promys he had made before,
Vnto Sygrem for his trew attendaunce; The horse he gave to Sygrem.
That he shuld be rewardid wele therfore, 5109
And to Sygrem, I say yow forthermore,
he gave that stede withoute more taryeng⸱,
The whiche he wanne of lamedon) the kyng⸱. 5112

Vppon) the towre on) highe stode lucidas, 5113 Lucidas saw all this, to her great delight.
And saw all this to hir grete plesaunce ;
Serenydes perseivid hough it was,
She seide noo word, nor made no contenaunce. 5116
And so furth on, to tell yow the substaunce,
The batell still endure[d] to And fro,
Moche pepyll slayn) And Alway moo And moo. 5119

Kyng⸱ lamedon), of whom) ye hard me speke, 5120 King Lamedon mounted another horse and rode at Generydes,
Was sette all now appon) anothe[r]¹ stede,
To that entent he wold hym) hym) self A wreke,
And to Generides he ranne in dede ; 5123
Ther hors came on) with suche a spede,
And sothely, atte first encownteryng⸱,
Generides strake lamedon) the kyng⸱ 5126 who smote him

¹ MS. originally A stede, but anothe[r] is written above.

to the brain,
so that he
fell dead.

Thorough the hede streyght in to the brayn;   5127
The kyng᾿ was dede withynne a litiłł space,
ffor hym was made grete hevynes certayn,
And for to tełł yow certayn as it was,   5130
Whanne he was dede they stode in hevy case;

His side then
fled to the city.

Thei lost the feld, and fled atte last
In to the Citee, and shette the gatez fast.   5133

They without
pitched their
tents,

Thanne thei withoute the tentys vppe y^ei pight,   5134
Eche after other streight abowt the town,
In ałł the hast possibiłł that thei myght;
And first of Ałł, the kynges pavilion   5137
Set for the kyng᾿ and ther vppon a crown;

and set up engines
to break down
the walls.

Engyins grete were purveyd for the nonys,
To breke the wałłys with casting᾿ of stonys.   5140

While they be-
sieged the city

And whiłł that thei besegid the Cite,   5141
These lordes and these knyghtes euerychone,

the news came to
Gwynan that
Generydes was
gone to India,

Ther cam tidengys in very certente,
Vnto Guynan the kyng᾿ be many on,   5144
hough in to ynde Generides is gon,
With meche people and many a nobyłł knyght
To helpe the kyng᾿ his fader in his right.   5147

so he resolved to
invade Persia,
and avenge his
father's death,
and get Clarionas.

Thanne in to perse purposith he to goo,   5148
his faders deth to venge if[1] that he myght,
And of Clarionas he thought also,
hir to haue he thought it was his right,   5151
he made a massinger redy day and nyght

He sent to
Sir Amelok,

Vnto ser Amelok, And hye hym fast
Streyght in to ynde in Ałł the possible hast.   5154

bidding him
hold out, and
he would come
to his rescue.

‘ Goo now to Amelok, and byd hym kepe hym close,
That in noo wise he stere not to And fro,
And kepe hym owt of daunger of his foys,

[1] MS. *of.*

ffor witẖ myꝺ ost streigẖt to perse I wiℓ goo,   5158
To wynne the Sowdoꝺ and his land Also ;
ffro thense I wiℓ into yndᵗ witẖout fey[n]ingᵗ,
And reskew hyꝺ froꝺ Auferius the kyngᵗ.'   5161

Now gotẖ the messenger oꝺ his viage   5162   The messenger
Streigẖt in to ynd, witẖoute more taryengᵗ,   came to Sir
And to ser Amelok seide his message,   Amelok,
Whiche likid hyꝺ rigẖt wele in euery thyngᵗ,   5165
And very glad he was of his comyngᵗ :   [leaf 28]
Grete chere also made quene Serenydes,   who was glad
ffor she purposid wele to leve in pece.   5168   of his coming.

Thañ furtẖ witẖ aℓ quod she to lucidas,   5169
'Telle me, doughter, of very frendlehede,   Serenydes asks
What Sygrem seid, and what his massage was,   Lucidas whät
And as longith to my womanhede,'   5172   Sygrem said.
With thoo wordes she wexe a litiℓ rede ;   She blushed,
'Madame,' quod she, 'if it please yow to here,   and told her of
I shaℓ teℓ yow the trowtẖ of this mater.   5175

There is a knyght of good and noble fame,   5176
In very trowtẖ hatẖ sent me here a ryngᵗ,   Sir Darell and
ffor noo slaunder ne hurt onto my name,   his ring.
Butt to wurchippe in aℓ his demeanengᵗ,   5179
And myꝺ honour above aℓ other thingᵗ,
This is his wiℓ and his desire certayꝺ.'
Thanne seid Serenydes to hir ayeyꝺ,   5182

'What is the knygẖtes name ? now teℓ it me.'   5183
'Trewly, Madame,' quod she, 'ser Dareℓ he higẖ[t],
And of Cesare the prince sonne is he,[1]
Of his handis callid a noble knygẖt,   .   5186
And ayre to his lande, I yow be higẖt ;
Now haue I told yow aℓ the circumstaunce,
I prae yow take it to no displeasaunce.'   5189

                    [1] MS. he is.

'Therof,' quod she, 'dowte ye neuer a dele,   5190
Butt my conseite wiłł I telle yow playne,

'If he love you,'
said Serenydes,
'let him get
If it be so that he love yow so wełł,
ye shałł rigħt sone haue knowlage in sertayne,   5193
your pleasur to perfourme he wiłł be fayn) ;
Send for Sygrem,' quod she, 'that he may goo
To ser Darełł your erand for to do.   5196

And as he owitħ yow feitħ and trew seruice,   5197
That of Generides he wiłł purchase
A ryng of gold, in eny maner wise,
Whiche he in perse had of Clarionas ;   5200
Why and wherefore I shałł tełł you ye cause,
I haue a frende, a fułł seke creature,
Grete payn) of ache ałłway he dotħ endure.   5203

who has been told
in a vision that it
will make him
whole.'
And by a vision) it come hym) too,   5204
he shhuld be hoole if he the ryng mygħt haue ;
And for certayn) it were grete pite also,
That he soo soone were dolvyn) in his grave,   5207
If suche a ryng mygħt hym) socour And save.
ffor the whiche doughter I yow require,
Send for Sygrem and tender this mater.'   5210

To hir anon) Answerd lucidas ayeyn),   5211
Whiche in this mater was fułł Innocente ;
'Madame,' quod she, 'I wiłł putt to my payn),
In that I canne to folow your entente.'   5214
Sygrem anon) on) this massage was sent,
And to ser Darełł dede his erande soo,
The ryng to borow withoute wordes moo.   5217

As for ser Darełł he thougħt noo thyng Amys,   5218
Nor he that brougħt the ryng, but wote ye what ?
ffułł ofte it hatħ be seide, and trew it is,

ffalshede and trougth is euer atte debate : 5221

And yet Sygrem was aɫway fortenate ;

ffor lucidas, whanne he brougħt hir the ryngᵗ,

Gave hym) a manteɫ of hir owne weryngᵗ. 5224

Serenides perseivid be the ryngᵗ, 5225

hir prayour was obseruyd and obeyde,

And furtħ with aɫ withoute more taryengᵗ,

She callid lucidas, and this she saide ; 5228

'Dougħter,' quod she, 'I am rigħt wele apayde,

ffor now I wote ye haue chose you a man),

That wiɫ please yow in aɫ that euer he canne. 5231

And fayre dougħter,' quod she, 'this I yow prae, 5232

As late me see the facyon of that ryngᵗ.'

'Madame,' quod she, 'ye wote rigħt wele alway,

I haue not disobeyde yow in noo thingᵗ ;' 5235

And from a lose anon) ther as it hyngᵗ,

Be cause she wold in no wise her displese,

She toke the ryng onto Serenydes. 5238

Whanne she it hadde thanne was she wele content,

And callid furtħ on) of hir Acqueyntaunce,

Suche on) as wold do after hir entent,

And brougħt vppe was vnder hir gouernaunce, 5242

A man) that cowde hym) self rigħt wele avaunce,

And born) he was, the story seitħ the same,

In Ethiope, and Gusare was his name. 5245

Ther witħ aɫ right this to hym) she sayde ; 5246

'On my massage,' quod she, 'now must ye goo

ffurtħ in to perse, and this may not be nayde,

And ye shaɫ bere witħ you this ryngᵗ Also.' 5249

'Madame,' quod he, 'your) pleasure for to doo,

I wold be glad in eny maner wise,

To ryde or goo ye shaɫ haue my seruice.' 5252

'Gusare,' quod she, 'in sothe this is the case,   5253

[leaf 28, back] haue here a ryng' and kepe it stiɫɫ opece,

To the tyme that ye come onto Clarionas,

ffor she it gave on to Generides ;   5256

that she might break the love between her and Generydes. The love of them is grete, but,[1] neuer the lese,

I wold ther were a variaunce fuɫɫ fayn,

So that the love were broke betwix them twayn.   5259

By this meane my pece I may purchase,   5260

And other wise I trow it wiɫɫ not be,

If ye do wele your' labour' in this case,

ffor your' rewarde yow shaɫɫ wele know and se,   5263

That ye shaɫɫ haue A cause to praye for me.'

'Madame,' quod he, 'this shaɫɫ be don right wele,

In this mater dowte ye neuer a dele.'   5266

Falshede and gile is now togeder mett,   5267

In A persone to awayte ther Avauntage.

vppon han hors [Gusare][2] hym self was sett,

When Gusare came to Persia he met a poor palmer, And rideth into perse on his massage.   5270

Whanne he come ther he mett in his viage

A pore palmer, goth in sympiɫɫ gise ;

To hym anon he sayde right in this wise :   5273

and asked him where the Sultan was. 'Now good fader, what contre come ye fro ?'   5274

'At Mountoner,' said he, 'ffro Mountoner,' quod he, 'the redy waye.'

'Good ser,' quod he, 'now or ye ferther goo,

Where lith,' he seide, 'the Sowdon ? I yow praye.'

'I left hym ther,' quod he, 'as yesterday ;

A grete people surely with hym ther was,

'with Clarionas.' And his doughter also, fayre Clarionas.'   5280

'And where is Generydes ?' 'He is gone to India to maintain his father's right.' 'Where is now hir love, Generides ?'   5281

'he is furth into ynd,' quod he, 'certayn ;

his faderys right to maynteyne and encrese,

MS. *but it.*   [2] *om.* MS.

ffor ther shall he be lord and souereyn.'   5284

'ffader,' quod he, 'of on thyng' yet ageyn,

This wold I vnderstonde in myne entent,

What token he gave hir whanne he went?'   5287

'What token did he leave with her?'

'In sothe,' quod he, 'that canne I tell some dele; 5288

Whanne he departid owt of the Citee,

With hir he left, I am remembryd wele,

A lityll dogge, and ther ye may hym see.'   5291

'A little dog,' said the palmer.

'ffader,' he seide, 'do now sum what for me;

we ij wolle chaunge our clothyng' or we goo.'

They change clothes,

Quod the palmer, 'I gree me wele therto.'   5294

Now is Gusare well onward on his way,   5295

and Gusare came

And gave the palmer money largely;

To mountoner he came the redy way,

to Mountoner,

Ther was brought tydengez sekerly,   5298

and heard of Gwynan's invasion.

That Gwynan was enteryd certaynly

Into the lande of perse withoute eny delay,

ffor to make a feld and wynne it by batell.   5301

And so furth on to say yow ferthermore,   5302

Gusare is now as besy as he may,

To do that he had promys[ed] before;

And as the palmer went in his Arraye,   5305

So goth Gusare, and toke the [redy] way

He goes to a temple where the Sultan and Clarionas were,

Into A tempill, wheare as the Sowdon was,

With hym ther was also Clarionas.   5308

On his fynger the ryng' anon he sett,   5309

and puts the ring on his finger, and posted himself so that Clarionas might see him.

And in the temple purveid hym A place

Among' the prese, for no man wold he let

That he myght stonde before clarionas;   5312

And ther he stode as for a certeyn space,

The ryng' vppon his fynger for to shewe,

She sawe the ryng' and saide butt wordez fewe.   5315

When she saw the ring

Yet in hir self she was gretly dismayde,   5316

And ther with aH she chaungyd countenaunce ;
Myrabyll sawe it wele, and this she saide,
'Madame, ye haue som cawse of displesaunce ;   5319
I prae yow, teH me what is your grevaunce.'
'That shaH ye knowe,' quod she, 'withoute fayle,
And wele I wote therof ye wiH merveH.   5322

I saw a palmer stondeng' in the prese,   5323
On his finger,' quod she, 'ther is a ryng',
The whiche I gave,' quod she, ' onto Generides,
And to non other creature that is levyng'.'   5326
'Madame,' quod she, 'that is a wonder thing',
yet for AH that dismay yow neuer a dele,
ye shaH se aH this shalbe right weH ;   5329

For I myself wiH speke with hym,' quod she ;   5330
' To your chaumber I shaH hym bryng' anon,
Ther shaH yow fele and knowe the certente,
In very trougth if it be so or noo.'   5333
So her vppon Mirabell is gon,
And taryd not, but as hir commandement was,

She brougt the palmer vnto Clarionas.   5336

Whanne he hir sawe, he knelyd on his kne,   5337
'Madame,' quod he, 'take ye not in disdayne
Of on fortune, whiche wiH non other be,

ffor in this case to yow I wiH be playn ;   5340
Generides is weddid in certeyn,
It passith not a fourthnyght sithe it was,
To Amelokkez doughter lucydas.   5343

It was ayenst his wiH in euery thing,   5344
The cause was suche that he myght not say nay,
his fader chargyd hym on his blissyng',

That pece myght be apoyntid for alway, 5347 to make peace.
If ye trost not the wordes that I say,
here is a ryng' whiche he sent yow be me, 'Here is the ring you gave him.
ye gave it hym) in very certente. 5350

And ferthermore also he chargid me, 5351 And he charged me to let you
To late you wete and suerly vnderstonde,
That ye may now stonde att your' liberte, know that you were free to wed.'
To wedde where euer ye will in eny lande.' 5354
Whanne she herd that noo lenger myght she stond,
Butt downe she felle swoninge for very payn) ; Clarionas fell down in a swoon.
Mirabell ranne and toke hir vppe ageyn), 5357

Comfortyng' hir in all that euer she myght, 5358
And whanne that she was recoueryd vp ayeyn), When she recovered
To hym) that brought the ryng' she went right,
And in noo wise she cowde not hir refrayn), 5361
And smote the ryng' owt of his handes twayn) ; she smote the ring out of Gusare's hands,
All sodenly the ryng' from) hym) was gone,
With that Mirabell toke it vppe anon), 5364 and Mirabell picked it up.

And putte the ryng' in full sure kepyng'. 5365
Thanne saide Gusare onto Clarionas,
'Madame,' quod he, 'I haue forgete a thing',
Whiche I shuld say as I commaundid was, 5368
Ye haue a litill dog', this is the case ; Gusare then asked for the dog,
My charge was this to tell yow euery dele,
In eny wise that ye shuld kepe hym) wele.' 5371

'As for the dog',' quod she, 'here it ys ; 5372
I will noo lenger kepe it sekerly,
Nor no thing' that I may knowe was his.'
To hym) she threw the dog' full hastely, 5375 which Clarionas threw to him, but Mirabell caught it.
With that Mirabell kaught it sodenly ;
'Thow shalt nomore,' quod she, 'come in his way,
ffor lucidas with the shall neuer playe, 5378

And I wiłł haue the att myn owen device.'   5379
Whanne Gusare saw that ther was non other[1] way,
he toke his leue anon in hasty wise,

Gusare then
returned to
India,
And so departid vppon his Iurnay,   5382
Ayeyn to ynd as fast as euer he may.

and Clarionas to
her chamber,
Clarionas is to the chaunber gone,
With syghys depe and thoughtes many on,   5385

a woful woman.
A wofułł woman fułł of hevynes,   5386
Generides alway now remembryng,
Complayneng gretly of his vnstabilnes,
Of wheche he was not gilty in noo thyng;   5389

Mirabell thought
And so Myrabełł alway demyng
Of this mater to vnderstonde it wele,

there was treason.
That it was do be treson euery dele.   5392

When the Sultan
heard of it
he came to
his daughter's
chamber,
And whanne the Sowdon hard of y[is] array,   5393
And hough his doughter toke suche a hevynes,
To hir chaunber he toke the redy waye,
As nature wold and also gentilnes,   5396
And fond hir in hir bed in grete distresse;

and asked what
was amiss.
'Doughter,' quod he, 'ther is some thing amys,
What euer it be now tełł me what it is.'   5399

'My lord,'
quoth she,
'Generydes
is false,
'My lord,' quod she, 'plese it yow to vnderstonde,
ye gaue me onys onto Generides
In mariage, with half your lande;
Now is he false alas, an[d] cawseles   5403
With hym ser Amelok hath made his pece,
And trewly accordid in euery case,

and married to
Lucidas.'
ffor he is weddid vnto lucidas.'   5406

'This aventure,' quod he, 'is passing new,   5407
And as me think a very wonder thing;

'But is it true?'
Butt wote ye verily that it is trew?'

                    [1] MS. eyer.

'Ye, ye, my lord,' quod she, 'withoute feyning'; 5410
And ferthermore he sent me here a ryng',
That I gave hym in very certente,
Where by I wote it may now other be.'   5413

To his doughter the Sowdon gave answer',   5414
'Who wold,' quod he, 'have thought in suche a knyght,
That he wold be ontrew in this mater?
A grete mervell to here, I yow be hight,   5417
ffor this is do [a]yenst all maner right,
And if he shew yow suche onkyndnes,
yet for all that take ye noo hevynes,   5420

For I will purvey for yow another waye,   5421
And moche better as after myn entent;
kyng Gwynan wold be glad, I dare well say,
That he and I shuld make apoy[nte]ment   5424
Betwix yow twayne, and if ye will assent,
That mariage, I cowde wele vnderstonde,
Shall bryng' a fyniall pece in to this land.'   5427

Clarionas seide neuer a worde ageyn,   5428
The whiche Mirabell liked neuer a dele;
To the Sowdon than spake she wordes playn,
'My lord,' quod she, 'as ferre as I canne fele, 5431
In this mater I canne think but wele;
And well I wote that he is suche a knyght,
he will not breke that he hath onys behight.'   5434

'Now, good Mirabell,' quod Clarionas,   5435
'ye wote right wele he sent me here a ryng'.'
'In very trought, madame, and trew it is;
Butt this I wote as wele as eny thing',   5438
All that he saide,' quod she, 'it is lesyng'.'
The Sowdon toke good hede of þt she saide,
Of hir wordes he was right wele apayde.   5441

'Yea, yea, my lord, here is the ring;

it cannot be otherwise.'

The Sultan marvelled that Generydes should be so untrue,

but, said he,

'Gwynan will be glad,

and if you will assent,

we may make a final peace.'

Clarionas said never a word, but Mirabell told the Sultan

[leaf 29, back]

it was all false.

The Sultan took heed of her words, and was well pleased.

'What is best
to be done,
Mirabell?'
'What think yow best, Mirabell?' thanne quod he,
'That shuld be do as towchyng¹ this mater?'
'Trewly,' quod she, 'the best that I canne se,

'Let me go,'
said she,
'and find out
the truth.
late me go furth and be the messanger;   5445
And whanne I come ayeyn) thanne shall ye here
The very trougth, and trew as it is
Doo as ye list, for this is myn) avise I wis.   5448

But if I go,
promise to put
off the marriage
Iff I shall goo, of one thing¹ I yow praye,   5449
That I may haue a surance or I passe,
The mariage to putte in delay

between my lady
and Gwynan.'
Betwix my lady here, Clarionas,   5452
And kyng Gwynan, rehersid here in this case,
And att my comyng¹ home ye shall wele know
All other maner tidynges as I trow.'   5455

The Sultan
assented,
and she went
off to India
Too hir desire the Sowdon) seid not nay,   5456
And furth with gave hir license for to goo;
In to the reame of ynde she toke hir way,

with two squires
and two pages.
With hir ther went ij squyers and noo mo,   5459
Save ij pages to kepe ther horses also,
On hir Iurnay to kepe the way full right,
In All the hast possible that she myght.   5462

Now I shall telle yow hough befelle yᵉ case;   5463
Generydes in
his sleep dreamed
that the Sultan
and his daughter
came to him,
complaining sore
that his promise
was not kept,
Generides was dremyd in his sleppe,
hym) thought the Sowdon) and Clarionas
Come hand in hand, and she with sighys depe   5466
Complayned sore, and first beganne to wepe,
And thanne anon) the Sowdon) to hym) spake,
'Awake,' quod he, 'Generides awake!   5469

Thy promys is not kept that thow behight,   5470
And namely to my doughter and to me,
and that he had
taken
ffor thu hast take, ayenst all maner right,

Another wiff in very certente,   5473   another wife.
By tresone colour' vnder a suerte.'
Thanne seid Clarionas, 'geve me my ring',   'Give me my
ffor suerly I wiłł haue Gwynan the kyng'.'   5476   ring,' said
                                                                   Clarionas,
                                                                   'for I will marry
                                                                   Gwynan.'

After ałł this hym) thought Gwynan yᵉ kyng'   5477   After this, he
In to Egipte shuld lede Clarionas :   thought that
                                                                   Gwynan led her
Thanne came Mirabełł as she was goyng',   into Eygpt,
And toke hir from) him) as hir fortune was ;   5480   but Mirabell
                                                                   took her from
he awoke and of this soden) case,   him.
To Darełł and to Natanełł ałł in fere,   When he awoke
                                                                   he told Darell
Of his dremys he told them) the mater.   5483   and Natanell.

Syr Darełł, as sone as he hard of yᵉ ryng',   5484   As soon as Darell
his hart anon) mysgave hym) furth with ałł,   heard of the ring,
                                                                   his heart mis-
hym) thought som) tresone was ymagenyng,[1]   gave him,
And fayn) he wold haue wist what was fałł ;   5487
Vppon) Sygrem anon) he beganne to calle,   and he called
Whanne he was come he told hem) mor And lesse,   Sygrem,
Of ałł the dreme of Generides.   5490

' Now, good Sygrem, I prae yow goo,' quod hee, 5491   and sent him
' To lucidas and speke for the ryng',   to Lucidas to
                                                                   get the ring
Besechyng' hir that she wiłł send it me,   again.
As euer I may do for hir eny thing'.'   5494
' Ser,' quod Sygrem, 'I say withoute feyning',
I wiłł do your' massage and see what she wiłł say,
And bryng' ayeyn) the ryng' if that ye may.'   5497

Thanne went Sygrem the way to lucidas,   5498   Sygrem went
ffrom) ser Darełł to telle his erande playn),   to Lucides.
In euery thyng' rehersid here the case,
And specially to haue the ryng' Ayeyn),   5501
It was his desire and his comyng' certayn).
Vppon) this anon) she gave an answere,
' I shałł,' quod she, ' speke for this mater.'   5504

                    [1] MS. *ymagenyd*.

and she to her
mother,
To hir moder anon) with aH she gothe,   5505
And tenderly she prayde here for the ryng',
Butt lucidas wheder she was lefe or lothe,
but could not
get it,
She cowde not haue it for no maner thyng',   5508
So partyd she and gretly complayneng',
Right grete vnkyndnes she thought also,
That vnder trost she shuld be seruyd so.   5511

And whanne she sawe it wold non) other be,   5512
and went her
way back to
Sygrem.
ffuH hevilly she went hir way ayeyn),
'I shaH telle yow the trowth, Sygrem,' quod she,
    This ryng' wiH nott be goten) for certayn,[1]   5515
I haue both lost my labour' and payn),
'There is some
treason, I pro-
mise you,
And wele I wote it is not aH a right,
ffor some tresone ther is I yow behight.   5518

And aH I trow be for Generides,   5519
and Darell will
bear the blame.
I canne weH think that DareH shaH bere ye name
Of this vnhappy werk, yet neuer the lese
Right wele I wote that he is not to blame ;   5522
And I suppose ye wiH reporte the same :
Butt this I prae yow hartely,' quod she,
But tell him
'Do my message as sone as ye hym) see,   5525

And say I send hym) word this in sertayn) ;   5526
that Gwynan
is gone to
Persia to destroy
the Sultan and
his land.
Gwynan the kyng' is gon), I vnderstonde,
ffourth in to perse, and his erande is playn),
The Sowdon) to distroye and his land :   5529
It to perfourme he hath made fuH covenaunt.
Beg him to get
leave to go to
[leaf 30]
Persia,
Now, good Sygrem, I prae yow say hym soo,
And that he gete hym) licence for to goo   5532

Furth in to perse withoute more taryeng',   5533
where he will
hear tidings of
the ring,
And say hym) suerly this is myn) avice,
Ther shaH he here some tidynges of the ryng',

[1] MS. certente.

And whoo that take on hym that enterprise, 5536
hough it was brought abought, and in what wise,
And he most dele with all so sekerly,

but he must deal
secretly.'

That no man knowe it save he and ye and I.' 5539

Now goth Sygrem, and noo thyng well apayd, 5540
he mette ser Darell rideng on the playn,

Sygrem meets
Darell,

And told hym all that lucidas had seide ;

and tells him
all that Lucidas
had said.

hough he had lost his labour and his payn, 5543
And hough the ryng wold not be goten ageyn ;
Whanne he had hard all this yan was he wroth,

As soon as he
heard all,

And to Generides anon he gothe. 5546

'I pray yow, ser, now geve me leve,' quod he, 5547
'ffurth into perse I purpose me¹ to goo,

he asked
Generydes leave
to go into Persia

hough it is ther to knowe the certente,

to see if his dream
were true.

ffor I am alway trobolyd to and to ; 5550
ffor your dremys right I drede also.'
Generides ther of was wele apayde,
'Goo on your way, in goddis name,' he seide, 5553

'Go on your way
in God's name,

'As fast as euer ye may, and com ayeyn, 5554
Owt of that lande sum tidyngez wold I here ;
I pray yow, darell, bryng me word sertayn,

and bring me
some tidings of

And of Clarionas my lady dere.' 5557

Clarionas.'

'That shall not be for gete in noo maner.'
Ser darell toke his leve, and went his way
Into the lande of perse, as I yow saye. 5560

Now is Gusare, that most on happy wight, 5561

Gusare is now
come out of
Persia,

Out of the lande of perce com² into ynd,
ffull fast seching, in all that euer he myght,
The redy way Generides to fynde, 5564
With new contrivid falshede hym to blynd,

and goes straight
with a new lie
to Generydes,

In all the hast to seche hym furth he went,
And atte [last] he founde hym in his tent. 5567

¹ MS. *ne*. ² MS. *is com*.

GENERYDES. 12

'My lord,' q*uo*d he, 'fro perse now am I come,   5568
ffro the Sowdon) with tidynges y^t be there,
ffor I wiłł tełł yow playnle ałł and som),

that Clarionas
is married to
Gwynan.

Gwynan the kyng⟨ is ther w*ith* grete powre,   5571
They ben) accordid ałł bothe in on) man*er*,
The pece is made and cryed in eu*er*y place,
The kyng⟨ is weddid on to Clarionas.   5574

These tydingez sendith yow s*er* Anasore ;   5575
Anoder erand haue I for to do,

The dog which
Clarionas sent,

A litiłł dog⟨ Clarionas hath ther,
She bad I shuld bryng hym) w*ith* me Also,   5578
Butte be the tyme I shuld part And goo,
Thanne shuld I haue brought it w*ith* me verily,

he had had taken
from him.

And it was taken) ayeyn) from me sodenly.'   5581

Generides hard wele ałł that he seide,   5582

Generydes was
sore abashed,

And in hym) self he was abasshed sore,
Thanne furth with ałł the message[r] he prayde ;

and asked when
the wedding was.

'Good s*er*,' q*uo*d he, 'yet telle me ferthermore,   5585
Whanne she was weddid and hough [long] before,
Of your⟨ departeng⟨ sey me the certente.'
'Ther of I słałł tełł yow the trouthe,' q*uo*d he ;   5588

'I come fro thense apoy*n*ted as thei were,   5589

'The same day
that I left,'
said Gusare.

The same day thei were weddid fułł sekyrly ;
My hast was suche that I myght not be ther,
To see the rewle and it was trewly.'   5592
Generides toke it fułł hevily,
In petuose wise complayneng⟨ eu*er* in on),
Thanne Natanełł comfortid hym) Anon).   5595

Now let us speak
of Mirabell.

Off Mirabełł now late vs speke a while,   5596
Whiche is reden), in ałł that eu*er* she may,
Into the reme of ynd⟨ fułł many A myle ;

Whanne she came nygħ the ende of hir Iurnay,   5599   *When she came near the end of her journey she met Darell,*
Ther mette she witħ Dareħ vppoɲ the waye,
A ferde she was in very certente,
ffor Atte first she wist not yat it was he.[1]   5602

Whanne she hyɲ sawe she was rigħt wele apayde,   5603   *and was well pleased.*
And herd hym speke thanne very glad was she ;
'hougħ dotħ my lord, the Sowdoɲ, now ?' he said,   *'How doth my lord ?' said he,*
'And my lady Clarionas,' quod he,   5606   *'and is my lady Clarionas married ?'*
'Is she weddid ? teħ me the very certente.'
'Weddid ?' quod she, 'nay, nay, I yow ensure,   *'No,' said Mirabell,*
Nor neuer wilbe to noɲ erthely creature,   5609   *'and never will*

Save only on to my lord Generides,   5610   *except to Generydes.*
In whoɲ suerly is aħ hir fyence,
ffor this I canne yow teħ in sothfastnes,
ffuħ seldom is he owt of hir remembraunce,   5613
And as for eny new[2] foundeɲ Acqueyntaunce,
Ther is noo suche, I saye yow feithfully,
ffor wele I wote she had moche lever dye   5616   *She would rather die.*

Butt now I prae yow telle me,' quod she,   5617   *And now tell me, is Generydes married ?*
'Generides is he weddid, or noo ?'
'Nay,' quod Dareħ, 'for certayɲ levith me,   *'Nay,' said Darell,*
It came neuer in his thought so for to do ;   5620   *'it never came into his thought.*
And for to say the very trowtħ Also,
ffor hyɲ I dare wele answere in this case,
he wiħ noɲ other but fayre Clarionas.'   5623   *He will have none but Clarionas.'*

'The pece is not appoynted thanne,' quod she,   5624   *[leaf 30, back] 'Then the peace is not made between Sir Amelok and him?'*
'Of ser Amelok and of Generides ?'
'Nay,' quod Dareħ, 'trewly it wiħ not be ;   *'Nay,' quoth Darell.*
holde oɲ your' way,' quod she, 'stiħ opece,   5627   *'Hold on your way,' said she, 'and set my lady at rest,*
And sette my lady[3] more in hartes ease ;
ffor oɲ thyng' shaħ I say yow that is sure,
Ye shaħ fynde hir a wofuħ creature.'   5630   *for you will find her a woful creature.'*

[1] MS. *she.*   [2] MS. *now.*   [3] MS. *lorde.*

'I will,' said
Darell,
'in all the haste
I can.
Generydes is
now sad for his
dream.'

'In aꝉ the hast,' quod DareꝈ, 'that I canne,　　5631
To hir I wiꝉ withoute eny more ;
Generides is now an hevy man),
As for a dreme whiche trobelyd hym) fuꝉ sore,　　5634
No thyngᵗ so meche sitħ he was boore ;
And wenyngᵗ in his dreme, this is yᵉ case,
kyngᵗ Gwynan had weddid clarionas.　　　　　5637

The Sowdon) was agreyd weꝉ therto,　　　　5638
Aꝉ hym) thougħt was trew in euery thingᵗ,
Now may ye teꝉ hym) it is noo thyngᵗ soo,
And putt Away aꝉ this Imagenyngᵗ.'　　　　5641

They parted,

he for Persia,
she for India,
to seek
Generydes.

Thanne departid thei and noo taryengᵗ,
he went to perse and she went to ynd,
The redy way Generides to fynde.　　　　　5644

Whanne she cam) yer, into yᵉ ost she went,　　5645
Generides to seche she ded here payn),

She found him
in his tent with
the false Gusare,

Atte last she founde hym) in his tente,
And ther she founde that false Gusare ageyn),　　5648
The massenger, wherof she was fuꝉ fayne ;
And bothe here squyers furtħ with aꝉ she prayde,
'lay on handes on) that false theff,' she saide.　　5651

Whanne he hir saw he drew hym) owt aside,　　5652
hir comyngᵗ theder likid hym) fuꝉ iꝉ ;
Mirabeꝉ thanne anon) hym) had asspyde,

whom she seized
by the head.
One that knew
her wish
hit him a blow
that put him
beyond the help
of doctors.

She toke hym) be the hede and held hym) stiꝉ,　　5655
Thanne on) that knewe hir purpose and wiꝉ,
he smote Gusare so harde vppon) the cheke,
That leche craft hym) nede non) other seeke.　　5658

And ther he dyed withynne a litiꝉ stounde,　　5659

Generides had merveꝉ what it ment ;
As he came owt Mirabeꝉ ther he founde ;

And as sche was comyng⸱ inward to his tent,   5662
Of hir he was fuꝉ gladde in his entente,
And seid, 'mayde Mirabeꝉ, benedicite ;
What thyng⸱ hath brought yow into this contre ?' 5665

and asked Mirabell what had brought her thither.

'I shaꝉ,' quod she, 'telle yow the mater playn),   5666
And of my comyng⸱ heder aꝉ the case ;
This fals traytour that here this day was slayn),
he came and told to my lady Clarionas,   5669
That ye were weddid onto lucidas,
And on his fynger ther he brought a ryng⸱,
Whiche she gave yow Att your' both departyng⸱. 5672

She told him
all Gusare's
treason,

and all about
the ring

For aꝉ his bost from) hym) I toke the ryng⸱,   5673
My lady it forsoke, she was so wroth ;
The litiꝉ dog⸱ she toke that he shuld bryng⸱ ;
Butt as for that,' quod she, 'I hadde them) both : 5676
Now haue I told yow hough the mater goth.'
And he hir thankyd right curtesly,
And hir rewardid as she was worthy.   5679

and the dog,

'As for the ryng⸱,' quod she, 'loo here it is ;'   5680
And furth with aꝉ delyueryd hym) the ryng⸱.
Generides knowe wele that it was his ;
'This ryng⸱,' quod he, 'Dareꝉ had in kepyng⸱ :   5683
Wherefore,' quod he, 'me think it is a wonder thyng⸱,
his trouth I knowe and haue don) many a day,
The fawte is not in hym) I dare wele say.   5686

and gave him
back the ring.

Now, fayre myrabeꝉ, go to hir ayeyn),   5687
ffor this I canne vnderstonde and fele,
She wiꝉ not leve noo tidyngez in sertayn),
Butt if she here yow speke, this wote I weꝉ ;   5690
And yet Dareꝉ wiꝉ teꝉ hir euery dele,
Yet wiꝉ she geve noo credence I am sure,
Butt ye be ther, ellys to noo creature.   5693

'Go to her again,
fair Mirabell,

and tell her how unkind she is to mistrust me.'
And ferthermore I prae yow telle hir this,   5694
Me to mystroste trewly she is vnkynd,
ffor o thing¹ shaH I say, and trew it is,
Vntrew to hir she shaH me neuer fynde,   5697
And this I wiH remembre in my mende
Eche creature of nature hym delititĥ,
That on good turne another quytitĥ.'   5700

At this Mirabell took her leave.
Witĥ these wordes Mirabell ganne to smyle,   5701
hir leve she toke, and furtĥ she gotĥ hir waye;
Of ser DareH now late vs speke a while,
Whiche hastitĥ hym as fast as euer he may,   5704
So ferre fourtĥ he was on his¹ Iurnay,
Sir Darell came to Mountoner,
That into the land of perse aryvid he,
And came to Mountoner the fayre Citee.   5707

and went straight to Clarionas.
Full streygĥt he went onto Clarionas,   5708
And to her chaunber toke the redy waye,
he knockyd softely as the maner was,
Thanne came a mayde and this to hym gan say;   5711
Her maid would not admit him,
'Go fro the dore,' quod she, 'ser, I yow praye,
My lady had noo rest of aH this nygĥt,
Nor slept not to now, I yow be hight.'   5714

FuH fast he prayde, but neuer the neer he was,   5715
[leaf 31]
And whanne he sawe it wold non oyer wise be,
but he called upon Clarionas,
he callyd alow vppon Clarionas;
'Madame,' quod he, 'please yow for to see;   5718
I am DareH, now speke a word with me.'
who heard, and said to the maid, 'Open the door.'
Thanne spake Clarionas onto the mayde,
'Goo vpon the chaumber dore,' she saide.   5721

Then Darell came in,
Thanne DareH came in and knelid on his kne,   5722
And thus he saide onto fayre Clarionas,
'ffrom ynd I come to this contre,

¹ MS. hir.

Generides commaunditĥ hym on to your grace ; 5725

and told her all about Generydes.

As for my comyng now this is the case,
Off yow he hatĥ be dremyd passing sore,
Whiche dayly hym noyetĥ more and more.' 5728

Thanne he told hir the mater hougĥ it was, 5729
She hard hym speke aĦ his entente to fele ;
'lete be these wordes,' quod Clarionas,

She professed at first not to believe him.

'This that ye say is lesyng euery dele, 5732
Suppose ye not I vnderstonde yow wele ;
Generides, this is the mater playn,

'It is plain,' said she, 'that Generydes is married to Lucidas.

To lucydas is weddid for certeyn. 5735

To hir it is this message shuld be do, 5736

This message should be to her.'

And not to me, for I haue not to don witĥ aĦ.'
'Now good madame,' [quod he,] 'why say yow soo ?
My message is to yow in especiaĦ, 5739
Now please it yow onto your mynd to caĦ,
hough good, hougĥ trew he was to yow alwaye,
And yet is he the same this dare I say. 5742

Off lucidas,' quod he, 'ye may be sure, 5743

Darell then told of his own love for Lucidas,

ffor I shaĦ teĦ yow trougtĥ withoute feyning,
I love hir best of eny creature ;
She sent to me, noo malyce supposyng, 5746

and how the ring had been obtained.

By hir moderys subtile ymagening,
The ryng to borow of Generides,
Seying she had a frende in grete distresse. 5749

The ryng, she said, wold make hym hoole ayeyn, 5750
And for that cause I sent it lucidas ;
Now wote ye wele, it was but for a trayn
Serenydes it had, this is the case ; 5753
That false Gusare the messanger he was,
ffor yow and for Generides also,
To make a variaunce betwix yow bo.[1] 5756

[1] MS. bothe.

This is,' quod he, 'the trowth that I have seide, 5757
And putt me to what othe that ye list.'
In here conseite thanne was she weⅡ apayde,
'To you,' quod she, 'now haue I noo mystrost.' 5760
'Trewly, Madame,' quod he, 'and I had it wist,
That ye shuld me mystrost in my message,
I had not A take vppon) me this viage.' 5763

With that she
became friendly,

Witħ that she made hym) very frendly chere, 5764
And whanne the Sowdon) wist of his comyng¹,
To hir he went som) tidynggez for to here,

and the Sultan
welcomed Sir
Darell,

And gave ser DareⅡ anone his welcomyng¹; 5767
'What tidynges now,' quod he, 'do yow bryng¹?'
'ffor certayn, ser,' he seide, 'suche as thei be,
To yow I wiⅡ declare the very certente. 5770

who told him
that Parentyne
was closely
besieged,

The Sege is leyde to parentyne,' quod he, 5771
'A grete dele nerrer thanne it was before,
The gates ar aⅡ shett of that Citee,
And of vitayle thei haue but easy store, 5774
Nor non) may haue, to say yow ferthermore;
So streyte them kepitħ auferius the kyng¹,
That owt thei may not for noo maner thing¹. 5777

and that
Generydes was
at Vice.

Generides lithe atte Citee of vice, 5778
Whiche is the strongetħ Citee of aⅡ the land;
he ħatħ besegyd it in suche a wise,
That thei may not skape I vnderstonde, 5781
The contre hoole obeyetħ to his hand.'
The Sowdon) hard hym wele, and this he seid,
'Of these tidynges I am rigħt wele apayde; 5784

'I would he
were here,'
said the Sultan,
'for Gwynan is
in the land,

Butt now I wold¹ he were here witħ me, 5785
TeⅡ hym) so, DareⅡ, in eny maner wise.
Gwynan) the kyng¹ is now in this contre,

And to my land he doth grete preiudice,   5788
Therfore haue I nede of his seruice.'
'Ser,' quod Darell, 'as fast as I canne goo,
In all the hast your' erande shalbe doo.'   5791

and I have need
of his service.'

Syr Darell toke his leve and went his way,   5792
Whiche euer hath be founde both good and trew;
Mirabell is homeward in hir Iurnay,
Ser Darell and she mette togeder now,   5795
Echeon) told suche tidynggez as thei cowde,
Betwix them) was noo lenger abideng',
Butt furth they rode withoute more taryeng'.   5798

Sir Darell took
his leave,

and met Mirabell
coming home-
ward.

Ser Amelok came owt of the Citee of vice,   5799
With sertayn) of his pepill furth he went,
ffor it was told hym) in credibill[1] wise,
Generides lay seke in his own) tent,   5802
Whiche boldith hym) the more in his entent;
yet were thei blynd in that opynyon),
ffor he was rideng' owt before the town).   5805

Sir Amelok heard
that Generydes
lay sick,

and came out of
the city.

Now is ser Darell come ayeyn) to ynd,   5806
And furth withall into the feld he went,
ffull fast rideng' Generides to fynde,
And furth withall he sought hym) in to ye tent,   5809
To telle hym) all the effecte of his entent,
Butt ther he founde non) erthely creature,
So furth he rode seching' his aventure;   5812

[leaf 31, back]

Sir Darell rode
over the field in
search of
Generydes,

And with a Duke of Ethiope he mette,   5813
Vppon) a courser crossyng' hym) the way;
Eche vppon) other ferly on) they sett,
And or thei partid, shortly for to say,   5816
The duke was slayn) and in the feld he lay:
Whanne lucidas hym) saw thanne was she fayn),
And glad she was of his comyng' ageyn).   5819

and met with
a duke of
Ethiopia,

whom he slew.

Lucidas saw this
and was glad.

[1] MS. credilbill.

Generydes rode
to meet him,
Generides thought wele that it was he,   5820
And furth with all came rideng⸍ apace,
' Darell,' he seid, ' right welcom⸍ be ye,

and asked news
of Clarionas.
What tydinges bryng⸍ yow fro Clarionas ? '   5823
' To telle yow,' quod he, ' I haue noo space,
Goo now on⸍ and take your⸍ seasone as¹ it is ;

' All is well,'
said Darell.
ffor all is well, ther is noo thyng⸍ Amysse.'   5826

Generydes was
well pleased,
Full wele apayde thanne was Generides,   5827
And in his mynd reioysid passing wele,

and rode into
the press,
and met with
Ananyell,
In to the feld he rode among⸍ the prece,
And in his way he mette ananyell,   5830
A manly knyght, the story canne yow tell,
A wise man⸍ and sadde in euery case,

the brother of
Amelok.
And broder onto ser Amelok he was.   5833

Anon⸍ thei ranne togeder in the feld   5834
With sperys sharpe, and made no more delay ;

He narrowly
escaped his
spear,
he smote Generides vppon⸍ the sheld,
The sheld to brast and fro hym⸍ fell away ;   5837
And as his grace and fortune was that day,
The spere ranne down⸍ by generides side,
And ellys withoute fayle ther had he dyed.   5840

And furth with all² or they departid yer,   5841

but struck him
dead in return.
Generides thanne smote hym⸍ so ayeyn⸍,
That thorough owt the body ranne the spere,
And with that stroke Ananyell was slayn⸍,   5844
Down⸍ from⸍ his hors he felle vppon the playn⸍ ;

Sir Amelok
saw this,
And whanne ser Amelok saw all the case,
ffor his broder an hevy man⸍ he was,   5847

and ran at Sir
Darell.
And to ser Darell he ranne with spere & sheld ; 5848
Thanne lucydas was sory in hir hert,
To see them⸍ twayn⸍ togeder in yᵉ feld,

¹ MS. at.   ² MS. all all.

And fast she prayde that thei myght sone departe,
like as nature required for hir part :
Butt bote was now to pray ne for to trete,
And bothe thei mette anow with speris grete.   5854

Full long¹ thei foughte, to say yow ferthermore,   5855
And lenger wold² haue dow as by ther will
Vnder them bothe ther stedys feynted sore,
That bothe togeder to the grownde ganne yᵉⁱ fall, 5858
Ser Darell in the feld ther lay he still,
The prese was suche he myght not gete away,
Butt still defendid hym ther as he lay.   5861

> They fought till their horses fell under them.

> The crowd was so great, Sir Darell could not get away.

Syr amelok was holpyn att his nede,   5862
his knyghtes came and fechid hym anow ;
Sone after that ser Darell was ow his stede,
With that Generides came rideng ow,   5865
They made hym rome among¹ them euerychone,
And where that euer he rode in eny side,
Ther was non in the feld wold² hym abide.   5868

> At length Generydes came up, and they made room for him.

The dede body vppow a sheld² they layde,   5869
Toward the Citee thei caried it anow ;
Ser amelokkez men were so dismayde,
To the Citee thei fled his pepill euerychow,   5872
And yet ther were distroyed many ow,
And or thei myght gete the Citee, this is sertayn,
An C knyghtes were take and slayn.   5875

> Ananyell's body was carried to the city,

Whanne thei were in thei shette ye gates fast,   5876
Ananyell thei beried furth with all ;
Thanne afterward in all the possible hast,
Too knyghtes thei sent echone in generall,   5879
This was the message in especiall,
ffull tenderly Generides for to praye,
To graunt them truse for ij monethis day,   5882

> and buried.

> Two knights were sent to Generydes to ask for two months' truce,

His knyghtes for to bery euerychone.   5883

which was
granted.

he grauntid them) and was rigĥt wele apayde,
Ser Dareĺĺ thanne he callid furtĥ anon),
And Nataneĺĺ Also, and this he saide ;   5886
' The trewse is now appoyntid and prevyed
Betwix the Cite and Me ij monethys day,
And now I wiĺĺ goo see Clarionas I say.   5889

Generydes left
Darell in
command,

Wherefore, Dareĺĺ, I prae yow now,' quod he,   5890
' That ye wiĺĺ do so moche as take the payn),
To rewle these men), that hir be vnder me,
In my absence as lord and cheff¹ capteyn),   5893
Or ought it be long¹ I wiĺĺ be here ayayn),
And if ther fortune eny hasty nede,
Thanne wiĺĺ I come as fast as I may spede.   5896

and ordered
Sygrem to come
with him with 100
knights to go to
Clarionas.

Off¹ knyghtes And squyers that be here,   5897
Of them) will I haue A C and no moo ;
ffuĺĺ secretly,' he seid, ' in aĺĺ maner,

[leaf 32]

I wolđ they were warnyd witĥ me to goo ;   5900
And say to Sygrem that he come also
In eny wise, that he may be my gide,
ffuĺĺ wele he knowitĥ the wayes on) euery side.'   5903

Meantime,
Mirabell came
home and told
the whole story.

In this meane tyme thanne was come home ayeyn)
Mirabeĺĺ on) to fayre Clarionas ;
She saide, ' Madame, Generides for certayn)
hym recomaundid onto your³ good grace   5907
In humble wise, and as for lucidas,
hir for to wedde came neuer in his thougĥt ;
The messenger is slayn) that the tidynges brougĥt.

And so furtĥ on) she told aĺĺ the hole processe,   5911
hougĥ that she founde Generides sertayn),
Aĺĺ discomfortid in rigĥt grete hevynes ;

Thanne saide Clarionas to hir ayeyn),   5914
' Moche thank to yow for your labour' a[nd] payn).'
And thus I leve them) bothe in hartys ease,
And ferthermore I will speke of Generides.   5917

Now toward perse ridith Generides,   5918   As Generydes
Takyng' his viage in the evyn) tide,   was riding
And of his[1] Iurnay wold he neuer sese,   towards Persia
Till he came ther wher he shuld abide ;   5921
With hym) ther went Sygrem to be his gide,
Costyng' the contre many dyuers way,
And so came he in to perse the redy waye.   5924

The contre was distroyed in that tide,   5925
And as he rode vppon) the way,
A lady he sawe rideng' be a forest side,   he saw a lady
Grete hast she had on) hir Iurnay,   5928   by a forest side,
To hir he rode withoute more delay,   and rode after
Whanne she hym) saw come toward hir so fast,   her.
Away fro hem) she fledde in all the hast.   5931   She fled,

With hir ther were xviij. in company,   5932
Generides rode after hir so fast,
And on) his way so fast he ganne hym) hye,
he ouer toke the lady atte last ;   5935   but he overtook
' Madame,' he seid, ' be ye noo thyng' agast,   her,
Why ride ye thus and in so hasty wise ?   and told her no
Ther shall no man do yow harme o warantise.'   5938   one should do
                                                                 her harm.

' In trowth I am a wedow, ser,' quod she,   5939   ' I am a widow,
' The Sowdon) is myn) vncle in certayn) ;   said she, ' and
kyng' Gwynan wold that I weddid shuld be   the Sultan is my
To his Cosyn), and me he wold' constreyne   5942   uncle.
So for to do ; this is the mater playn) :   King Gwynan
                                                                 wishes to marry
And thus fro hym) in all the hast I went,   me to his cousin,
Because I wold not folow his entent.   5945   but I will not,
                                                                 and therefore am
                                                                 fleeing to
                                                                 Mountoner.'

[1] MS. hus.

Too Mountoner now I wiłł take my way,   5946
And witħ my�</br>) vnkiłł ther I wiłł abide,
ffor here I leve in drede and in affray.'

'Madam,' quoth
he, 'I pray you
be our guide to
Gwynan.'

'Madame,' quod he, 'I prae god be your' gide,   5949
After kyng' Gwynan I purpose me to ryde,
ffayne I woldꝰ knowe the way and not to mys.'
'I shałł yow tell,' quod she, 'where that he is.   5952

'He is here in a
castle a mile or
two off,

In a castełł here be a forest side,   5953
ffroꝰ) hens it passitħ not a myle or twayne,
hold oꝰ) your' way streigħt as ye ride,
And ther ye shałł hyꝰ) fynde, this is certayꝰ),   5956

waiting for the
king of Spain,

A bideng' ther Otran the kyng' of spayne,
Whiche comytħ the kyng' to helpe I vnderstonde,
To warre vppoꝰ) my vncle and his lande.'   5959

'Now, Madame,' thanne seid Generides,   5960
'What pepyłł hatħ he ther? I prae yow say.'
'Trewly,' quod she, 'as ferre as I canne gesse,

with 200 men,

he passitħ not CC men) this day,   5963
And Chosen) men) they be in good arraye,
he is noo thyng' a drede in certente,

and every day he
goes hunting.'

ffor euery day on huntyng' ridetħ he.'   5966

'Madame,' quod he, 'thanne I beseche yow this,   5967
That it may plese yow do so meche for me,
Whanne ye be ther as your' vncle is,
That I to hyꝰ) may recomaundid be,   5970
A knygħt of Surre gladly wold hyꝰ) see,
Butt now I may not come, the cause is soo,
ffor I wiłł seche the kyng' where euer he goo.'   5973

The lady went on
to Mountoner,

Too Mountoner the lady toke the waye,   5974
And to the forest Generides is gon),
And whanne it was ferre past on) the day,

In a buschement he layde his men) eche on),   5977

And thanne he callid Sygrem furth anon) ;

'Sygrem,' quod he, 'afore all other thyng',

I prae yow wete where lith Gwynan the kyng'.   5980

and Generydes
laid his men
in ambush,

and sent Sygrem
to find where
Gwynan was.

Off his demeanyng' I wold wete also,   5981

And with my felisshepe I will abide.'

'Ser,' quod Segyrem, 'anon) it shalbe doo ;

Att your' commaundment now I will ride,   5984

And bryng' yow worde her be the forest side.'

Now goth Segrym), withoute more taryeng',

To monperson), and ther he founde the kyng'.   5987

He found him at
Monperson,

The town) was fast by the castell wher he lay,   5988

Thorough owt the town) he went among ye prese,

And whanne that he had Aspyed all yer array,

Agayn) he came vnto Generides ;   5991

'I shall yow telle,' quod he, 'that is noo leese,

I left them) ther att dyner euerychon),

And to this forest he will come anon).   5994

and came and
told Generydes
[leaf 32, back]
they were all
at dinner,

Armyd thei be eche on) atte poynte device,   5995

here will thei hunte I say yow verily ;

Butt this I councell yow be myn) avise,

Whanne yow them) se late them) go by and by,   5998

Till thei be passid thanne may ye them) askry.

And this suerly if ye do after me,

Betwix them) and the Castell shall ye be.   6001

and were coming
out to hunt.

And ferthermore,' as my Auctor doth write,   6002

'Gwynan if ye will [know] whereuer he be,

his owne Array is all togeder white,

hors and harnes and so is non) but he,   6005

his spere also is white, that ye shall see,

Now haue I sayde, do as ye semes best,

here will he come anon) in to this forest.'   6008

Gwynan dressed
all in white.

The king rode out, Anon) vppon) [on] huntyng⸍ rode the kyng⸍,   6009
                    Generides was ware therof anon),

and Generydes   No noyse was made nor ther was noo steryng⸍,
kept his men
quiet till they   To tyme the kyng⸍ and aH his men) were goon) ;   6012
were all past,   And whanne that thei were passid euerychon),

when he called to Generides anon) hym) ganne Askerye,
them to turn.
                   And bad them) 'turne, for tyme it is trewly.'   6015

The king turned   With that the kyng⸍ his hors he turnyd then),   6016
his horse,   And to his knygħtes aH thanne he saye,
                   'Serys, now is tyme to shewe that we be men),
                   ffor yender folk will lette vs of our' way.'   6019
                   Anone thei mette them) withoute more delay,

and in the first   And atte first encounteryng⸍ certayn),
encounter lost
20 of his knights, kyng⸍ Gwynan had xx. of his knygthes slayn) :   6022

and 15 were   And xv more were taken) furtħ witħ aH,   6023
taken.   Where witħ the kyng⸍ was greuyd passyng⸍ sore,
                   And sware his othe what euer shuld hym) falle,
                   he wold⸍ suerly avenge hym) therfore,   6026
In revenge the   And in that hete, to say yow ferthermore,
king slew Lucas,
                   Anon) he ranne to lucas witħ a spere,
                   And bare hym) thorougħ and slewe hym) ther.   6029

                   Whanne he was dede ther was grete hevynes,   6030
and Generydes   And witħ Generides was fuH hevy chere,
was full sad
thereat,   Remembryng⸍ the grete love and kyndnes,
remembering all   Whiche he had shewid to hym) in aH maner ;   6033
his love and
kindness.   And specially whanne he was prisoner,
                   And by his meane the Sowdon) gave hym) grace,
                   Whanne he so long⸍ lay in prisone for Clarionas.   6036

He then ran   And for by cause kyng⸍ Gwynan had hym) slayn),   6037
at Gwynan,   To go vn quyte he thougħt noo wurchippe in,
                   And witħ his spere ranne toward hym) ageyn),

Thanne was ther on of the kynggez kynne,   6040   but one of his
kin came between,
Betwene them̅ bothe his wurchippe for to wynne,
And witħ a spere in myddes of the prese,
ffurtħ with aħ he ranne vnto Generides.   6043

And bothe thei mette to geder in the feld,   6044
And for to teħ yow aħ the mater playn̅),
Generides stroke hym̅ thorougħ the sheldᵗ   and was pierced
by the spear.
Owt atte bak, and slew hym̅ for certeyn̅);   6047
And whanne ther felawes were take And slayn̅),   At this the king's
men drew back,
A bak thei drewe, and sperkelyd her and yer,   and scattered
themselves.
Thanne was the kyngᵗ fuħ wrothe in his maner,   6050

And blew his horn̅) to geder them to bryngᵗ,   6051
ffuħ sory he was to se them̅ goo so wide;
Thanne seid Sampson̅) these wordes to yᵉ kyngᵗ,
Off Cornyssħ was he born̅), and of that side;   6054
'It is noo tyme here for vs to Abide,
Drawe to yourᵖ Casteħwardᵗ, and that anon̅),
ffor here we do butt lese oure men̅) euerychon̅).'   6057

Too monpersone the kyngᵗ witħ drew hym̅ yan̅),   6058   The king
withdrew to
Generides hym̅ folowid in the chase;   Monperson,
pursued by
'Syr,' quod Sygrem, 'thus shaħ yow lese your men̅),   Generydes.
And wery them̅), withynne a short space: 6061
Butt this me think better in this case;
Gete yow be fore, this wold I yow avise,   'Get between
him and the
Betwix hym̅) and the town̅) in eny wise.'   6064   town,' said
Sygrem.

Generides dede after Sygrems counceħ,   6065
And to blanchard his stede he saide,   Generydes called
upon his steed
'Blanchard,' quod he, 'thow dost me neuer fayle,   Blanchard,
Nor vppon̅) the I was neuer ovtrayde.'   6068
Witħ these wordes thoughtfuħ in A brayde
A nother way he rode, and in a while   and outstripped
Gwynan by half
he was be fore the kyngᵗ welle half a myle.   6071   a mile.

GENERYDES.   13

He crossed
his path,

And whanne the kyng' perseivid that it was he,　6072
Adrede he was, And litiH wold' he say ;
And verily he thought not hym) for to Asse,
Nor hym) to mete he thought no more yᵗ day :　6075
Generides thanne crossid hym) the way ;

and told him
he should go
no further,
except he did
battle for
Clarionas.

' This way,' q*u*od he, ' thu shalt noo ferther pas,
Or thu do armys for fayre Clarionas.'　6078

The kyng' sawe weH he mygͪt now) oy*er* way,　6079
Nor to the town) he mygͪt not ride in pece ;
Anon) he dressid hym) in his arraye,

[leaf 33]

And thanne he turnyd vnto Generides :　6082

At the first
encounter both
their spears
broke,

Ther mette thei bothe withoute the prese,
And shortly the processe for to make,
Atte first encount*er*yng' bothe ther sperys brake.　6085

and they went
to work with
their swords.

Witͪ y*er* swerdes to geder thei went,　6086
And layde eu*er*ychone on) other strokes grete,

The sparks flew
from them,

The fyre sparkelid and fro the harneys glynt ;
Betwix them) twayne it was noo tyme to trete,　6089
AH man*er* love and frenshippe was forgete,
The kyng' in his conseite he was stronge,
he thougͪt noman) shuld figͪt witͪ hym) so long'.　6092

and Generydes'
shield was
broken.

Hee strake Generides vppon) the sheld',　6093
It aH to brast in peces to and fro,
The handdeH it feH in to the feld',
A grace of god that he askapyd soo,　6096
That witͪ that stroke his arme was not a twoo !

'Go now,' said
the king.

Thanne seid the kyng', ' if thu wilt leve in rest,
Goo now thy way and hold it for the best.'　6099

Generydes
was wroth,

Generides wrothe was in his man*er*,　6100
That he shuld byd hym) voyde owt of yᵉ place,
Remembryng' whiche was to hym) soo dere,

That fayre lady, that mayde Clarionas,   6103
he thought to ease his hert as in this case,
And ther with aH, withoute more taryeng¹,   *and struck him on the helmet,*
Vppon) the helme he smote Gwynan the kyng¹,   6106

And the helme to brast that was good and strong,
A quarter of it feH vppon) the grene,   *cutting off a quarter of it,*
The swerde ranne down) and clave ye sheld along,   *and cleaving his shield*
And ij fyngers he smete¹ of quyte and clene,   6110   *and two of his fingers.*
Thanne was he bare his visage myght be sene,
AH discomfeyte and aH forbled Also,
That in noo wise he wist not what to do.   6113

Thanne spake the kyng¹, and seid in y^{is} maner,   6114   *'Who are you?' said the king,*
'what maner a man), be ye? I prae yow say;
ffor I wiH fight with yow noo lenger here,   *'I will fight no more.*
My swerd² and aH I yeld it vppe this daye;   6117   *Here is my sword.'*
What is your¹ name?' quod he, 'I prae you say'
'Trewly my name,' quod he, 'I wiH not layn),   *'My name is Generydes.'*
Generides men) calle me for certayn).'   6120

The kyng¹ toke hym) his swerd, and seid ayeyn),   6121   *Gwynan gave up his sword, and said,*
'Though I have ben) Ayenst yow in this case,
yet am I not blame worthy in certayn),   *'I am not to blame,*
By yow only my fader slayn) was,   6124   *you slew my father.*
Butt now it is for gevyn) certayn) y^t trespas,
And this I wold desire of yow also,   *Let me go to my land, and I will*
In to my land that I may savely goo.   6127

AH this I wiH ensure yow be myn) othe,   6128   *never trouble the Sultan more.'*
ShaH I neuer the Sowdon) trobiH more,
hym nor his land; and for his ayris bothe,
I wiH be sworne like as I seid before,   6131
ffor I saw neuer that day sithe I was bore²,
Atte my fuH age and was att mannys myght,
That euer I medled with soo good a knyght.'³   6134

¹ MS. *swete.*   ² MS. *born.*   ³ MS. *kyng.*

Generydes in
jest asked,
'What say you
now about
Clarionas ? '
Generides in Iapyng¹ said agayn),   6135
'What sey ye now as for Clarionas ? '
'Syr,' quod the kyng¹, 'with grete trobiH,

'You have bought
her full dear,'
said the king;
'she is yours.'
ffuH dere ye haue hir bought, this is yᵉ case ;   6138
Now is she yourez by fortune and by grace,
And I am weH content that it be soo,
And as for my part now ther with I haue doo.'   6141

Peace was
proclaimed,
After aH this whanne pece was made and AH,   6142
The kyng therof sent tydinges to his ost,
Thanne were thei glad his men in esspeciaH,
Among them) AH whiche of them) myght be most,
The pece was cryed abought in euery cost,
and they rode
together to
Monperson.
The kyng¹ and he no longer ther abode,
To monpersone to geder thanne they rode.   6148

Theder were come the kynges men) before ;   6149
As sone as he hym) see he seide anon),
'Now serys,' quod he, 'withoute eny more
I wold¹ that ye went homeward¹ euerychon) :   6152
The pece is made and aH the werre is gon).
Now hye yow fast, I canne noo ferder say,
And I shaH come as sone as euer I may.'   6155

The Sultan had
dreamed that
Gwynan and
Generydes fought,
Now speke we of the Sowdon) in this case,   6156
Whiche hard¹ no maner thing¹ of AH yⁱˢ pece,
And in this mater dremyd sore he was ;
hym thought kyng¹ Gwynan and Generides   6159
had fought hand to hand, yet neuer the lesse
and that Gwynan
was thrown into
a river.
Right this hym) thought it happid atte last,
That in A Ryuer Generides hym) cast.   6162

The kyng¹ hym) thought for mercy yanne he prayde,
Generides thanne toke hym) vppe to grace ;
Whanne this was do, this dreme Aforeseid

he told them AH in to fayre Clarionas ;   6166   He tells it to Clarionas,
Thanne was the lady present in the place,   and then the lady who had
whiche with Generides spake on the way,   spoken with
She had forgete hir erande for to say.   6169   Generydes

FuH vmbely of pardon she hym prayde,   6170   remembered the message of the
'To yow I haue offendid, ser,' quod she,   strange knight.
'ffor Amessage the whiche I shuld haue seide ;
Ther is a knyght come in to this contre,   6173
To yow he recomaundid hym be me,   [leaf 33, back]
his name he wold not telle me, ne what he hight,
Of Surre he¹ was born the gentiH knyght.   6176

Right wele armed this knyght is also,   6177
And gladly wold haue sene yow or he went,
Butt nedis he must owt of this contre goo.'
Thanne was Clarionas not weH contente,   6180   Clarionas guessed who it was.
ffor wele she vnderstode in hir entent,
And euer in one she thought stiH opece,
That it shuld be hir love Generides.   6183

And for by cause she had hym in mystrost,   6184
Allway she demyd the² wold hir quyte,
hym to Absente awhile while that hym list,
And so to putte his comyng in respite ;   6187
Thanne ferthermore, as my auctour doth wete,   Gwynan and Generydes stay at
The kyng and Generides for ther disporte and play,   Monperson
Att Mounperson to geder bothe thei lay,   6190   two days or more,

Att ther pleasure ij dayes or a litiH more,   6191
And thanne to Mountoner he toke the way ;   and then go to Mountoner,
Sygrem was made the messenger before,   sending Sygrem
Onward to goo as fast as euer he may   6194   before to say that the war was
To the Sowdon, commaundyng them to say :   over.
"The warre is att anende, and aH is pece
Betwix kyng Gwynan and Generides,   6197

¹ MS. of he, but of is struck out.   ² So MS. for that he ?

Neuer to vex the Sowdoᵤ and his land,   6198
With grete suerte in euery maner thyngᵗ.'

Now hath Sygrem this message take in hand,
To the Sowdoᵤ the tidyngges doth he bryngᵗ;   6201
Thanne was he glad, as eny mañ levingᵗ,

and the Sultan
goes and tells
Clarionas.

hymᵤ self he goth onto Clarionas,
And told hir aH these tidyngges hough it was ;   6204

And hough the kyngᵗ and he shuld mete Also,   6205
In the forest appoyntid betwix themᵤ twaynᵤ :
'Butt trow ye, ser¹, that it be now soo ? '
'yae, dought ye not,' quod he, 'it is certaynᵤ ;   6208
Sygrem is come which is bothe trew and playnᵤ,
ffro thense he come, he knowith aH in fere,
he shaH teH yow the trougth of this mater.'   6211

Now goth Sygrem as fast as euer he may   6212
To hir chaunber, and toldᵗ hir this processe ;
'The warre is done,' quod she, 'this here I say;'
'Madame,' he seid, 'for certaynᵤ aH is pece ;   6215

'Butt now,' quod she, 'where is Generides ? '
'ffor sothe,' he seide, 'I left hymᵤ with yᵉ kyngᵗ,
To Mounpersoᵤ he is withoute feynengᵗ.'   6218

'Butt wiH he not come heder now ? ' quod she; 6219
'Madame,' quod he, 'of that I canne not say,
ffor atte this tyme I trow it wiH not be ;

'No, madam,
he is going back
again to India as
fast as he can.'

his purpose is to ryde another waye,   6222
ffourth in to ynd as fast as euer he may,
ffor to his ost he must take hede amongᵗ,
his people after hymᵤ think fuH longᵗ.'   6225

From hir he went withoute wordes moo,   6226
To the Sowdoᵤ furth he goth his way ;
'My lord,' quod he, 'it is good tyme to goo,

¹ MS. sero.

ffor ye wiH mete witħ hym) I dare weH say.'   6229
Now gotħ the Sowdon) furtħ in good array,
Witħ lordes and witħ knygħtes many on),
Toward the forest rode thei euerychone.   6232

The Sultan and his lordes ride forth to the forest to meet him.

In this meane while abode Clarionas   6233
In hir chaunber, noo thyng⟩ in hartes ease,
Gretly musyng⟩ and in fuH hevy case,
Whanne she be thougħt hir on) Generides;   6236
And Alway she remembryd stiH opece,
hougħ she had mystrostid hym) before,
Supposyng⟩ well he¹ wold se hir nomore.   6239

Meanwhile Clarionas was ill at ease in her chamber.

To MirabeH thanne told⟩ she aH hir hart,   6240
In euery thing⟩ as it felle in hir mynde;
' Madame,' quod she, ' for eny wo or smerte
That euer he had, I wist hym) neuer on kynde,   6243
So vncurtese ye shaH hym) neuer fynde;
And ferthermore I warantt yow,' quod she,
' Or it be long⟩ here witħ yow wiH he be.'   6246

Mirabell consoles her, saying, that Generydes will soon be here.

To the forest the Sowdon) dotħ ride,   6247
And first of aH he mette Generides,
Thanne came the kyng⟩ along⟩ by yᵉ forestes side,
And whanne that thei were mett in aH yᵉ prese,   6250
And made betwix them) bothe a fyniaH pece,
And witħ a suraunce sworn) in broderhode,
Togeder bothe in grete frendshippe thei rode.   6253

The Sultan met Generydes and the King in the forest, and peace was made.

Thanne they departid bothe the kyng⟩ and he,   6254
In aH maters to ben) of on) assentt;
The kyng⟩ gothe homeward in to his contre,
The Sowdon) streigħt to Mountoner he went;   6257
Generides ther was witħ hym) present,
And prayetħ hym) of licence for to goo,
The Sowdon) mervelid why he shuld do so.   6260

The King goes home, and Generydes asks leave to depart.

'Will you not
come and see
Clarionas ?'

'WyH[1] ye not come and see Clarionas ?'   6261
'Noo trewly, ser,' he seid, 'that may not be;
I must praye yow of pardon in this case,

'No, sir, I must
go back to India.'

ffor in to ynd now must I goo,' quod hee :   6264
Another tyme I purpose hir to see ;

[leaf 34]

And in certayn, herof ye may be sure,
I love hir best of eny creature.'   6267

Fro the Sowdon Generides is gon,   6268

He then sends his
men back to
Monperson,

And to his men he seid this for certayn ;
'To Mounperson I wiH that ye goo euerychon,
And ther to Abide in to the tyme I come Ayeyn ; 6271

and he and
Sygrem go
secretly to
Montoner,

Sygrem and I, this is the mater playn,
To Mowntoner we wiH goo sekyrly,
In secrete wise noman but he and I.'   6274

Now is Sygrem gon witH Generides,   6275
To Mountoner he take the way fuH rigHt,
Savyng¹ thei twoo ther was non other preese,

and at night he
stands in the
garden, near her
chamber,

Theder thei came be thanne² it was nygHt;   6278
Generides whanne it was sterre ligHt,
hym self anon gothe vnto Clarionas,
ThorougH owt the gardeyn wher hir chaunber was. 6281

and hears a
woman's voice
complaining.

Whanne he came ther he hard a womannes voyce, 6282
In pytues wise complayneng¹ more and more,
Save only detH ther was non other choyse,
She had so meche hevynes in store,   6285
vnkyndnes had greuyd hir so sore,
That Generides was in the countre her²,
Butt see hir wold he not in noo maner².   6288

And whanne Generides had hard hir speke,   6289

He knew it was
Clarionas,

Thanne wist he wele it was fayre Clarionas, .
ffor very payn hym thougHt his hert wold breke,

          ¹ MS. Uyll.   ² MS. be twanne.

And in hyɯ self discomfeyte sore he was,   6292
Speke myght he not as for a certeyn space,
Butt down he fell and ther withall he cryed ;
Myrabell hyɯ hard and sone hyɯ had Aspyde.   6295

and for very pain he fell down with a cry.

'Myrabell,' she seid, 'what may this be ?   6296
Whanne I hyɯ hard mervell it was.'
'In hevy plight my lady is,' quod she.
'Whom speke ye to ?' thanne seid Clarionas :   6299
'Madame,' quod she, 'in sothe this is the case,
Now shall ye fynde me trew in my seruice,
here atte wyndow is generides.'   6302

Mirabell heard him, and said,

'Here is Generydes at the window.'

Thanne with thoo wordes arose Clarionas,   6303
And to the wyndow came she all dismayde ;
Generides full redely ther he was,
Ther was kyssyng' butt noo wordes were seid ;   6306
Eche of oyer wer' full well apayd :
Anone thei putt All hevynes away,
And thanne Clarionas beganne to saye :   6309

At these words Clarionas came to the window,

and then there was kissing, but not a word said.

Then Clarionas began,

'Generides, why are ye so vnkynd,   6310
In this contre so long' As ye haue be ?
Me thought I was full litill in your mynde,
And all be cause ye wold not come to me.'   6313
Thanne seid Generides, 'Madame,' quod he,
'I yow beseche of pardon in this case,
In very trought a litill thyng' ther was.   6316

'Generydes, why are you so unkind ?'

'Madam,

Ye wend that I had be weddid in certayn   6317
To lucidas, whiche grevid me full soore ;
To yow alway I haue be trew and playn,
[1] Now haue I lete yow wete why and wherfore,   6320
And yet I am mystrostid euermore,
In easyng' of myn hert I haue don this,
ffor now is all for geven that is amys.   6323

you thought I was married to Lucidas.

I have always been true to you,

and yet you mistrust me.

But all is forgiven.

[1] This and the following line should be transposed.

You must give me leave to go back to India.	Off yow I must haue licence for to go	6324
	ffurth in to ynd, and therof haue I nede ;	
	My felisshepe they wote not who to do,	
	The treson of ser Amelok I drede :	6327
	In aH the hast homeward I wiH me spede,	
The sooner I go the sooner I shall be back.'	ffor euer the sonner that I goo certeyn),	
	Meche the sonner thanne I wiH come ayeyn).'	6330

Quoth she,	Quod she ayeyn), 'my reson) doth me bynde,	6331
	And as ferre furth as I canne vnderstonde,	
	I canne wele think your' goyng¹ in to ynd	
	Shalbe wurchippe and profight to your' land,	6334
	Your' pepiH glad to wete yow so nygh hande :	
'I must not refuse.'	wherfore,' quod she, 'if I me weH avise,	
	I may nott be ayenst it in noo wise.'	6337

That night, in all innocence, they were together in great pleasure.	That nyght they were to geder as I rede,	6338
	Nor sownyng¹ to [no] villany ne shame,	
	In grete pleasure and in aH goodlyhede ;	
	She made hym) chere and he dede hir yᵉ same,	6341
	In feithfuH wise withoute spotte or blame,	
	Anone with aH withoute spotte or eviH fame bothe ;[1]	
	Whanne it was day, though thei were neuer so loth.	

Generydes and Sygrem ride to Monperson to his men,	To Mounperson) rideth Generides,	6345
	In company with hym) Sygrem is gon),	
	his men) were ther abideng¹ stiH opece,	
	like as he had commaundid hym) before icheon),	6348
and so away to India.	Thei made no taryeng¹ but furth anon),	
	With hors and harnes in ther best Array,	
	Streight in to ynde thei toke the [redy] way.	6351

The people were glad of his return.	Whanne he was come ther as the pepiH lay,	6352
	Thanne were thei IoyfuH euery creature ;	
	Ser amelok fuH bold¹ he was that daye,	

[1] This line is corrupted by the copyist from the preceding.

ffor vnder a trete at All aventure 6355
Of ser Darell he thought he had be sure :
Butt of his werkyng¹ ser Darell knew it well,
And so he brake his purpose euery dele. 6358

Generides rode streight into the feld 6359
With his knyghtes, for noo thyng wold he lette,
his stede was blak, his spere and eke his sheld,
Anone with all with Sampson ther he mett ; 6362
Generides full fresshely on hym he sett,
Owt Atte bak he bare hym quyte and clene,
Sampsone felle down and dyed vppon the grene. 6365

Generydes rode straight into the [leaf 34, back] field,

and runs Sampson through.

Thanne came ser Amelok into the prese, 6366
And thought he wold a be avengyd for his sake,
Vppon the hede he smote Generides,
A quarter of his helme ther with he brake : 6369
Generides ther with to hym he spak,
'Thu wend,' quod he, 'that I had lakkid sight,
ffor now I may se better thanne I myght.' 6372

Up came Sir Amelok to avenge him,

and struck Generydes on the head, cutting off a quarter of his helmet.

And ther with all he smote ser Amelok 6373
Vppon the hede, and brast [his] helme in twayn ;
Downe by the cheke his ere away he strake,
All quyte and clene it felle vppon the playn ; 6376
And with that stroke, I say yow the certayn,
his Arme was smette fro the body clene,
So from his hors he felle vppon the grene. 6379

In return Generydes cleaves his helmet,

and cuts off his ear and arm,

so that he fell.

Thanne was ser Amelok full woo begon, 6380
All ouer come for angwissh and payn ;
his men were ther and reskewyd hym Anon,
vppon his sheld thei brought hym home ayeyn, 6383
All for wondid and sore in euery vayne :
Thanne seid he this, complayneng¹ passing¹ sore,
'I haue deseruyd this though it were more.' 6386

His men rescued him, and took him home.

Sir Darell knew
not of Generydes,

Syr Dareƚƚ wist not of Generides, 6387
B[utt] Alway demyd that[1] it shuld be he;
To Sygrem thanne he came in to the prese,

and asked Sygrem
who the knight
was on the black
horse.

'Sygrem,' seid he, 'teƚƚ me the very sertente, 6390
What knygħt is that that I may yender see?
his stede is blak; good Sygrem, teƚƚ me this,
I canne weƚƚ think Generides it is.' 6393

'It is Generydes,'
quoth Sygrem.

'Syr,' quod Sygrem, 'it is as ye haue rede, 6394
Generides it is withoute fayle;
he come butt late and rigħt weƚƚ hath he spedd,
Wherby his honour gretly dotħ prevayle, 6397
ffor he hatħ wonne kyng' Gwynan in bateƚƚ;
The corde is made, the mortuaƚƚ werre is sese,
Betwix hym and the Sowdon Aƚƚ is pece.' 6400

Sir Amelok,
on his bed,
repented of the
time past,

Now litħ ser Amelok vppon his bed; 6401
Of tyme past fuƚƚ sore he dotħ repente,
Wery and feynt, his wondys Aƚƚ for bled,
A basshed passyng' sore in his entent, 6404

and sent for
Serenydes,

And for Serenydes anon he sent,
Whiche in hir mende fuƚƚ gretly was dismayde;
Whanne she was come rigħt thus to hir he seid: 6407

'Madame,' quod he, 'ye vnderstonde fuƚƚ weƚƚ, 6408
Sithe I beganne to love yow first of Aƚƚ,
I haue my hert, my seruice, euery dele,
To yow allonly in especiaƚƚ;[2] 6411

and told her they
had both done
wrong.

And now reasone constreyneth me to caƚƚ
Vnto my mend and to my remembraunce this,
Bothe ye and I haue done ferre Amys. 6414

'I made you
leave my lord
Auferius

Ye were the wyff of auferius the kyng', 6415
Whiche was my very lord and souereyn,
And trayturly first Atte begynneng'

---

[1] MS. *that that.*   [2] MS. *especially.*

I made yow to forsake hym in sertayn, 6418

And thanne vnder a false compassion trayn,

and the land to rebel.

The lande anon and I were atte accorde,

To be rebell ayenst our' soueryn lord. 6421

I take noo hede of all this werk before, 6422

Wherfore I am in bytter paynes strong';

And though that I shuld suffer[1] meche more,

In very trouth I thinke it were noo wrong', 6425

As for my dayes thei will not now be long',

And fayne I wold my consciens were clere,.

Wherfore anon do calle a messenger, 6428

And to ser Darell chargid hym to goo, 6429 Send now to Sir Darell

Besechyng hym that he will speke with me ;

After his councell gladly wold I doo,

To pray the kyng' of grace and it wold be, 6432 to pray the king of grace.'

On me to shew his mercy and pitee.'

A Carefull woman was Serenydes, Serenydes was sad, and wept.

And euer wept that no man cowde hir sese. 6435

To lucydas she seid in this maner, 6436 To Lucidas she said, ' Daughter,

' Doughter,' quod she, ' this is now myn entent ;

Your' fader wold, as towchyng' this mater,

That to ser Darell a messenger were sent ; 6439 send Sygrem to Darell,

It were well done that Sygrem theder went,

And to your' fader prae hym for to come, and pray him to come to your father.'

In all the hast, loo this is all and som.' 6442

Now on this message Sygrem furth [is] went, 6443 Sygrem goes on his message to Sir Darell,

To[2] ser Darell and this to hym he seid ;

' The mayde lucidas now heder me sent,

And hir commaundement I haue obeyde ; 6446

ffor hir fader now good hath so purveyde,

A febyll man he is, I yow ensure,

And in this liff he may not long' endure. 6449

---

[1] MS. suster. [2] MS. And to.

This is the effecte of my massage,   6450
That ye wiħ doo so mekiħ as take yᵉ payɲ,
To come so ferre hir fader for to se,
The whiche gretly shuld counfort hyɲ certayɲ; 6453
[leaf 35] To speke witħ yow truly he wold be fayɲ,
That wote I wele, and she wold purvey so,
That ye shaħ savely come and savely goo.'   6456

Off these tidynges was he weħ contente,   6457
And part also as for his hartes ease;
Yet he remembryd hyɲ or euer he went,
who asks leave of he wold haue licence of Generides,   6460
Generydes,   ffor in noo wise he wold not hyɲ displease;
And her vppoɲ he made noo lenger space,
To hyɲ he gotħ and told hyɲ aħ the case   6463

Off ser Amelok and of his repentaunce :   6464
Generides answerd, and this he seid;
' If I may fynde his wordes of substaunce,
In very trougtħ I wiħ be weħ apayde.'   6467
'ffor my comyngᵗ his dougħter hatħ so purveyde,
Ser,' quod Dareħ, ' and that in suche wise
I shaħ goo save and come o warantise.   6470

And to be playɲ to yow in euery wise,   6471
This is the cause that he hatħ sent for me;
telling him of his I owe his doughter trewly my seruice,
love for Lucidas. So ye were weħ content ther witħ,' quod he; 6474
'Ellys wiħ I not goo in very certente.'[1]
Off his wordis Generides was fuħ fayɲ,
And smylingᵗ softely answerd thus ageyɲ :   6477

' Dareħ,' quod he, ' I know this very sure,   6478
She is not longᵗ owt of yourᵖ remembraunce,
Ye love hir best of eny creature;

---

[1] MS. certentente.

Wherin, god woote, I take noo displesaunce,   6481
ffor Aff that may be for your foryeraunce,   'Go on, in God's
I am contente to helpe yow to the same ;   name,' said
                                      Generydes.
Wherefore,' quod he, 'goth on in goddis name.'   6484

To the Castelf ser Darelf now is gon,   6485   Darell came to
Whanne he was come first atte begynneng',   the castle, where
                                      Lucidas met him,
his doughter lucidas mette hym Anon,
And thankfully she gave hym his welecomyng',   6488
Thanne furth with aff withoute eny more taryeng',   and brought him
She brought hym to hir fader ther he lay,   to her father.
Seke and febyff, fuff nye his endyng' day.   6491

Syr amelok was glad of his comyng' ;   6492
'Ser Darelf, I prae yow, bere me witnesse,   Amelok begged
This I desire above aff other thyng',   him to pray
                                      Generydes to
ffor to haue my pardon of Generides :   6495   make his peace
I haue affendid sore, yet neuer the lesse   with Auferius.
Of Aff thynges that is past what euer it be,
Besechyng' hym now of mercy and pite ;   6498

And of his fader auferius the kyng',   6499
If it wold be, fayne I wold haue his grace ;
ffor more vntrew ther was neuer non levyng',
Thanne I haue ben to hym as in this case :   6502
My life woff now endure butt short space,
Besechyng' yow to prae Generides,
That he wold with his fader to make my pece.   6505

And for to do your dever in this case,   6506
Remembryng' this mater euery dele,
here is,' quod he, 'my doughter lucidas,   'Here is my
                                      daughter Lucidas,
The whiche, if I may vnderstonde and fele,   6509   whom you love:
That ye with hert and thought y^t ye love hir wele,
She shaff be youres, lo this shalbe your wage,   I will give her to
                                      you, and all my
And aff my land with hir in mariage.   6512   land.

Pray also that
Serenydes may be
forgiven.'
And also, DareĦ, as for Serenydes,   6513

This I beseche yow hartely,' q*u*od he,

'That ye speke witħ hir that she may haue hir pece,

And so to leve in rest and it wilbe :   6516

And pray Generides to speke witħ me,

So wold god that he were here p*r*esent,

loo her is aĦ the effecte of myɲ entente.'   6519

To lucidas he seid in this maner ;   6520

'Dougħter,' q*u*od he, 'here is a nobiĦ knygħt,

his aunccetours were meɲ of grete powre ;

And of princes he is descendid fuĦ rigħt,   6523

Ye shaĦ be his, this I haue hyɲ be higħt,

In marriage, this is the mater playɲ,

And of my land I say yow for certeyɲ.   6526

And be ye so agreyd ther to,   6527

And as ye think now teĦ me you*r* avise.'

Lucidas agrees.
'Syr,' q*u*od she, 'as it plese yow to do,

I am contente ther witħ in eue*r*y wise,   6530

like as ye wiĦ appoynte it and devise ;

In eue*r*y thing⟨ to folow you*r* entent,

I am hooly atte you*r* co*m*maundment.'   6533

Darell goes back
to Generydes,
Thanne s*er* DareĦ departid home ayeyɲ,   6534

Vnto Generides the redy way,

And ther he told hyɲ aĦ to geder playɲ

Of s*er* Amelok, and in what plight he lay ;   6537

'And this,' q*u*od he, 'he prayde me to say,

In vmbiĦ wise, desireng⟨ tenderly

That ye wold⟨ come and see hyɲ or he dye.   6540

and at length
prevails upon him
to visit
Sir Amelok.
He was in great
distress,
Wyth long⟨ prayou*r* he brought hyɲ atte last   6541

Vnto s*er* Amelok ther as he lay,

In grete distresse musyng⟨ of tymes past,

And to Generides this ganne he say, 6544
like as a man) had ben) half in affray ;
'Mercy,' quod he, 'mercy, gentiH Generides,
Graunt me that I witħ yow may haue my pece, 6547

[leaf 35, back]
and cried
'Mercy, mercy,
gentle Generydes,
let me have peace
with you

And witħ your' fader auferius the kyng', 6548
ffor hym) I haue offendid specially,
To non) so moche a creature levyng',
This land I hym) be raft fuH traytourly ; 6551
To god and hym) I yeld me now gilty,
Pray hym) of grace and ellys, I wote certayn),
My sowle shaH lye in euer lastyng' payn). 6554

and with Auferius,

whom I have
specially offended.

I yield myself to
God and him.

And o thyng' I wold, this is the case, 6555
Ye mygħt haue knowlage or [I] feryer goo,
DareH shaH haue my dougħter lucidas
In mariage, and aH my land also, 6558
Besechyng' yow to be good lord therto,
And shewe your' grace onto Serenydes,
That sne may prae for yow and leve in pece. 6561

Darell shall
marry Lucidas.

Be good lord to
them,

And ferthermore, now I remember me, 6562
how I smote yow witħ villany and shame,
Withynne the courte that euery man) mygħt see,
Nougħt remembryng' the wurchippe of your' name, 6565
And therfore on) that side I am lame,
ffuH vmbely besechyng' your' goodnes,
That of aH this I may haue forgevenes.' 6568

and forgive me
for smiting you
in the court.'

Witħ that he feH in swounyng' for very payn), 6569
Wherof Generides had grete pitye,
And whanne he sawe he[1] was awake ayeyn) ;
'Ser Amelok,' he seid, 'now as for me, 6572
AH that is past shaH clene forgevyn) be,
And witħ my fader I shaH make your' pece,
ffor yow and also for Serenydes. 6575

'All that is past,
Sir Amelok,

and I will make
your peace with
my father.

[1] MS. hym he.

GENERYDES. 14

And or ye dye this I desire also,[1]   6576
That ye for geve me or I ferther passe.'

'Trewly,' quod he, 'ser, that may sone be doo,
As for to me ye haue do noo trespace ;   6579
And [as] ferfurth as god will geve me grace,
With all the world, with highe and low degree,
I shall departe with loue and charite.'   6582

A Carefull woman was Serenydes ;   6583
She rent hire here, a petuose thing to see,[2]

And with a nakyd swerd came to Generides,
'I yow requere for goddis loue,' quod she,   6586
'haue here this swerd, and make an ende of me
Now or ye goo, and bryng me owt of payn,
ffor I haue well deseruyd it for certayn.'   6589

'Do away, Madame,' quod he, 'god defende ;'   6590
Ther with he toke hir in his armys twayne,
'All that is amys,' quod he, 'may be amend,
And so ye must comfort your self ayeyn,   6593

ffor this I haue promysed for certayn,
Vnto my lord and fader for to goo,
To make the pece for yow and hym Also.'   6596

Generides departid furth his way,   6597
Ser amelok lay in angwissh and in payn,
Sighyng full oft vppon his bed he laye,

And shortly to say yow the certayn,   6600
he dyed anon withynne a day or twayne.
Thanne who was hevy butt Serenydes,
ffor more and more hir sorow ded increase.   6603

And ouer wharte his body ther [s]he lay,   6604
All in swoune, grete pite to be hold,
And in noo wise she wold not thens away,

---

[1] MS. *desire of yow also.*
[2] MS. *rent hire a petuose thing to here*

Moche sorow was made of yong⁹ and old⁹ :   6607   and in an hour
after Serenydes
With that hir face wex all to geder cold⁹,   died of grief.

helpe was ther now, reskewe ne socour⁹,

Bothe he and she were dede withynne An owre.   6610

A woofull creature was fayre lucydas,   6611   Fair Lucidas was
very sad,
To se the maner of ther departeng⁹,

And bothe to geder in a full litill space ;

So all the day alone she sate wepyng⁹,   9614   and sat all day
weeping and
She had noo comfort of erthely¹ thyng⁹,   thinking of
Darell.
Save euer more was ser Darell in hir mynde,

he was to hir so curtes and soo kynd.   6617

Generides sent furth a messenger,   6618   Generydes sent to
the king
To telle the kyng⁹ his fader tideng⁹,   to tell him of
Sir Amelok's
hough ser Amelok hath yeld vppe All in fere   repentance.

The Reme of ynd, and knowith hym for his kyng⁹, 6621

With petuese wordes gretly repentyng⁹,

And of all his offence and trespace,

ffull vmbly besechyng⁹ yow of grace.   6624

Off these tidengys the kyng⁹ was well apayd,   6625   The king was
well pleased,
And toward Surre dressid hym to ride,   and prepared to
ride to Syria,
Thanne to the messenger right² yuus he seid ;

'Sey to my sonne that he here abide,   6628   leaving Generydes
to rule India.
And sette the lande in rewle on euery side,

hole to be and vnder his obeysaunce,   [leaf 36]

And take it as his owen inheritaunce.'   6631

Kyng⁹ auferius fell seke anon vppon,   6632   Anon after he fell
sick,
Yet not withstondyng so as it myght be,

With hym he tooke his knyghtes euerychon,

The streight way toward surre rideth he,   6635   but went back to
Syria,
And whanne that he was come in to yᵗ cuntre,

Tydynges he hard whiche grevid hym right sore,   where he found
queen Sereyne
The quene Sereyne was dede a day before.   6638   had died the day
before.

¹ MS. *etherly.*

² MS. *this right*, the former word being marked for erasure.

Grete hevynes ther was for hir deceas,   6639

He went where
she lay,
and swooned
twice,
The kyng⟨ went to the place ther she laye,

And twyes he swouned among⟨ the prece,

ffull sory were his meñ to se that day,   6642

Be one assent thei had hym⟩ thens awaye,

And furth with all in to his chaunber y^{ei} hym⟩ brought,

All disfortles he was and full of thought.   6645

And alway still he febelid passyng⟨ sore,   6646

So what with thought and feyntid *with* sekenes,

and within two
days died,
Withynne ij dayes he dyed or litill more ;

Thanne was the lande in grete hevynes,   6649

To think vppon⟩ so noble a princez

That dyed be fore, and ther kyng⟨ Also,

So woo thei were thei wist not what to do.   6652

and they were
both buried.
For hym⟩ and hir was made grete ordena*u*nce,   6653

Prelett*es*, prestis, syngeng⟨ ther se*r*uice,

And grete lordes doth ther obs*er*uaunce,

ladys also in full lamentabill wise,   6656

Eue*r*ychon⟩ of them⟩ in blak as is ther gise ;

Now late vs leue them⟩ in rest and pece,

And speke wee ferther of Generides,   6659

Generydes,
in India,
set the land in
order,
Whiche is in ynd, and doth grete diligence   6660

Thorough owt the land to sette good ordena*u*nce,

In ponyssheng⟨ of them⟩ that doo amys,

Suche as be good of witte and goue*r*naunce,   6663

Them⟩ to charisshe and putte to fortheraunce,

All this remembert he both day And nyght,

And for to see that eue*r*y man⟩ haue right.   6666

So wele he dede in eue*r*y man*er* thing⟨,   6667

The land of hym⟩ were passing⟨ well content,

and was crowned
king.
As rightwise ayre thei toke hym⟩ for y*er* kyng⟨,

And Crownyd hym̄ be all the hooll assent;   6670
Thus were thei All att his commaundment,
he was soo good soo curtese and soo fre,
he had the loue of all the hoole contre.   6673

The same forster that came on to [the] kyngꞇ,   6674 The faithful
                                                        forester was
And toldꞇ of All the treson̄ that was do,   rewarded with
                                                        100 pounds,
he lost his office ther and his levyngꞇ,
And with quene-Sereyne he went Also;   6677
Ther for his trowth withoute wordes moo,   and restored to
                                                        his office.
A C pownde of fee he had ther fore,
With his office like as he had before.   6680

Owt of Cesare thanne cam̄ barons iij,   6681 Three barons of
                                                        Cæsarea bring
And in ther Iurnay thei rode passingꞇ fast,   tidings to Darell
To tell ser Darell the very certente,
hough his fader owt of his life[1] is past;   6684 of his father's
                                                        death.
Desirengꞇ hym̄ to come in all the hast,
And by the Assent of All his baronage,
Of that contre to cleyme his eritage.   6687

Whanne thei had told ther message hole and playn̄),
Ye may well wete ser Darell was not glad;
Vnto Generides he went certayn̄,   He asks leave of
                                                        Generydes to go
And told hym̄ of the tidynges that he had,   6691 home,
Besechyngꞇ hym̄, with countenaunce right sadde,
Of licence in Cesare for to goo;
Generides consentid well ther too.   6694

And whanne his leve of hym̄ thus takyn̄ was,   6695
ffor All the payñ he sufferyd and the smert,
Ye shall well knowe the fayre mayde lucidas   and sorrowfully
                                                        parted with
Right endly was inprentid in his hert;   6698 Lucidas.
Vnto hir chaunber sone he made a stert,
And curtesly of hir his leve he toke,
With kyssengꞇ fele as witnes[eth] the book.   6701

                    [1] MS. list.

In to Casare now ser Dareᵭ is gooᴻ,   6702
The countre hole was glad of his comyngᵗ,
He was made king of Cæsarea, And for ther prince thei toke hymᴻ euerychoᴻ,
And gave hymᴻ ther trouth withoute feynengᵗ,   6705
he was soo good to themᴻ in euery thingᵗ,
Shewyngᵗ themᴻ favourᵖ and grete gentilnes,
he had the hartes hoole of more and lesse.   6708

Whanne he had sett the rule and gouernaunce,   6709
Thorough owt the land to mayteyᴻ rest and pese,
And made his officers to his plesaunce
Suche as hymᴻ thought his honour wold encrease, 6712
and then went back to Generydes, Thanne ageyᴻ he went onto Generides,
And in his Iurnay rideth he fuᵭ fast,
ffurth in to ynd in aᵭ the possibiᵭ hast.   6715

Now is the prince of Cesare come ayeᴻ,   6716
Vnto the kyngᵗ of ynde Generides,
[leaf 36, back] The whiche in sothe of his comyᴻ,
ffor he abode his comyngᵗ stiᵭ opece ;   6719
and without delay was wedded to Lucidas. And for to teᵭe yow shortly the processe,
Withoute delay or lenger space,
The prince was weddid onto lucidas.   6722

And whanne the fest was aᵭ to geder do,[1]   6723
ffor tender love and speciaᵭ remembraunce,
With hymᴻ and here he gave the lande also,
Whiche was hir faders oldᵗ inheritaunce ;   6726
He is made governor of India in the absence of Generydes, The prince also, his honour to avaunce,
he gave hymᴻ fuᵭ powre signyd with his hande,
In his absence to gouerne aᵭ his lande.   6729

who goes to Syria, Now goth Generides, the kyngᵗ of ynde,   6730
Toward Surre withoute more delay ;
And in the story leke as I do fynde,

---

[1] MS. *done.*

Too Counstables ther mette hym̄ be the way, 6733
One of them̄ twayne, the very troutħ to say,
Of aħ Surre cheff gou*er*no*ur* he was,
The toder kept the Citee of Damas. 6736

and is met by two constables,

Aħ sad thei were, and made fuħ hevy chere, 6737
Generides had merveħ what it ment ;
To his *pr*esence he bad thei shuld come nere,
That he mygħt knowe the effecte of *yer* entente, 6740
And vppon̄ that A streigħt co*m*maundment,
Gevyng¹ them̄ charge to teħ hym̄ aħ the case,
Trewly and playn̄ what man*er* a thyng¹ it was. 6743

who told him

Fuħ lothe thei were to teħ the certente, 6744
ffor hevy tidinges came to sone Alway,
Butte whanne thei sawe it mygħt non oy*er* be,
To hym̄ thei spake, ' s*er*, please it yow,' q*u*od thei, 6747
' To take it in pacient that we shaħ saye,
The kyng¹ you*r* fader dede is for certeyn,
And you*r* moder also the quene Sereyne ; 6750

of the death of his father and mother.

Bothe he and she, withynne iij dayes of space : 6751
It is grete hurt to the land were it goddes wiħ.'
And whanne Generides wist hougħ it was,
Down̄ from̄ his hors in swounyng¹ ther he feħ, 6754
To tyme he was awake ther lay he stiħ ;
Thanne eu*er*y man̄ dede grete diligence and payn̄),
And vppon̄ his hors thei sette hym̄ Ageyn̄. 6757

He fell from his horse in a swoon,

They brougħt hym̄ to the Cite of Damas 6758
And passing¹ seke in his pales he laye,
Aħ pale and wanne, owt of likeng¹ he was,
his fressh colou*r* it fatid al away, 6761
And thanne to Nataneħ this ganne he sey,
' Goo now, I prae yow hartely,' q*u*od he,
' And sey to Segrem that he come to me.' 6764

and was carried to Damascus, where he lay sick.

He sent for Sygrem,

Whanne he was come thanne seid Generides,   6765

and gave him a
ring to take to
Clarionas,
'Sygrem,' quod he, 'I haue sent for yow here;
God wote I am noo thing¹ in hartes ease,
And very seke ye se, and in what man*er*;   6768
Goo to Clarionas myn owen lady dere,
haue here this ryng¹, bere it here for me,
I am aferde I shaH hir neuer see.   6771

TeH ye hir soo in very certente,   6772
Me recomaundyng¹ in fuH humble wise,
beseeching her to
pray for him.
Besechyng¹ hir that she wiH pray for me,
I aske no more for aH my trew *ser*uice;'   6775
Ser,' quod Sygrem, 'rigHt as ye wiH devise,
What I shaH do or say for your³ entent,
I am redy att your³ owne *com*maundment.'   6778

Sygrem goes into
Persia
Now gotH Sygrem withoute wordes moo,   6779
ffurtH in to Perce he riditH on a pace,
To Mounton*er* Citee now is he goo,
On his massage As he *com*maundid was,   6782
and tells Clarionas
all.
So StreigHt he gotH on to Clarionas,
And ther he told³ hir aH the circumstaunce
Of his sekenes witH hevy countenaunce.   6785

And whanne Sygrem had aH to geder seïde,   6786
She swoons,
Anon she feH in swounyng¹ for very payn w*ith* aH,
Where witH MirabeH gretly was dismayde,
and Mirabell
counsels her
'Madame,' quod she, 'what thing¹ that eu*er* faH?' 6789
And on hir lady fast beganne to caH,
'hurt not your³ self, I p*ra*e yow, in this case;'
WitH thoo wordes a woke Clarionas.   6792

'AH way your³ comfort is fuH good,' quod she,   6793
'Butt in this case I wote not what to sey.'
'Madame,' quod she, 'woH ye do After me?'

'Gladly,' she seide, 'all that I canne or may.'   6796
'Be my councell thanne shall ye take your' way   to go to Syria
secretly.
To Surre warde,' quod she, 'be myn) Avyse,
In pore clothing' and in full secrete wise.   6799

And haue with yow Gwynot your chaunberleyn),   6800
And one to kepe your' hors it shall suffice,
Take vppon) yow the labour and the payn),
And ye shall make hym) hoole o warantice.'   6803   She agrees,
'I will,' quod she, 'do like as ye haue device,
And certenly, withoute eny wordes moo,
To morow erly forward will we goo.'   6806

Fro Mountoner gothe Clarionas,   6807   and goes from
With hir rode Sygrem to hir gide,   Mountoner with
                                                               [leaf 37]
ffull secretly as she appoynted was,   Sygrem,
That noman) of the Cite hir aspide ;   6810
ffurth on ther way to surreward thei hied,
And in all goodly hast as it myght be,   till they come to
ffull sone thei came to Damas the Citee.   6813   Damascus.

Sygrem from hir departid furth with all,   6814
Streight to the Castell gothe Clarionas,   Clarionas goes
Vppon) the porter she beganne to calle,   straight to the
                                                  castle,
And he ayenward askid what[1] she was :   6817
'ffor certeyn), ser,' quod she, 'this is the case,   and tells the
The kyng' is seke, it is infourmyd me,   porter
                                                 she is come to
I trost to god to make hym) hole,' quod she.   6820   cure the king.

'In strenthe or erbys that ben profeitable,   6821
In them I knowe the vertu that is sure,
In euery kynd whiche is most comfortabill,
And accordeng' to euery creature,   6824
And often tyme I haue putte it in vre ;
Wherefore, I prae yow, do my eraunde,[2]
That I may see the kyng' now or I goo.'   6827

[1] MS. was.   [2] So MS. ? my eraunde to do.

'Damesell,' quod he, 'your erande shall be do [1];' 6828

With that the porter goth vnto the place,
And spake with Natanell a worde or twoo,

And brought hym furth onto Clarionas,   6831
Vnknowen to them bothe what that she was ;

'Ye are right welcom, suster myn,' quod he,
'What is your will ? I prae yow telle it me.'   6834

'Trowly,' quod she, 'I am a pore woman,   6835
The kyng is seke, whom gretly I complayne ;

And I wold Shewe suche connyng As I canne,
Trosting to god to make hym hoole ayeyn.'   6838

Thanne he beheld hir ferthermore certayn,
A ryng he knew whiche on hir fynger was,
Yet wist he not that it was Clarionas.   6841

From hir he went streight onto the kyng,   6842
'Ser, please it yow to vnderstonde,' quod he,
'Ther is a woman whiche is full connyng
In euery sekenes and, as thinkith me,   6845
By here wordes her semyth so to be ;
here atte Castell gate with hir I spakke,
To make yow hoole this wolle she vndertake.   6848

'On hir fynger ther is a ryng,' quod he,   6849
'The whiche in sothe me think a straunge case ;
And this I wote in very certente,
Ye gave suche on vnto Clarionas,   6852
And in myself I mervell hough it was.'

Thanne seid the kyng, 'I woll now y^t ye goo,
Bryng hir to me withoute wordes moo.'   6855

Now Natanell goth to the Castell gate,   6856

And brought this woman streight onto the kyng,
Butt she was wympelyd soo that woote ye what,

[1] MS. *don.*

That he had no maner knowlaching¹,   6859   so that he did not
                                                              know her,
With that anon̄ he had aspyed the ryng¹,
The whiche hym̄ thought he gaye Clarionas,
Yet for aH that he wist not what she was.   6862

'I pray yow, ser, be of good chere,' quod she,   6863
'And if it please your goodnes for to here
I am a woman̄ of ferre contre ;'
And ther withaH, in fuH curtes maner,   6866   and offered to
                                                              kiss him.
She proferyd hym̄ to kysse with louyng¹ chere ;
'Nay, suster myn̄,' quod he, 'with goddes grace,
I must pray yow of pardon̄ in this case :   6869

For I wiH kysse no woman̄ be ye sure,   6870   He refused to
                                                              kiss any one
Though she myght make me hoole as euer I was,   but Clārionas.
Butt only hir whiche is that creature
That I loue best, the mayde Clarionas ;   6873
And if that she were present in this place,
If I here kyssid, I think, so god me save,   She, perhaps,
                                                              could cure him.
It were the best fisykke that I cowde haue.'   6876

'I haue,' she seid, 'brought with me hir ymage :'   6877
'Ye,' quod the kyng¹, 'I prae yow, late me see ;'
Anone she dede vnWympiH hir visage,   She unveiled
                                                             herself,
'Withoute fayle I am the same,' quod she :   6880
Thanne seid the kyng¹, 'Aye, Benedicite !
hough haue ye take vppon̄ yow aH this payn̄ ?'
Ther with he toke hir in his armes twayn̄.   6883   and he took her
                                                              in his arms

Thanne he kyssid hir withoute more taryeng¹,   6884   and kissed her,
And aH that nyght, tiH day beganne to rise,   and they sat
                                                             together till
They twayne were sett withoute departeng¹,   daybreak.
As glad and mery as thei cowde device,   6887
To bothe ther pleasurez in aH goodly wise ;
And on̄ the morow, sothely for to say,   On the morrow
                                                              she went back to
To mountoner she toke the redy way.   6890   Mountoner.

Generydes recovered,	And hole he was and very weH att ease,	6891
	And atte his hartes rest in especiaH;	
and was crowned king,	The iij^{de} day after Generides	
	Was crownyd kyng' of Surry furtĥ witĥ AH;	6894
	Thanne the lordes echon) in generaH,	
	Witĥ very dew and feithfuH obseruaunce,	
	Dede hym) omage with vmble obeysaunce.	6897

	Whanne he had sette the land in gouernaunce,	6898
and soon after set off for Persia,	ffurtĥ in to perce he takith his Iurnay,	
	In grete estate And in grete ordenaunce,	
	With his lordes and in suche array,	6901
	Thus rideth he the redy way	
to wed Clarionas.	To Mountoner, ther as the Sowdon) was,	
[leaf 37, back]	Ther for to wedde the mayde Clarionas.	6904

	Whanne he was come, the Cite was fuH fayn),	6905
	ffor att aH tymes of necessite	
	he toke on) hym) the labour' and the payne,	
	And was ther sheld from) aH aduersite;	6908
	So thanne withynne the space of dayes iij,	
	As rially as thei cowde device,	
	The mariage was made in solempne wise.	6911

Gwynan was there,	Gwynan the kyng' was atte mariage,	6912
	The kyng' of Trace also withoute lese,	
and Ismael the Savage,	Whiche callid was IsmaeH the savage,	
	Broder he was onto the kyng'¹ Generides,	6915
and Darell was steward of the feast,	And so to gide and gouerne aH the prece	
	Appoynted was, likke as thei thought it best,	
	The prince of Cesare cheff stiward of ye fest.	6918

and many others.	And other grete estatis ther were moo,	6919
	Bothe of lordes and ladyes many on),	
	Grete Iustis ther the Sowdon) made also,	

¹ Omit *the kyng.*

And all the plesure that cowde be thougħt vppon);
And to be hold the pepill euerychon),
Whiche came to se the fest of yong¹ and old,
It was a very wonder to be hold.   6925

Sone after whanne the fest was don) and All,   6926   Soon after,
And euery man) gon) home in to his cuntre,   when all had gone
                                                           home,
Withynne a while, as aventur² gan) fall,
The Sowdon) dyed, whiche was grete pite;   6929   the Sultan died,
Grete mone was made of men) of the Cite,
Save ther comfort and trost in¹ euery thyng¹,
Was only on) Generides the kyng¹,   6932

Whiche sesid all the lande in his demeane,   6933   and Generydes
                                                           took his land,
Be rigħt wise titell of his mariage,   by right of his
                                                           marriage.
Takyng¹ homage, as lord and souereyn),
Thorough owt the lande of all the Baronage :   6936
Bothe yong¹ and old and euery man) of age,
As glad thei were of hym), I yow ensure,
As euer was land of eny levyng¹ creature.   6939

He was to them) so lovyng¹ and so kynd,   6940
The laugħ abseruyd will bothe ferre and nere,
No man) had Wrong that eny man) cowd fynde,
ffewe compleyntes or non) that men) myght here,   6943
Gentill ther with, curtes in All maner,
If eny man) wold wrong¹ oyer day or nygħt,
he was redy for to forfete his rigħt.   6946

And for be cause it shuld not owt of mynd,   6947   He married
                                                           Natanell
The good seruice so feitħfull and so playn)   to Mirabell,
Off Natanell, whiche he had founde so kynde,
And for his love hadde grete labour³ and payn),   6950
he thougħt he wold remember it ayeyn),
In suche a wise as hym) thougħt honorable,
And maryed hym) to the made Mirabell.   6953

¹ MS. *was in.*

and gave them
the city of Seure.
Too hym and her he gave a faire Citee,   6954
Withynne the Reme of Surre callid Sevre,
A bougħt the town a dosen myle fre
Vnto hym self, and yerly of valour[1]   6957
vj thousand pownde, to maynteyn yer honour ;
And of that land he made hym cheff Iustice,
To maynteyn in euery maner wise.   6960

Sir Anasore was
made lord of a
great barony.
Syr Anasore with hym was not for gete,   6961
he made hym lord of A grete baronye,
The whiche was fallyn in perce be eschete,
Whanne lucas dyed that was of ydonye ;   6964
And for grete trost that he hadde specially
In hym), Aħ myn Auctour reherse,
he gave hym ther the Stiwardshepe of perce.   6967

Sygrem was
wedded to the
laundress,
Sygram also was in his remembraunce,   6968
Vn to the lavender weddid ther he was,
Whiche vtterly for soke hir acqueyntaunce,
And toke hir Iurnay witħ Clarionas ;   6971
and had a fair
lordship given
him by the king.
The king¹ hym grauntid, of his speciaħ grace,
A fayre lordshippe onto them bothe in fere,
The whiche was wurth an Cħ be yere.   6974

Thus quyte he them that were to hym so kynd, 6975
And, for to seie[1] yow in shorte conclusion,
A better prince was neuer had in mynd,
Thanne he was on that euer bare crown ;   6978
And thus he was a man of grete renown,
Sowdon of perce with aħ his signory,
And also kyng¹ of ynd and of surre.   6981

Generydes and
Clarionas lived
many a year in
prosperity,
In grete wurchipe Clarionas and he   6982
Good lyff thei ledde to geder many a yere,
In hartes ease and moche prosperite,

¹ MS. valowe.   ² MS. seia.

Issue they had whiche was to them full dere,   6985 and had issue.
Right grete lordes and ladyes thei were,
Whiche on of them of xv yere of age,   The daughter was married to the
The kyng᾿ of Egipt had in mariage.   6988 king of Egypt,

The remenaunt grew to grete hono*ur*,   6989 and the others grew up in great
And thus I make an ende of this processe,   honour.
Besechyng᾿ hym that is our saviour᾿,
All oure synnes of pardon to relese,[1]   6992
And in the Ioy and blisse that[2] is endlese,
he graunt vs a place *per*petuall,
In paradise where all his seyntes dwell.   6995

**Explicit the boke of Gene-
rides and of his faire lady Clarionas.**

[1] MS. *be relese*, but the first word is struck out.   [2] MS. *this*.

VARIOUS READINGS FROM THE PRINTED FRAG-
MENTS OF SIR GENERYDES,

GIVEN IN THE PREFACE AND POSTSCRIPT TO MR FURNIVALL'S EDITION
OF THE HELMINGHAM MS. FOR THE ROXBURGHE CLUB.

2016. *claymeth it of*] they clayme this
2017. *Also to be made*] And also to be
„ *your*] his
2018. *voward*] forwarde
2019. *of right it longith*] it longeth of
ryght
2021. *so it*] me so
2022. *may withoute*] may bere without
2025. *it is but*] for it is
2026. *full curtes*] curteys
2027. *they ganne*] gan they
2029, 30. *withoute ... Batell*] withou[t
dowte] Unto the kynge of
kynges to gyue a strou[te]
2031. *ganne them*] gan
2032. *princes*] knyghtes
2033. *other dyuerce*] dyuers
2034. *Dukes and Erles*] erles
„ *anon*] many one
2035. *that they hadde vppon*] so that
they shone
2036. *perlys*] grete perles
2037. *in the fressest*] on the best
2038. *through owt in*] thrughe
2040. *enmys for*] enemyes
2042. *ffro*] Forth of
2043. *rideth*] rode
„ *to his pavilion*] vnto his tente
2044. *With ... rome*] With his lordes
aboute hym wente
2045. *redy*] all redy
2046. *a companye*] company
2047. *were*] brought
2049. *All redy to gye*] to guyde truly
2052. *att his demenyng*] in his ledynge
2056. *he was baneer*] dyde the baner
bere

2058. *ij thowsand ... companye*] [Sir
Crove]s with thre thousande
in theyr company
2059. *ward*] batayll
„ *ser Anasore*] anazere
2061. *they were thore*] that there were
2062. *withoute*] withouten
2064. *bothe the rule of more*] the reule
more
2067. *all*] and
2072. *by and by*] ryght hardely
2073. *after hym*] after
2075. *begely*] vgly
„ *bothe in*] in
2105. *was Baner*] bare the banere
2314. *they twayne*] they
2345. *sheld and thu goo*] shelde
agayne and go
5339. *on fortune*] a fortune
5343. *Amelokkez*] syr Amelokes
5344. *It was ayenst*] This was
5345. *cause*] case
„ *certente*] certayne
5351. *also he*] he
5352. *late*] let
5354. *where euer*] where that
„ *eny lande*] ony londe
5355. *noo lenger myght she*] she myght
no lenger
5356. *for very payn*] for grete doloure
5357. *ageyn*] that houre
5359. *that she*] she
„ *vp ayeyn*] agayne
5361. *refrayn*] restrayne
5365. *full sure*] sure
5371. *shuld kepe*] kepe
5372. *here*] lo here

5374. *that*] elles that
5375. *full hastely*] hastely
5378. *with the shall neuer*] shall neuer
  with the
5379. *haue*] kepe
5382. *vppon*] on
5383. *as he*] as euer he
5384. *the chaunber*] her chaumbre
5386. *full of hevynes*] and full of per-
  plexcyte
5387. *alway now*] alway
5388. *of his vnstabilnes*] his duplycyte
5389. *not gilty*] giltles
5390. *alway*] had alway
5392. *do be*] done by
5394. *a hevynes*] mornynge
5396. *also gentilnes*] as a gentyll kynge
5690. *here you speke*] here you
5692. *I am sure*] be ye sure
5694. *ferthermore*] forthermore
  „ *this*] so
5696. *o*] one
  „ *is*] is also
5701. *these wordes*] this worde
  „ *ganne*] began
5702. *goth*] wente
5703. *late*] let
5704. *hastith*] hasted
5705. *So*] And so
  „ *hir*] his
5706. *into*] in
5707. *the*] that
5708. *onto*] to
5709. *redy waye*] way redy
5711. *this to hym gan say*] to hym
  sayde preuely
5712. *the dore*] this dore
  „ *I yow praye*] I pray you hertely
5714. *to now*] tyll nowe
5715. *the neer he was*] the nerer he
  coude
5716. *otherwise*] other
5720. *onto the*] to hir
5721. *vpon*] open nowe
5722. *Thanne Darell*] When he
  „ *and*] he
5723. *onto fayre*] vnto
5724. *ffrom ynd . . . contre*] Fro ynde
  I come now as faste as I can
  [te]
5725. *on to*] to
5726. *now this*] this
5727. *be dremyd*] ben drenchyd
5728. *hym noyeth*] and nyghtly is

5731. *quod*] nowe quod
5732. *lesyng*] lesynges
5733. *yow*] it
5736. *this message*] the erande
5737. *not to don*] done
5738. *why*] quod he why
  „ *yow*] ye
5740. *onto*] to
5742. *is he*] he is
  „ *this dare I*] I dare well
5744. *I shall tell yow trougth*] in very
  trouthe
5752. *wote ye*] wote I
5753. *Serenydes*] Senerydes
5754. *he was*] was
5755. *ffor*] Fro
  „ *for*] fro
5756. *betwix*] bytwene
5757. *the trowth*] trouthe
5758. *that*] that euer
5759. *she*] the
5761. *and I had it*] if I had
5762. *shuld me mystrost*] mysdeme me
  sholde
  „ *my*] ony
5763. *not A take vppon*] nat taken on
5767. *ser Darell*] hym
5768. *now quod*] quod
  „ *yow*] ye now
5769. *he seide suche*] suche
5770. *very certente*] certente
5772. *nerrer*] nere
5775. *to say*] I say
5780. *it*] them
5782. *to*] vp to
  „ *hand*] honde
5784. *right wele*] well
5785. *he*] that he
5786. *eny maner*] ony
5788. *preiudice*] dyspyse
5789. *nede*] great nede
5790. *canne goo*] may gone
5791. *doo*] done
5793. *both good*] euer gode
5794. *is homeward in*] [home]warde
  gothe on
5795. *now*] a newe
5796. *cowde*] knewe
5799. *Citee*] towne
5800. *went*] sente
5802. *his own*] his
5803. [ ]nes to hym verament
5804. *that*] theyr

GLOSSARIAL INDEX.

A = He, 800.

A, Ah ! 3049, 6096.

A = of, 1150, 2752. A = in, 4810; unless this is an example of the indefinite article used redundantly with a numeral. A = have, 3483, 3955, 4829, 4883, 5763 (redundant).

ABASSHID, *v. pret.* was abashed or confounded, 127. ABASSHED, 4091; confounded, 3451. *pp.* ABASSHED, cast down, 6404.

ABELL, son of the prince of Turkey, 1921; constable and standard-bearer to the Persian army, 2017, 2023; slain by Belen, 2963.

ABIDENG, *sb.* dwelling, 4199; *part.* awaiting, 5957.

ABISSHID, *v. pret.* was abashed or confounded, 1260.

ABODE, *v. pret.* remained, 6147.

ABRAYDE, *v. pret.* started, 2320, 4717.

ABSERUYD, *v. pret.* observed, 6941.

ACCORDENG, *adj.* corresponding, 143, 1936, 2179, 6824.

ACCORDYNG, *adj.* appropriate, becoming, 245, 395.

A COMPAYNED, *pp.* accompanied, 1283.

ACQUEYNTAUNCE, *sb.* familiar friends, 6970.

ADO, *sb.* dealings, 2518. We use 'to do' in the same sense.

ADRED, *pp.* afraid, 844. ADREDE, 3867, 5965, 6073.

AFERDE, *adj.* afraid, 85, 1435, 5601, 6771.

AFFENDID, *pp.* offended, 4580, 6496.

AFFRAY, *sb.* affright, terror, 6545.

AFFRONTE, *adv.* in front, 4811.

AFORE, *prep.* before, 5979.

AFRAYE, *sb.* assault, attack, 2533.

AFTER, *adv.* afterwards, 3407.

AFTER, *prep.* 'After me,' according to my advice, 6795.

AGAST, *adj.* aghast, frightened, 5936.

AGE. 'Wele in age,' advanced in years, 1905.

AGEYN, *prep.* against, 1476; 'ther ageyn' = against it, 973.

AGREYD, *pp.* 'Was agreyd' = had agreed, 5638.

A HYE, *adv.* on high, 3051.

AISSHES, *sb.* ashes, 4406.

A LANDE, *adv.* on shore, 93.

A LATE, *adv.* of late, 4635.

ALIGHT, *v. pret.* alighted, 4562, 4576.

ALL AND SOM, everything, generally and particularly, 5570, 6442.

ALL IN ONE, *adv.* altogether, 1319.

ALLONLY, *adv.* only, 6411.

ALL ONLY, *adv.* only, alone, 881, 1432.

ALLOWE, *v. t.* to approve, 2783.

ALL SONE, as soon, 3778.

ALL THE HAST. 'In all the hast,' in all haste, 1293, 1444, 2807, 2886, 5566, 5878, 5931, 6442, 6685.

ALL THE HOOLE, all the whole, 3600, 6673. ALL THE HOLE, 5911. ALL THE HOOLL, 6670.

ALL UTTERLY, *adv.* entirely, 1500, 1757, 1867.

ALOW, *adv.* in a low voice, 5717.

ALTO, *adv.* altogether, 1559. ALL TO, 4272, 6094.

ALWAY, *adv.* always, 415, 490, 899, 1044. In 3948 it appears to be an error for 'all away.'

AMELOK, the false steward of Auferius, and usurping King of India, 28, 2129. AMALOK, 2381.

AMEND, *pp.* amended, 6592.

AMONG, *adv.* 'Euer among,' continually from time to time, 1373, 1853. Palsgrave gives, 'Amonge, parfoys.' See also Prof. Zupitza's note to Guy of Warwick, l. 950.

AMYSELL, sworn brother to Ananyell, 4833.

ANANYELL, brother of Amelok, slain by Generydes, 4825, 5016, 5830, 5844.

ANASORE, a knight of Persia, keeper of the prison, 1460, 5575, 6961. Son of Croves, 1906. ANASAR, 1471. ANASOR, 1503. ANOSORE, 2852, 3023, 3029.

ANCERS, *sb.* anchors, 3653.

ANCETORS, *sb.* ancestors, 3139.

AND, *conj.* if, 214, 354, 889, 3415, 4436, 6432.

AN HUNTYNG, 37.

ANONE VPPON, *adv.* immediately after, 78. ANON VPON, 141. See VPPON.

A PASE, *adv.* apace, swiftly, 988, 4453. A PACE, 2316, 3076.

APAYDE, *pp.* pleased, 848, 3485, 4206, 4419, 5072. APAYD, 1932. APAYED, 856, 1162, 2430, 2828.

APAYN, an error for 'and payn,' 5915.

APOYNTEMENT, *sb.* arrangement, 5424.

APOYNTID, *pp.* arranged, 5347. APOYNTED, 5589. APPOYNTED, 5624. APPOYNTID, 5887.

APPARELL, *sb.* provision, 641. In the next line the word is repeated, apparently in error, perhaps for 'peril;' or it may merely be used in the other sense of 'preparation,' like Fr. *appareil.*

AQUYTE, *v. pret.* requited, 1876.

ARABYE, Arabia, 1901.

ARAY, *sb.* condition, 1193. ARRAYE, 1258.

ARAYED, *pp.* 'Thus hath arayed me,' hath made me in this guise, 515.

ARKADYE, Arcadia, 1952.

ARMYS. 'To do armys' = to do battle, 6078.

AS, redundant in the phrases 'as for that nyght,' 138, 152, 383; 'As for a nyghtis space,' 230; 'as in this case,' 442, 582; 'as for a space,' 568; 'as after hir avise,' 702; 'as for a tyme,' 902; 'where as,' 1191; 'as for his hartys ease,' 1354; 'as for the landes right,' 1846; 'as for more witnesse,' 2382; 'As now,' 2409; 'as towching,' 2805, 5443; 'as after myn avise,' 2892; 'as for a daye or twayne,' 2990; 'as for this landis right,' 3345; 'as for a litill space,' 3789; 'as for this day,' 3887; 'as for that nyght,' 3897; 'as this nyght,' 3902; 'As for the cheve guerdon,' 3912; 'as for on nyghte reste,' 4030; 'as for Generides,' 4623; 'As late me see,' 5233; 'as yesterday,' 5278; 'as for a certeyn space,' 5313; 'As for a dreme,' 5634; 'as for a certeyn space,' 6293; 'As for to me,' 6579.

ASKAPYD, *v. pret.* escaped, 6096.

ASKRY, *v.* to descry, 5999. ASKERYE, 6014.

ASPIED, *v. pret.* espied, spied, 437.

ASPIED, *pp.* 2476. ASPYED, 2674.

ASPYE, *v.* to spy, watch, 1357, 1409, 2600.

ASSE, *v.* to assay, 6074.

ASSEMELYD, *pp.* assembled, 1317. ASSEMELID, 2046.

ASSENT, *sb.* 'Ar of hir assent,' are in league with her, 983.

ASSIRYE, Assyria, 2166. ASIRYE, 2545.

ASTATE, *sb.* state, 389.

BE RAFT, *v. pret.* bereft, 6551.

BERY, *v.* to bury, 5883; *pret.* BERIED, 5877.

BESEN, *pp.* beseen, provided, 1978. BE SENE, 2068.

BESETTE, *v.* to set, bestow, 5021.

BESY, *adj.* busy, 5303.

BESYNESSE, *sb.* in the phrase 'did all ther besynesse' = busied themselves, exerted themselves to the utmost, 1167.

BE TROST, *pp.* trusted, 1049, 3615.

BETWIX, *prep.* between, 108, 905, 3117, 5259.

BE TYME, *adv.* betimes, in good time, 522.

BEWRAYED, *pp.* exposed, 3885.

BE WREYE, *v.* to expose, betray, 4155.

BLAME, *sb.* 'To take a blame' = to take blame, 1628.

BLANCHARD, the name of King Belen's steed, 2458; given to Gwynan, 2265; and won by Generydes, 2247, 6066.

BLODE, ON. 'Braste on blode,' burst out bleeding, 546.

BLYSSYNG, *sb.* blessing, 236. BLISSYNG. 'On his blissyng,' as he expected to receive his blessing, 5346.

BOLDITH, *v. pres.* emboldens, 5803.

BOLEYN, BOLYN. See BELEN.

BOORE, *pp.* born, 5635. BORE, 6132.

BOTE, *sb.* use, advantage, 4681, 5853; *v.* 'It botith not,' is of no use, 4901.

BOTELER, *sb.* butler, 424.

BOUNDEN, *pp.* bound, 1458.

BOUSTOUS, *adj.* boisterous, rough, 2152.

BRAKE, *pp.* broken, 3489.

BRAST, *v. pret.* broke, 2326, 2677, 3047, 4926, 6094, &c.

BRASTE, *v. pret.* burst out, 546.

BRAYDE, *sb.* a sudden movement, a start, 2218, 2342, 2736, 6069.

BRAYDED, *v. pret.* started, 165.

BREDE, *sb.* breadth, 2075.

BRODER, *sb.* brother, 4826, 6915.

BRODEREN, *sb.* brethren, 2656.

BRODERHODE, *sb.* brotherhood, 6252.

BROWGTH, *pp.* brought, 4874.

BUSCOMMEST, *adj.* buxomest, most compliant or obedient, 2505.

BUSSHMENT, *sb.* ambush, 950. BUSCHEMENT, 5977.

BUT IF, *conj.* except, 322, 332.

BY AND BY, *adv.* 2048, 2072, 3287, 4766.

BYTWIX, *prep.* between, 2188.

BY WARE, *v.* beware, 4590.

CALLED *or* CALLID, reputed; in the phrases 'called passing wight,' 4573; 'callid good,' 4994. See 5186.

CAME, *v. pres.* come, 6745.

CAPADOCE, Cappadocia, 2087.

CAPADOOR, Cappadocia, 1954. Elsewhere CAPADOCE.

CAREFULL, *adj.* full of care, sorrowful, 4161, 6434, 6583.

CASARE, elsewhere CESARE, 6702.

CAST, *v.* to intend, purpose, 4423; *pret.* 3654.

CAWDE, could, 373. A scribe's error for 'Cowde.'

CERTAYNE. 'In certayne,' 462, 476, 4856; 'For certeyn,' 419; 'For certayn,' 4934; 'The certayn,' 2036, 6600.

CERUICE, *sb.* service, 4675.

CESALL, one of the Sultan of Persia's allies, 1965.

CESARE, Cesarea, 1926, 6681.

CESELL, Sicily, 2070.

CHARGID. Perhaps for 'chargeth,' the imperative, 6429.

CHARISSHE, *v.* to cherish, 6664.

CHARITE, OWT OF, 502. SEYNT CHARITE, 4282.

CHASE, *v. pret.* chose, 1325.

CHASTELYN, *sb.* the keeper of a castle, 1520, 1609. CHASTELAYN, 1632.

CHAUNBOUR, *sb.* chamber, 1407.

CHAUNBYR, *sb.* chamber, 69; CHAUNBER, 71, 3792, 4629.

CHEFF, *adj.* chief, 5893, 6735.

CHER,*sb.* aspect, countenance, 129; condition, 2594, 6031. CHERE, 239, 433, 2953; happiness, 2580. 'To make chere' = to be cheerful, 571; 'To make better chere' = to treat better, 2660; 'To take chere,' 751; 'To make frendly chere' = to treat in a friendly manner, 5764; 'To make chere' = to cheer, 6341; 'Made hevy chere,' were sad in countenance, 6737.

CHERYDONE, Prince of Cesarea, and father of Darell, 1928.

CHESE, *v.* choose, 1232, 1316.

CHESE, an error for 'Chek,' 4778.

CHEVE, *adj.* chief, 3912.

CHOSE, *pp.* chosen, 5230.

CLARIONAS, daughter to the Sultan of Persia, 686, &c.

CLARIONAT, a town in Persia, 3677.

CLARYET, the name of Generydes' sword, 3481.

CLAYMETH, *v.* 3 *pl.* claim, 2016.

CLEFE, *v. pret.* clave, cleft, 4598.

CLEUE, *v. pret.* clave, 3035, 3523.

COME, *v. pret.* came, 3017, 3042, 3829, 4214, 4281, 5204, 6396.

COMENAUTE, *sb.* the commonalty or commons, 254.

COMFORT, *v. pret.* comforted, 3854.

COMMANDITH, commendeth, 444. COMMAUNDITH, 5725.

COMNE, *pp.* come, 9.

COMPANABLE, *adj.* companionable, 2261.

COMPASSING, *adj.* 'False compassing' = with a false design, 4163.

COMPASSION, 6419; an error for 'compassing.' See 4163.

COMPLAYNE, *v. t.* to lament for, 6836.

CON. 'To con thanke' = to thank, 878.

CONFORTABLE, *adj.* comfortable, able to help, 2212.

CONFORTYNG, *pr. p.* comforting, 2514.

CONNYNG, *adj.* skilful, wise, 338.

CONNYNG, *sb.* skill, wisdom, 404, 1020.

CONNYNGLY, *adv.* wisely, 398.

CONSEYTE,*sb.* imagination, opinion, 696, 6091. CONSAITE, 4352. CONSEITE, good opinion, favour, 4638, 4739, 4902.

CONTENAUNCE, *sb.* 'Made no contenaunce,' did not change the expression of her face, 5116.

COPPE, *sb.* a cup, 4406.

CORAGEUS, *adj.* courageous, 2093.

CORDE, *sb.* accord, 6399.

CORNYSSH, the native county of Sampson, 6054. Called CORNYTH in the MS. l. 3137.

CORYNTH, Corinth, 3137. The MS. has CORNYTH, and elsewhere CORNYSSH.

COST, *sb.* coast, border, 6146.

COSTOM, *sb.* custom, 2974.

COSTYNG, *part.* traversing, 5923.

COUENAUNDE, *sb.* covenant, agreement, 3807.

COUERTURE, *sb.* pretext, 4596.

COUMFORT, *v.* comfort, 1019; *sb.* comfort, 1023.

COUNFORT, *sb.* comfort, 61, 3565.

COUNFORT, *v.* to comfort, 76, 1014.

COURSE. 'Toke ther course, or coursis,' a term of tilting, when the combatants rode at each other with their spears, 2462, 2627, 3360, 3383; 'Rode a course,' 5098.

COWDE, could, 381.

COWD GOOD SKILL, was skilful, 932.

CRAFT, *sb.* 'A craft' = a cunning contrivance, 4233.

CREDENCE, *sb.* 'To take credence' = to believe, 4680.

CROPPE, *sb.* the top of a plant or tree. "Croppe and rote," 4940.

CROSSYNG HYM THE WAY, crossing his path, 5814. See 6076.

CROVES, King of Arabia, 1901.

CRYED, *pp.* proclaimed, 5573, 6146.

CRYES, *sb.* proclamations, 4757.

CURTESLY, *adv.* courteously, 166, 392, 602, 694, 5091, 6700.

CURTEYS, *adj.* courteous, 3, 307. COURTEYSE, 338. CURTES, 425, 2026, 6617, 6866. CURTESE, 1946, 6672.

DALAY, *sb.* delay, 1842.

DAMAS, Damascus, 4744.

DAMASK, Damascus, 3140.

DANGER, *sb.* 'Made danger = made a difficulty, hesitated, 5073.

DARELL, a knight of Persia, son of Cherydone, Prince of Cesarea, 1505, 1929, 5058.

DAUID, eldest son of the Prince of Turkey, 1920.

DAY, *sb.* space of time; in the phrases 'ij monethis day,' 5882, 5888; 'a moneth day,' 1717, 1890.

DAYLE, a mistake for 'daye,' 3959.

DEBATE, *sb.* quarrel, strife, 2296, 5221.

DEBONERLY, *adv.* 279; perhaps for 'deboner' = debonair.

DED, 'Don to ded' = put to death, 1487.

DEDE, *v. pret.* did, 692, 1327, 5216; 'Dede of' = put off, 4343. DED, 3925, 4798.

DEFAUTE, *sb.* fault, 875.

DEFENDE, *v.* to forbid, 900, 4479, 6590.

DEFENSABLE, *adj.* 'In defensable wise,' in a defensive manner, fully armed, 1888.

DELAY. In l. 5300 'eny delay' is found to rhyme with 'batell,' where it must be a mistake for 'fayle.'

DELE, *sb.* a part or portion. 'Euery dele,' every bit, 112, 605, 892, 2717; 'Some dele,' somewhat, 261. DEELL, 698.

DEME, *v.* to judge, 461, 1614; *pret.* DEMYD, 1455, 4710.

DEMEANE, *v.* to deal with, treat, manage, 788, 4622.

DEMEANYD, *pp.* 'To be demeanyd' = to behave, conduct oneself, 1719.

DEMEANYNG, *sb.* demeanour, 398, 2195, 5981. DEMEANENG, 662, 5179. DEMEANING, 929. DEMENING, 1345. 'Att his demening,' under his command, 2052.

DEPARTE, *v. t.* to part, separate, 2747, 5851; and *i.* to share, divide, 3418; *pp.* DEPARTID, 3080, 6254.

DEPARTENG, *sb.* parting, separation, 209, 2661.

DETERMYTTE, *v. t.* to put an end to, 1695.

DEVER, *sb.* endeavour, 6506.

DEWTE, *sb.* 'Of dewte,' as their due, 2016.

DIGHT, *v.* to make ready, prepare, 382, 1110, 2027; *pp.* prepared, 3636.

DILIGENCE, *sb.* 'Dede diligence' = was diligent, 6756.

DISCOMFETE, *pp.* discomfited, 2411.

DISCOMFETURE, *sb.* 'Were att discomfeture' = were discomfited, 2511.

DISCOMFEYTE, *pp.* discomfited, distressed, 6112, 6292.

DISCOMFORTID, *pp.* deprived of comfort, 5913.

DISCOMFORTURE, *sb.* discomfiture, 2571.

DISENTE, *sb.* descent, 1314.

DISFORTLES, an error for 'comfortles,' 6645.

DISMAY, *v.* used as a reflexive verb, 5328.

DISPLESAUNCE, *sb.* displeasure, 4268, 4691, 5189, 5319, 6481.

DISPORTE, *sb.* sport, 36, 3836. 'Disporteng place,' pleasure ground, 647.

DISSENTE, 956; apparently an error for 'assent.' See 983.

DISSESE, *sb.* discomfort, 292, 713, 878.

FALL, rhyming with 'will' and 'still,' 5858.

FALOW, *sb.* fellows, 1766.

FALSED, *sb.* falsehood, 958.

FALSHEDE, *sb.* falsehood, 1539, 5221, 5267.

FANTESIES, *sb.* fancies, 4652. FANTESYCE, 4676.

FARDE, *v. pret.* behaved, seemed, 4786.

FARE, *sb.* course of life, 4495.

FATID, *v. pret.* faded, 6761.

FAWTE, *sb.* fault, 4386, 5686.

FAYNE, *adj.* glad, 27, 3801, 5649. FAYN, 1145, 1284, 2329, 4560.

FEBELID, *v. pret.* grew feeble, 6646.

FELASHEPE, *sb.* company, 1667, 1956. FELASSHEPE, 2855.

FELAW, *sb.* companion, 134, 4833.

FELD, *sb.* field. To 'sette a feld' is to put an army in order of battle, 2914, 2921, 4806; 'Made ther feld,' 4813; 'made a feld,' 4817; 'To make a feld,' 5301.

FELE, *adj.* much, 6701.

FELISCHEPE, *sb.* company, 1886. FELISSHEPE, 2540, 4830, 5982, 6326. FELISSHEPPE, 2869, 2969.

FENDE, *sb.* fiend, 3069; *pl.* FENDEZ, 2520.

FENYALL, *adj.* final, 5038.

FER, *adv.* far, 911.

FERD, *adj.* afraid, 3389. FERDE, 4425.

FERDER, *adv.* further, 6154.

FERE. 'In fere' or 'in feere' = together, 422, 527, 728, 1326, 1378, 2113, 4353, 4604, 6210, 6620, 6973.

FERLY, *adv.* strangely, wonderfully; and hence, impetuously, 2203, 5815.

FERRE, *adj.* far. 'Ferre in age,' advanced in life, 66, 228, 3666; *adv.* 3118.

FEYNTID, *pp.* rendered faint, 6647.

FISYKKE, *sb.* physic, 6876.

FLATRISE, *sb.* flattery, 4042.

FOR BECAUSE, *conj.* because, 2959, 6947.

FOR BLED, *pp.* weakened by loss of blood, 4946, 6112; bleeding, 6403.

FOR BLODE. It is difficult to say whether 'sore for blode' (3528) signifies 'sore for loss of blood,' or 'having bled sore.' Most likely the latter. Compare 'sore forbled,' 4946.

FOR BY CAUSE, *conj.* because, 6037, 6184.

FORDER, *v.* to further, 336.

FORGETE, *pp.* forgotten, 2352, 5367, 5558, 6090, 6961.

FORGEVE, *pp.* forgiven, 4730.

FORGEVYN, *pp.* forgiven, 6125. FORGEVEN, 6323.

FORGROWE, *pp.* misshapen, 3667.

FORMEST, *adj.* first, foremost, 1998, 2023, 2971.

FORS, *sb.* care. 'Gave butt litill fors,' took but little care, 2268.

FORSAKE, *pp.* forsaken, 4671.

FORSOKE, *pret.* gave up, abandoned, 5674.

FORSTER, *sb.* forester, 975, 4803, 6674.

FORTHERAUNCE, *sb.* furtherance, advancement, 6664.

FORTHERMORE, *adv.* furthermore, 103.

FOR THOUGHT, *v. pret.* repented, 1456.

FORTUNE, *v.* to chance, happen, 3977, 4234, 5895.

FOR WHYE, *conj.* because, 996.

FOR WONDID, *pp.* severely wounded, 6384.

FORYERAUNCE, *sb.* furtherance. 6482.

FOR YETE, *pp.* forgotten, 1916.

FOUGHTEN, *pret.* 3 *pl.* fought, 3512.

FOUNDEN, *pp.* found, 5614.

FOUNDRED, *v. pret.* were worn out with fatigue; used of horses, 3385.

FOURTHNYGHT, *sb.* fortnight, 5342.

FOYS, *sb.* foes, 2491, 5157.

FRAUNCHESSE, *sb.* franchise, 1273.

FRE, an error for 'fere' or 'faire,' 5100.

FRELY, *adv.* 2415; perhaps for 'ferly.'

FRENDLEHEDE, *sb.* friendship, 5170.

FRESSEST, *adj.* freshest, 2037, 3562.

FRO, *prep.* from, 792, 5712. FROO, 3483, 3945.

FURMABELY, *adv.* formally, conformably to precedent, 1728.

FYENCE, *sb.* affiance, trust, 5611.

FYLLE, *v. pret.* fell, 4095.

FYND, *v.* to provide, 1013.

FYNE, *sb.* end, 1757.

FYNIALL, *adj.* final, 5427, 6251.

GADERID, *v. pret.* gathered, 2917.

GADERYNG, *sb.* gathering, 1335.

GAILE, *sb.* gaol, 1696. ·

GALAD, King of Assyria, 2167, 2545.

GANNE, *v. pret.* began, 243, 390, 933, 1998, 4870, 5701. GAN, 5711.

GEERE, *sb.* gear, equipment, 2104, 2670. GERE, 2857, 4563.

GENERYDES, son of Auferius and Sereyne, 291, &c.

GETE, *v. imper.* get, 6063.

GETEN, *pp.* gotten, begotten, 187.

GEVE, *v.* to give, 4249; *pp.* given, 3581, 4642.

GIDE, *sb.* guide, 4803.

GIDID, *v. pret.* guided, 4800.

GIRDE, *pp.* girt, 3557.

GISE, *sb.* guise, 2974, 4203.

GLAD, *sb.* gladness, joy, 1255.

GLYNT, *v. pret.* glanced, 2421; flashed, 6088.

GOFFORE, the Sultan of Persia, 651.

GOO, in the phrase 'goo sett,' 2914.

GOO, *pp.* gone, 4003, 4783, 6781.

GOOD, *sb.* goods, possessions, 237.

GOOD, *interj.* 2770.

GOODLYHEED, *sb.* goodness, 679. GOODLY HEDE, 2803, 6340.

GOOD MAN, *sb.* master, proprietor, 1122.

GOTEN, *pp.* begotten, 4287.

GOTH, *v. imper.* go, 6484.

GOUERNAUNCE, *sb.* government, 674, 1094, 1948.

GOULYS, *adj.* gules, 2306.

GRAMERCY, *int.* Fr. grand merci, great thanks, 452, 2653.

GRAUNT, *pp.* granted, 1671.

GRE, *v.* to agree, 1141.

GRE, *sb.* pleasure; to take in gre = to be pleased, 103, 998.

GREE, *v.* to agree, 5294.

GREKE, *sb.* Greece, 356, 402.

GRESELY, *adj.* grisly, 2153.

GRESES, *sb.* steps, 1531.

GRISSELL, the name of Generydes' horse, 3301.

GROW, *pp.* grown, 804. GROWE, 1343.

GUSARE, an Ethiopian in the service of Serenydes, 5245.

GWYNAN, son of Belen, King of Egypt, 2127, 3595, 5787. GUYNAN, 2238, 4198. GWAYNAN, 2241.

GWYNOT, chamberlain to Clarionas, 2688, 3244, 6800.

GYE, *v. t.* to guide, 2049.

HAKENEY, *sb.* hackney, 1249.

HAN, an, 5269.

HAND. To 'bere in hand' = to treat, 2780.

HAND BE HAND = hand to hand, 1827.

HANDE. 'Of his hande,' 1930; 'Of his handis,' 5186; 'Aside hand of' = beside, 2453, 2825.

HANGED, *adj.* 'An hanged bedde,' a bed with curtains, 71.

HAP, *v.* to happen, 156.

HAPPYD, *v. pret.* happened, 435, 3622. 'Hym happyd in,' he lighted upon, 57. HAPPID, 3524, 6161.

HARD, *v. pret.* heard, 516, 659, 2740, 3347, 3663, 5730. HARDE, 49.

HARD, *pp.* heard, 897.

HARKENYD, *v. pret.* heard: followed by ' of,' 2949.

HARKYN, *v.* to hear: followed by ' of,' 4016.

HARMES, *sb.* arms, 614, 2305. HARMYS, 2405.

HARMONES, the king of higher Ind, 2956.

HARNES, *sb.* armour, 605, 2028, 2965. HARNESSE, 2945. HARNEYS, 6088.

HAROWED, *sb.* a herald, 2249.

HARTID, *pp.* encouraged, 2418.

HATH, 3 *pl.* 2659.

HAUE. In the phrase ' have here' = take here, 6587, 6770. ' Had hym awaye,' took him away, 6643. HAUE, apparently for ' hath,' 1710.

HEDYR, *adv.* hither, 75. HEDER, 168, 5667, 6219.

HEERE, *sb.* hair, 545. HERE, 501, 6584.

HELME, *sb.* helmet, 6106, 6107.

HELVYS, *sb.* helves, handles, 2162.

HEM, *pron.* them, 5931.

HEM SELF, *pron.* himself, 4786.

HERE, *pron.* her, 4247.

HERE BEFORE, *adv.* heretofore, 1134.

HERIS, hers, 4675.

HEVILLY, *adv.* sorrowfully, 5513.

HEVY, *adj.* sorrowful, 239, 595, 2665, 3038, 5847, 6602.

HEUYNESSE, *sb.* sorrow, 887, 2548, 2604, 2987. HEVYNES, 2969, 3585, 4625.

HIDE, *sb.* head, 2342.

HIGH. ' On a high' = on high, aloud, 2456.

HIGHE, *v.* to hie, go, 4067.

HIGHT, *v. pret.* was called, 21, 639, 1291; *v. pres.* am or is called, 2756, 4144, 4159, 4694, 5063.

HIR, *pron.* their, 635, 4789; *adv.* here, 5892.

HIRE, *v.* to hear, 576.

HIS, is, 4675.

HOLD, *pp.* holden, 495, 1710, 1930.

HOLPYN, *pp.* holpen, helped, 5862.

HOLTYS, *sb.* holts, woods, 43.

HOLY, *adv.* wholly, 76.

HONOUR, *sb.* ' Hir honour' = for her credit, 4511.

HOO, *adv.* how, 868. HOUGH, 1068.

HOOLE, *adv.* wholly, 124.

HOOLE, *adj.* whole, sound, 5205.

HOOLY, *adv.* wholly, 32, 6533.

HOUGH, *adv.* how, 1069.

HOVYD, *v. pret.* tarried, 4028.

HUDE, *sb.* hue, colour, 1560.

HUSHT, *adj.* hushed, silent; and so, secret, 320.

HYE, *v.* to go, 41, 1955, 3056, 5153, 5934.

HYM, *pron.* them, 2919, 3280, 4542, 6150, 6348.

HYMSELF, *pron.* themselves, 3083.

HYNG, *v. pret.* hung, 5236.

IAPE, *sb.* a jest, 3377.

IAPYNG, *sb.* jesting, jest, 6135.

ICHE, *pron.* each, 2662, 4381.

ICHEON, each one, 1800, 1942. ICHON, 1691.

IE, 1980. IEE, *sb.* eye, 1874, 2772.

IENTILEST, *adj.* gentlest, 929.

IENTILL, *adj.* gentle, 3, 307, 664.

IENTILLES, *sb.* gentles, gentlemen, 1326.

IENTILLY, *adv.* gently, 1261. IENTELLY, 3428.

ILL FARYNG, *adj.* ill-conditioned, ugly looking, 2152, 3020, 3025.

IMAGENINGE, *sb.* plotting, devising, 122.

IMPORTABILL, *adj.* intolerable, 1477.

IN. ' In swounyng,' 1257, 6754, 6787; ' In falling,' 4425.

INCONTENENT, *adv.* incontinently, immediately, 2865.

INDE, *sb.* India, 2.

INDERLY, *adv.* 675. Like INLY.

INLY, *adv.* inwardly, thoroughly, 3361, 4986. See ENDLY.

I NOW, *adv.* enough, 2006, 3637.

INPERT, *v.* to injure, 4480.

INPRENTID, *pp.* imprinted, 6698.

INTENT, *sb.* endeavour, 1263.

INTO, *prep.* unto, 3593, 6166, 6271.

IOATAN, a knight overthrown by Sir Darell, 4977.

IONATHAS, a knight of Ethiopia, 3143.

Is, *pron.* his, 237.

ISMAELL the Savage, brother to Generydes and King of Thrace, 1344, 2621, 6914.

IT. Apparently an error for 'yet,' 4723.

IUELL. See YUELL.

IULYAN, Emperor of Rome, 3402.

IURNAY, *sb.* journey, 607.

I WIS, *adv.* certainly, surely, 718, 732, 5448. I WISE, 2774.

KECHEWE, an error for 'kerchewe,' a kerchief, 4424.

KERCHE, *sb.* kerchief, 3827, 4398.

KIRTILL, *sb.* kirtle, mantle, 4380, 4393, 4395.

KNOW, 3365. KNOWE, *pp.* known, 262; *pret.* knew, 323, 450, 974, 1170.

KNOWIT, *v. pres.* 3 *sing.* knoweth, 87. Probably an error of the scribe for 'knoweth it.'

KNOWITH, acknowledgeth, 6621.

KNOWLACHE, *sb.* knowledge, 1251, 5050.

KNOWLACHING, KNOWLACHYNG, *sb.* knowledge, 1236, 2182, 2606, 2640, 3218, 4118, &c.

KNOWLEGINGE, *sb.* knowledge, 235, 277, 316.

KNYGHTWOODE, *sb.* knighthood, 5032.

LAMADONE, King of Libya, 2171. LAMADON, 3123. LAMEDON, 4842, 5098.

LARGE, *adj.* 'ij myle large,' a space of two miles, 3223.

LARGELY, *adv.* liberally, 3418, 5296.

LATE, *v.* to let; *inf.* 132; *imper.* 607, 940, 2806, 3592, 4405.

LAUGH, *sb.* law, 6941.

LAUNDE, *sb.* lawn, 73.

LAVENDER, *sb.* laundress, 282 1167, 4363, 6969. LAVENDERE, 4354.

LAWDE, *sb.* praise, 2877.

LAYEN. 'Withoute layen,' without concealing, 2302.

LAYNE, *v.* to conceal, 717, 772, 810, 2646. LAYN, 4385, 4885.

LECHE CRAFT, *sb.* doctor's skill, 5658.

LEESE, *sb.* falsehood, 5992.

LEFE, *v.* to learn, 1316.

LEFE, *adj.* In the phrase 'wheder she were lefe or lothe,' whether she were willing or unwilling, 5507.

LEKE, *v. i.* to like, 2010.

LEKE, *adv.* like, 6732.

LEKELY, *adv.* likely, 670.

LEKID, *v. pret.* liked, 661.

LENAGE, *sb.* lineage, 413, 2438, 2639, 3114, 3873.

LENGER, *adv.* longer, 190, 572, 2897, 5355. LENGGER, 2712.

LENGEST, *adv.* longest, 4374.

LEPPE, *v. pret.* leaped, 2262.

LESE, *sb.* to lose, 13, 1133, 2573, 6057.

LESE, *sb.* falsehood, 20, 289, 319, 794, 4936. LEESE, 2622, 2652.

LESING, *sb.* falsehood; 4661. LESYNG, 5732.

LESSE, *sb.* falsehood, 3902.

LESSE, a mistake for LESTE, 39.

LEST, *v.* to last, 899.

LEST, *adj.* active, nimble. Fr. *leste*, 1923, 2146.

LESTE, *subj.* would please, 406.

LET, *v. pret.* let be, allowed it to be supposed, 5067.

LETE, *v. imper.* let, 5731.

LETT, 2200. LETTE, *sb.* hindrance, 11, 2873.

LETTE, *v. t.* to hinder, stop, 1752,

2671, 6019; *v. i.* to stop, cease, 2470.

LEVE, *v.* to believe, 186, 1389; to live, 589, 1074, 5948; *imper.* LEVITH, 5619.

LEVING, *part.* living, 4210.

LEVER, *adv.* rather, 5616.

LEYNE, *v.* to conceal, 2284.

LEYSER, *sb.* leisure, 358, 838. LEYSERE, 3276.

LIFF, *sb.* life, 3181. LYFFE, 2699.

LIFT, *v. pret.* left, 4131.

LIGGING, *pr. p.* lying, 2475. LIG-GENG, 3027.

LIGHT, *v. pret.* lighted, 3046.

LIKE, *v.* to please; *pret.* LIKID, 5165, 5653.

LIKENG, *sb.* condition, 6760.

LIST, *v.* to desire, 154, 656, 5758. 'What here lyst,' what she pleased, 266.

LIST, *sb.* pleasure. 'On my list' = at my pleasure, 2459.

LONDYD, *v. pret.* landed, 4193.

LONG, *adv.* 'To think long' = to long, 6225.

LONG, *v.* to belong; *pres.* LONGITH, 347; *pret.* LONGYD, 26.

LOSE, *sb.* a string or lace, 5236.

LOTHE, *adj.* loathsome, 4302.

LUCAS, a knight of Persia, slain by Gwynan, 1652, 6028, 6964.

LUCIDAS, daughter of Amelok, 4843.

LYBIE, Libya, 2171.

LYGHT, lieth, 1027.

LYSTE, *v. pret.* desired, 33.

LYVEZ. 'A lyvez creature' = a living creature, 3381. Compare Chaucer, Clerk's Tale.

MADANE, King of Thrace, 2144. In the Roxburghe Club version he is called King of Greece. MADAN, 2920.

MAGRY, *sb.* ill will, 877.

MALICHIAS, a knight of Persia, slain by Generydes, 938, 1484.

MANASSEN, one of the King of Egypt's allies, 2169. Slain by Lucas, 2482. MANESSEN, 2476.

MANER. 'Some maner trayne,' some kind of snare or plot, 83, 1438; 'In no maner a wyse,' 259; 'No maner harnesse,' no kind of armour, 2945; 'All maner vitayle,' all kinds of provisions, 3111; 'Some maner waye,' in some way or other, 4478; 'What maner thing,' 4708; 'All maner right,' 5472.

MANERLY, *adv.* in a becoming maner, 653.

MASEDEYN, Macedon, 1952. MASE-DOYNE, 2085.

MASSAGE, *sb.* message, 364, 2377, 3165, &c.

MASSENGER, *sb.* messenger, 1892, 5162. MASSANGER, 3173, 3329. MASSINGER, 5152.

MASTEREYS, *sb.* efforts, displays of skill, 2778.

MEANE, *sb.* means, 594, 952, 3160, 6035.

MECHE, *adj.* much, 1275, 1670, 1949, 5146; *adv.* 3199, 3419, 3445, 5635.

MEDEN, Sereyne's maid, 264. MEDEYN, 274, 298, 299, 304. MEDEYNE, 281.

MEDLED, *v. pret.* 'Medled with' = encountered, 6134.

MEKILL, *adv.* much, 6451.

MEND, *sb.* mind, memory, 412, 1073, 3032, 6413; mention, 2506. 'Sithe tyme of mend' = since time within memory, 1772. MENDE, 3198, 3434, 4796, 6406. Rhyming with 'fynde,' 5698.

MENY, *sb.* retinue, attendants, 277; company, 3002.

MERCAUNDEZ, *sb.* merchants, 4203.

MERTHIS, *sb.* joyful songs and cries, 3563.

MERVELYS, *sb.* marvels, 109.

MESELL, *sb.* a leper, 4237, 4311.

MESSAVENTURE, *sb.* misadventure, 3848.

METELY, *adj.* Of good measure, tall, 432; moderate, 768.

ME THINK, methinks, 2362, 3243.

MEVE, *v. t.* to move, 1760, 4909.

MIRABELL, Clarionas's maid, 716, &c. MYRABELL, 797. MIRABILL, 3804.

MO, *adj.* more, 2722, 3908.

MOAB, King of Cappadocia, 1954.

MONE, *sb.* sorrow, complaint, 2695. 'To make mone' = to complain, lament, 2662.

MONPERSON, a town of Persia, 5987. MONPERSONE, 6058. MOUNPERSON, 6190.

MOO, *adj.* more, 955, 1110, 1977.

MORE, with a comparative, more bolder, 1628; more wrother, 1568; more stronger, 2160.

MORELL, the name of King Belen's horse, 3286.

MORTUALL, *adj.* mortal, deadly, 6399.

MOST, with a superlative, 929.

MOST, *adj.* greatest, 2708.

MOTE, *v.* may, 668. 'So mote I goo,' 2900, 4639, 5043.

MOUNTENER, the chief city of Persia, 639, &c.

MYDDES, *sb.* midst, 538, 852, 6042.

MYNDE, *sb.* 'To make mynde' = to make mention, 2131. MYND, 3016, 4866.

MYSGOUERNAUNCE, *sb.* misgovernment, 4873.

MYSTREST, *v.* to mistrust, 1399, 1413.

MYSTREST, *sb.* mistrust, 1673.

MYSTROST, *sb.* mistrust. An error for 'mystrest,' as it rhymes with 'list,' 5760, 6184.

MYSTROSTE, *v.* to mistrust, 5695, 5762; *pp.* MYSTROSTID, 6238.

NATANELL, tutor to Generydes, 337, &c.

NAY *or* NAYE. 'That is noo nay,' there is no denying it, 2277; 'This is noo nay,' 4159, 4288,

4539; 'Said nay' = opposed, 4755, 5456.

NAYED, *pp.* denied, refused, 1797. NAYDE, 5248.

NE, *conj.* nor, 4368.

NEDE, *v.* 'That hym nede,' that may be needful for him, 350; 'Them nede,' they needed, 4400.

NEE, *conj.* nor, 3317.

NEER, *adv.* nearer, 5715.

Negative, double, 3317, 3413, 4205, 5361, 5374.

NEW. 'We are new to begynne,' we have to begin anew, 3108.

NICOMEDE, Nicomedia, 1940. NYCOMEDE, 2073.

NONYS. 'For the nonys,' for the occasion, 3289, 5139.

NORISE, *sb.* nurse, 288. NORYSE, 286.

NOT FOR THY, *adv.* nevertheless, 235, 813, 917, 3127.

NOTHER, *conj.* neither, 1749, 1817, 3181.

NOTHER, *pron.* other, 1749.

NOWNBER, *v. t.* to number, 1561.

NOYETH, *v. pres.* annoyeth, 5728.

NOYTHER, *conj.* neither, 4470.

NYE HANDE, *adv.* near, 2273.

NYERE, *adv.* near, 2531.

NYGH HANDE, *adv.* near, 62, 6335.

NYHAND, *adv.* near, 951.

O. 'o length' = at length, 1778; 'o trough' = in truth, 4286, 4501; 'o my trowth,' 4723.

OBEISEAUNCE, *sb.* obedience, 1096. OBEYSAUNCE, 6630. OBYSEAUNCE, 2435.

OBESEAUNCE, *sb.* obeisance, 652. OBEYSAUNCE, 2020, 6897.

OBETH, King of Sicily, 1934.

OBEY, TO, *v.* For this construction see 19, 5782.

OBSERVAUNCE, *sb.* 'To do observaunce' = to shew respect, 6655.

OF = for, in construction with 'beseech,' 325, 6315, 6498; 'thank,' 5093; 'praye,' 6263, 6432; = on, in construction with 'avenge,' 565; 'Sory of,' 597; 'To be of assent' = to assent, 3609; 'Abiding of,' 4328; 'Purveyd of' = provided with, 4649.

OF, *prep.* off, 2798.

OFFEND, followed by 'to,' 6171.

ON. In the phrases 'on huntyng,' 962, 965, 3765, 3775, 5966; 'On lyve' = alive, 3375; 'On sleppe' = asleep, 4063.

ON, *adj.* one, 1316, 4791; redundant in 2909, 6978.

ON, *prep.* in. 'On twayn' = in two, 2242, 2632, 4569, 4926; 'On twoo,' 2933, 4598. Of, 4597.

ON- in compounds = un.

ONCOPELYD, *pp.* uncoupled, 42.

ONFORTUNE, *sb.* misfortune, 5339.

ONHAPPY, *adj.* unhappy, unlucky, 4874; mischievous, 5561.

ONHORSID, *pp.* unhorsed, 2464.

ONNESE, *adv.* perhaps for 'vn-nethe,' scarcely, 3453.

ONNETHE, *adv.* scarcely, 977.

ONTO, *prep.* unto, until, 282, 1288, 3136, 5178.

ON TOKE, *v. pret.* took on, 3951.

ONTREW, *adj.* untrue, 120.

ONTROWTH, *sb.* untruth, 4896.

ONYS, *adv.* once, 1182, 2492, 2785, 4242, 4303, 5401.

O PECE, *adv.* quietly, uninterruptedly (? Fr. *en paix*), 1385, 1681, 2417, 2544, 2620, 2766, 3739, 3755, 3920, 4189, 4328, 4581, 4911, 5254, 5627, 6182, 6237, 6347, 6719. OPEESE, 2313. OPESE, 3391, 3500, 4512, 4618.

OR, *prep.* before, 1185.

OR, *adv.* before, 917, 1005, 2232, 2968, 6540. OR EUER, 6459.

ORDENAUNCE, *sb.* array, 2084, 2142; arrangement, 4769.

ORKENAY, Orkney, 1961.

OSTAGE, *sb.* hostelry, 64.

OTHER, *pl.* others, 1587, 3132.

OTRAN, king of Spain, 3064, 5957.

OUER, *adj.* upper, 2996.

OUERTHROWE, *pp.* overthrown, 4979.

OUER WHARTE, *prep.* across, 6604.

OUGHT. 'As hym ought,' as was due to him, 142.

OUREZ, *pron.* ours, 2989; *sb.* hours, 4201.

OUTRAYTH, outrageth, 2426.

OWE, *v.* to regard as owing or due, 922, 1329.

OWTTRAYED, *pp.* outraged, violently treated, beaten, 3491. OUTRAYED, 4841. OVTRAYDE, 6068.

OYTHER, *conj.* either, 2610.

PACIENT, *adj.* 'In pacient' = patiently, 6748.

PALES, *sb.* palace, 4247, 6759.

PARAUENTURE, *adv.* peradventure, perhaps, 2586.

PARDE, *int.* verily! Fr. *par dieu,* 731, 3441.

PARENTYNE, the chief city of India, 5771. PARENTYNNE, 378. PAREYNTYN, 970.

PARTID, *v. pret.* departed, set out, 2113.

PARTISE, *sb.* parts, 1706.

PASSITH, *v. pres.* exceedith, 5954.

PAYDE, *adj.* pleased, 2246.

PAYN. 'On a payn,' in 1727, is on pain of something which is not mentioned.

PAYN, *sb.* pains, 68, 1018, 5213. PAYNE, 3412.

PECE, *adj.* quiet, 320.

PEERLYS, *sb.* pearls, 3306.

PEKYS, *sb.* pikes or pickaxes, 2509. See 2161.

PENSELL, *sb.* a small penon or flag, 2686, 2947, 3245.

PEOPILL, *sb.* a body of people, 2670.

PEOPLE. 'A grete people' = a large multitude, 5279.

PERAUENTURE, *adv.* perchance, 153, 781. PERAUENTOUR, 888.

PERCE, Persia, 6780.

PERISSHED, *v. pret.* pierced, 3367.

PERSE, *sb.* Persia, 620, &c.

PETEUOSE, *adj.* piteous, 3586.

PETEVOUS, 3953. PETUOSE, 5594, 6584. PETUESE, 6622.

PETEVOUSLY, adv. piteously, 1529.

PHARES, one of the Sultan of Persia's allies, 2097.

PIGHT, v. pret. pitched, 5134.

PITEVOUS, adj. piteous, 2954.

PLAYN, adj. honest, 6948.

PLEASE IT = may it please, 3720, 6843. PLESE IT, 4309, 5400. PLEASIT, 4060.

PLENTEUOUS, adj. plenteous, 620, 1031.

PLESAUNCE, sb. pleasure, delight, 31, 126, 654, 4650, 5114, 6711.

PONYSSHENG, sb. punishing, 6662.

Possessive case, mark of, omitted, 'Suster sonne,' 283; 'Hevyn kyng,' 2642, 4002, 4427; 'Sowdon powre,' 3420; 'maister harnes,' 3845; 'nyghte rest,' 4030; 'auferius right,' 4134; 'auferius comyng,' 4772; 'prince sonne,' 5185.

POSTRENE, sb. a postern, 2559.

POYNTE DEVISE, ATTE, perfectly, completely, 3307, 5995.

POYNTED, v. pret. appointed, 2125, 2149.

POYNTEMENT, sb. appointment. 'In ther poyntement,' under their command, 2100, 2178; arrangement, 3006, 3086, 4762.

PRATYE, adj. pretty, 302. PRATY, 4422.

PRECE, sb. crowd, 2453, 6641.

PREFF, sb. proof, 1453, 1496.

PRELETYS, sb. prelates, 3561.

PRESE, sb. press, crowd, 538, 852, 2708, 2726, 5311. PREESE, 2299, 6277.

PRESENT. 'In present' = present, 3104.

PREUYD, pp. proved, 4.

PREVYED, pp. provided, 5887.

PRICE, sb. value, worth, 2036.

PRIUITE, sb. secrecy, 263.

PROCESSE, sb. story, narrative, 1509, 4615, 5911, 6213.

PROMES, sb. promise, 1328; v. to promise, 4654.

PROWSE, sb. prowess, 4231, 4950.

PUESSENCE, sb. puissance, power, 3419.

PURCHASE, v. to acquire, procure, 877, 5198, 5260; sb. acquisition, 2812.

PURVAYE, v. to provide, 59, 1026, 1365; pret. PURVAYDE, provided, 1298. PURVAYED, 1288; pp. PURVAYDE, provided, 1771.

PURVEY, v. to provide, 6455; pret. PURVEID, provided, 5310. PURVEYD, 3220, 4276; pp. PURVEID, provided, 2082. PURVEYD, 1115, 2889, 3196, 4649, 5139.

PURVYAUNCE, sb. providence, 272.

PUSAUNCE, sb. power, 1951. PUYSAUNCE, 1970.

PUT TO, v. to apply, 4948, 5213.

PYTUES, adj. piteous, 6283.

QUARELL, sb. cause of quarrel, claim, 3536, 4561.

QUIETE, v. pret. acquitted, 2861.

QUYK, adj. alive, 2576.

QUYTE, v. t. to acquit, 1500; to requite, 3498, 5700; pret. requited, 2327; acquitted, 3013; yielded, gave up, 3608; pp. requited, 3495, 6975.

QUYTE AND CLENE, 6364, 6376.

REAMES, sb. realms, 4332.

REANE, sb. rein, 3474.

REBELL, adj. rebellious, 6421.

RECOMAUNDID, v. pret. commended, 5907, 6174.

REDE, v. to advise, 625, 871, 2575.

REDELY, adj. ready, 6305.

REDEN, pp. ridden, 5597.

REDY, adj. near, 3706, 6890.

REDYEST, adj. quickest, nearest, 3700.

REHERSID, pp. mentioned, 1114.

Relative omitted, 5272.

REME, sb. realm, 19, 496, 1028, 2649, &c.

REMEMBRYD, *pp.* reminded. 'Am remembryd' = remember, 619, 2690, 5290.

REMEVE, *v. t.* to remove from, 3223.

REMEVID, *v. pret.* removed, 3015.

REMEVYNG, *part.* removing, 5069.

RENNE, *v.* to run, 930.

REPORTE, *v.* to refer, 4526.

REPREFF, *sb.* reproof, 1451.

REQUERE, *v.* to require, 619, 6586.

RESAN, *sb.* reason, 1061.

RESKEWSE, *sb.* rescue, 4928.

RETEYNE, *v. t.* to restrain, 1543.

REUER, *sb.* river, 1151.

REWITH, *v. pres.* repenteth, 3971.

REWLE, *sb.* revel, 5592. The line is corrupt. Order, 6629.

REWLE, *v.* to rule, 5892.

REYNYNG, running, 3825.

RIALL, *adj.* royal, 1950.

RIALLY, *adv.* royally, 1308, 6910.

RIGHTWISE, *adj.* righteous, 1322; Rightful, 2960, 6669, 6934.

RISSH, *sb.* rush, 1680.

RODE, *sb.* rood, 2445; roadstead, 4106.

ROMANS, *sb.* romances, 1.

ROUGHT, *v. pret.* recked, cared, 50, 1076.

ROWNDE, *adv.* direct, straight, 3364; and so, swiftly. 'Ranne to rownde,' 2627. ROUNDE, 3362, 4922.

RUBEN, son of Manassen, 2170, 2792.

RUMBER, *sb.* turmoil, 1377.

RYALL, *adj.* royal, 245.

RYNESHED, *v. pret.* rinsed, 1182.

SAD, *adj.* grave, serious, 3926. SADDE, 5832.

SADNESSE, *sb.* soberness, gravity, 1346, 3141.

SAFF, *adj.* safe, 3147.

SAMPSON, one of the King of Egypt's knights, 6053; slain by Generydes, 6362, 6365. SAMPSONE, 3138.

SANYK, King of Africa, and father of Serenydes, 2136, 2931, 4864.

SAUGYS, *sb.* sages, wise men, 88.

SAVE, *adv.* safe, 6470.

SAVELY, *adv.* safely, 6127, 6456.

SAYE, *v. pret.* said, 6017.

SCOMFITE, *pp.* discomfited, 570.

SEASONE, *sb.* 'Take your seasone' = take your time, 5825.

SECHE, *v.* to seek, 3997, 4150, 5566. SECHEITH = seeketh, 2451.

SECHING, *part.* seeking, 5812.

SECRELY, *adv.* secretly, 3786.

SEIGH, *v.* to sigh, 1416.

SEKE, *adj.* sick, 714, 6632, 6759.

SEKERLY, *adv.* secretly, 359, 867, 5298, 5538; certainly, 2095, 2911, 3695, 3840, 5373. SEKYRLY, 6273.

SEME, *v.* 'Him seme,' appear to him, 1981; 'Me semyth' = it seemeth to me, 2427; 'Ye semes' = it seems to you, 6007; 'Her semyth' = she seemeth, 6846.

SEMELY, *adj.* comely, 1918, 2000, 4827.

SEMLANTE, *sb.* semblance, appearance, 4019.

SEMYD. 'Hym semyd' = it seemed to him, 40, 1988; = he seemed, 3311.

SEMYNG, *sb.* 'To his semyng,' as he thought, 4986.

SENDE, *v. pret.* sent, 1896.

SENT, sendeth, 445, 2812, 3334.

SEOSYNNE, *sb.* season, 271.

SERENYDES, wife of Auferius and afterwards of Amelok; daughter of the King of Africa, 21.

SEREYNE, the mother of Generydes, and Queen of Syria, 255; her death, 6638.

SERTEYN. 'In serteyn,' 4978.

SERUAGE, *sb.* servitude, 1848.

SERVAGE, *sb.* slavery, 3344.

SERYS, *sb.* sirs, 6018.

SESE, *v. i.* to cease, 941; *pp.* 6399.

SESE, *v. t.* to stop, 1489, 6435.

SESILL, Sicily, 1933.

SETT, 680. SETTE, *pp*. seated, 387.

SEVRE, a city of Syria given to Natanell on his marriage, 6955.

SHAPE, *pp*. shapen, 175.

SHENDE, *v. t.* to injure, ruin, 1657, 4403; *pp*. SHENT, 4669.

SHETT, *pp*. shut, 5773.

SHETTE, *v. pret.* shut, 5133, 5876.

SICHE, *adj*. such, 1126.

SIDE, *adj*. long and flowing, 4398.

SITHE, *conj*. since, 587, 800, 805, 1215. In 800 'a' is repeated in error.

SKAPE, *v. i.* to escape, 2534, 2849, 5781; *pret*. SKAPID, 4567.

SLEE, *v.* to slay, 520, 2367. SLE, 3913, 3927, 4591.

SLEPPE, *v. pret*. slept, 3934, 3937, 4037.

SLEPPYD, *v. pret*. slept, 161.

SMETE, *v. pret*. smote, 2388, 6110. SMETTE, 2355; *pp*. smitten, 579. SMETTE, 6378. SMETYN, 553.

So, *adv*. as, 4837.

SOFTELY, *adv*. gently, quietly, 2528.

SOKYD, *pp*. 234.

SOMTYME, *adv*. at one time, 4801.

SONE VPPON, *adv*. soon after, 243.

SONNER, *adv*. sooner, 6329, 6330.

SORGEONS, *sb*. surgeons, 3572.

SOTHE, *sb*. truth, 507, 612, 4885. SOTH, 996.

SOTHFASTNES, *sb*. truth, 4834, 5612.

SOTILTE, *sb*. subtilty, 122; trick, device, 1538.

SOWDON, *sb*. sultan, 640, &c.

SOWNNE, *v. i.* to sound, tend, 1750. SOWNYNG, *part*. 6339.

SPACE, *sb*. 'While I haue lyffe and space' = while I live and move, 2699, 3181.

SPECIALLY, error for 'special,' 3570.

SPERKELYD, *v. pret*. dispersed, scattered themselves, 6049.

SPORYD, *v. pret*. spurred, 217.

STERE, *v.* to stir, move, 5156.

STERT, *sb*. 'Made a stert' = rushed, 6699.

STOND, *v.* to stand, 4373. STOND-ENG, *part*. 5323.

STORE, *sb*. story, 3481.

STORY, *sb*. history, 2167.

STOUND, *sb*. space of time, 5659.

STRAKE, *pret*. struck, 2793, 2794, 2946, 3366, 5126, 6375.

STRAYTE, *adv*. strictly, 1462.

STRENTHE, *sb*. strength, 6821. A doubtful reading.

STRIFF, *sb*. strife, 3160.

STROKE, *pret*. struck, 2628, 3514.

STRONGETH, an error for 'strongest,' 5779.

STRYFF, *v.* to strive, 3373.

SUERTE, *sb*. surety, certainty, 2264; security, 4444.

SURAUNCE, *sb*. an assurance, bond, 6252.

SURE, *adj*. secure, safe, 2732, 4575, 4605.

SURRE, Syria, 93. SURRY, 99.

SUSTELY, 5070. Perhaps an error for 'softely.'

SUSTER, *sb*. sister, 4937.

SWARD, *sb*. sword, 519, 3400, 3406, 3921. SWARDE, 3480. SWERD, 2707, 3486.

SWONNE, *sb*. swoon, 2359.

SWORN BRODER. Knights who had taken an oath of brotherhood to each other were called 'sworn brothers,' 4834.

SWOUNE, *sb*. swoon, 4095, 6605.

SWOUNYD, *v. pret*. swooned, 4099.

SWOUNYNG, *sb*. an error for 'swoune,' 6569; in swounyng, 1257, 6754.

SYGHENYNG, *sb*. sighing, 162.

SYGREM, a herald, 2256, 4987, 5001, 5044. SEGREM, 6764. SEGRYM, 5986. SEGYREM, 5983.

TAK, *pp*. taken, 887.

TAKE, *v.* to deliver, 361, 447. TOKE, *pret*. 907.

TAKE, *pp.* taken, 226, 946, 2566, 3240, 3977, 5472, 5763, 6882; *pret.* took, 4070, 5536, 6422.

TARED, *v. pret.* tarried, 1287, 2757, 2926, 3352, 4347. TARYD, 2240, 2950.

TARYNG, *sb.* tarrying, 1293, 2513.

TEGER, Tigris, 1738.

TENDER, *v.* to treat kindly, 3734; to propose, 5210.

THANK, *sb.* thanks, 2879, 5915. THANKE, 3093, 3645.

THAT, redundant in 'what thing that euer fall,' 6789; 'what that she was,' 6832.

THE, *pron.* thy, 4086.

THEDER, *adv.* thither, 217, 1337, 6278.

THEDERWARD, *adv.* thitherward, 1269.

THEE, *v.* to thrive, 668.

THEMSELF, *pron.* themselves, 2596, 3057.

THER AS, *adv.* where, 2668.

THERFRO, *adv.* therefrom, 893.

THERYS, *pron.* theirs, 2989.

THING, *sb.* things, 1153.

THINK. 'Me think' = I think, 3243, 5408. THYNK. 'Vs thynk' = we think, 1782; 'Thinkith me' = seemeth to me, 3337; 'Hym thought' = seemed to him, 5639, 6861.

THIS, *pron.* these, 4402. THISE, 1706.

THO, *pron.* those, 26, 2486. THOO, 888, 1965, 2958, 4090, 4525, &c.

THO, *adv.* then, 2828.

THORE, *adv.* there, 3394, 4316.

THOROUGH, *prep.* through, 557, 2452.

THOROUGHOWT, *adv.* throughout, 2946.

THOUGHT, *sb.* anxiety, trouble of mind, 2725, 2985, 3234, 4612, 6647.

THREFTE, *adj.* thriving, 280, 1342.

THREFTY, *adj.* thrifty, 1134.

THRETE, *v. pret.* threatened, 500.

THRETING, *part.* threatening, 539.

THRETYNG, *sb.* threatening, 4086.

THROUGHELY, *adv.* thoroughly, 388.

THYNG, *sb. pl.* things, 202, 466.

TIDE, *sb.* time, 5925.

TIDENG, *sb.* tidings, 1159, 6619. TIDING, 2512.

TO, *prep.* until, 2781, 5714, 6012. 'Stroke to' = struck at, 3514; at, 6218; for, 6808.

TO AND TOO, more and more, 3378. TO AND TO, 5550.

TO BRAST, *v. pret.* broke asunder, 2356, 2495, 5837, 6107.

TODER, *adj.* other, 67, 1504, 2338, 3002, 3012, 3454, 3929, 6736.

TO GEDER, *adv.* together, 179, 1440.

TOKE, *v. pret.* delivered, 683, 1184, 2716, 5238.

TOKENYNG, *sb.* token, sign, 2608. TOKENNING, 4626.

TOKKYD, *pp.* tucked, 4397.

TONE, *adj.* one, 1957, 2338.

TOO, *adj.* two, 5879.

TRACE, *sb.* Thrace, 1028, &c. The Roxburghe Club version reads 'Tharse' in these passages, and this removes the difficulty in 2144 compared with 2288. TRASE, 2920.

TRAPPOUR, *sb.* trappings, 3305.

TRAVELL, *sb.* labour, toil, 111, 159.

TRAYN, *sb.* stratagem, artifice, 1069, 2140, 4503, 5752, 6419. TRAYNE, 4027.

TRAYTURLY, *adv.* traitorously, 2272, 4038, 6417. TRAYTOURLY, 6551. This is probably the reading in 2130.

TRESONE COLOUR. If this be the true reading it seems to mean 'treasonable pretext,' 5474.

TREST, *sb.* trust, 4621.

TRETE, *v.* to entreat, 5853.

TRETE, *sb.* treaty, 6355.

TREW, rhyming with 'now,' 5793.

TREWAGE, *sb.* tribute, 1792. TREVAGE, 3343.

TREWSE, *sb.* truce, 5887. TREWYS, 3006.

TRIFFOLYS, *sb.* trifles, 4664.

TROBELYD, *pp.* troubled, 54, 3737. TROBOLID, 3730. TROBOLYD, 5550.

TROST, *sb.* trust, 265, 786, perhaps for 'tryst,' or 'trest,' as it rhymes with 'lyst.'

TROST, *v.* to trust, 994, 3760. 'That is to trost' = that is to be trusted, 4356. Perhaps we should read 'trest,' as it rhymes with 'wist' and 'list,' as in 4621.

TROUGTH, *sb.* truth, 107, 816, 2279, 3722, 4473, 5447, &c. TROUGHT, 5437, 6316.

TROW, *v. i.* to think, 1598, 5455, 5519.

TROWLY, *adv.* truly, 144.

TRUSE, *sb.* truss, 4425; truce, 5882.

TRUSHED, *v. pret.* trussed, packed up, 605.

TWAYN, *adj.* two, 65. TWAYNE, 108, 1218, 1763. THWAYNE, 155.

TWYES, *adv.* twice, 3952, 3969, 6641.

TYME. 'To tyme,' or 'To the tyme' = until, 2471, 2746, 4228, 6755.

VAILE, *sb.* valley, 216.

VALOUR, *sb.* value, 6957.

VARIAUNCE, *sb.* strife, 5756.

VELANYE, *sb.* villany, 1358.

VENGE, *v.* to avenge, 5149.

Verb of motion omitted, 5282, 6606.

VERY, *adj.* true, actual, 2623.

VIAGE, *sb.* journey, 3146, 3331, 5162, 5271.

VICE, a city of India, 4770, 5778.

VISITE, *pp.* visited, 4293.

VITALLE, *sb.* victuals, 3637.

VMBLY, *adv.* humbly, 600. VM- BELY, 6170, 6567.

VNCURTESE, *adj.* uncourteous, 6244.

VNDERTAKE, *v. t.* to be surety for, 3583.

VNKYLL, *sb.* uncle, 5017. VNKILL, 5028.

VNNETHE, *adv.* scarcely, 2534, 4946.

VNQUYTE, *adj.* unrequited, un- avenged, 6038.

VNWURCHIPFULL, an error for 'And wurchipfull,' 4850.

VNWYMPILL, *v.* to unveil, 6879.

VOWARD, *sb.* vanguard, 2018.

VOYDE, *v.* to avoid, remove one- self, 6101.

VPON, an error for 'open,' 5721.

VPPON, *adv.* after, in point of time; in the phrases 'sone vppon,' 1926, 1041; 'anon vppon,' 6009, 6632. On, 2035. 'Came so hastely vppon' = came upon him so hastily, 4787.

VRE, *sb.* usage, custom, 2788, 4594; use, practice, 6825.

VTERLY, *adv.* entirely, fully, 3516.

WAGE, *sb.* wages, hire, 2441, 6511.

WALOPING, *part.* galloping, 3325.

WANNE, *v. pret.* won, 1133, 2130, 2237, 2609, 2814; conquered, 3688, 4766.

WARANTISE, *sb.* 'O warantise,' of a surety, 5938, 6470.

-WARD. 'As to me-ward' = as regards me, 4331.

WARE, *adj.* careful, cautious, 351, 1084; aware, 2315, 2625, 3040.

WARENTICE, *sb.* 'O warentice,' of a surety, 174; 'O warentyce,' 287, 6803.

WARK, *sb.* work, 1171.

WAWIS, *sb.* waves, 91.

WAX, *pret.* waxed, 2472.

WAY, *pl.* 5923.

WAYTITH AFTER = waiteth for, 2440.

WEDDER, *sb.* weather, 1403.

WEDE, *sb.* dress, 4258.

WEIGHT, *sb.* wight, person, 331, 3852.

WEIGHT, *adj.* active, nimble, 3361.

WELCOMYNG, *sb.* welcome, 392, 663.

WELE, *adv.* well, 5733.

WELEWILLYNG, *adj.* well-disposed, 964.

WELLYD, *pp.* 'Wele wellyd,' well-disposed, 2089.

WENE, *v.* to think, 4655; *pret.* WEND, 6317. WENDE, 3947. WENYNG, *part.* 2502, 5636.

WENT, *pp.* gone, 2667, 6443.

WERRE, *sb.* war, 898, 6153.

WERS, *adj.* worse, 1365.

WESHT, *v. pret.* washed, 1182. WESSH, 4316.

WETE, *v.* to know, 132, 180, 333, 714, 4153, 4432; *pres.* WOTE, 739, 777, 778 (read 'Ye wote ye what;' see 6858); WOOTE, 891; *pret.* WIST, 153; WYSTE, 53, 913; *imper.* 2 *pl.* WETE, 1300, 2739.

WEX, *pret.* waxed, 3349, 5065, 6608. WEXE, 5173.

WEXEN, *pp.* waxen, grown, 306, 430, 2765.

WHAT SOME EUER, *pron.* whatsoever, 4556.

WHAT TYME, whenever, 4225.

WHECHE, *pron.* which, 5389.

WHEDER, whether, 914.

WHELS, *adv.* whiles, 4037.

WHERE, *adv.* whereas, 1134.

WHO IS, whose, 353.

WIDDED, *pp.* wedded, 1080.

WIGHT, *sb.* weight, 2163.

WIGHT, *adj.* nimble, swift, 3634, 4573, 5055.

WILL, *adv.* well, 371, 899, 1835, 3698, 6941. WILE, 581. WILL, 'And it wilbe' = if it may be, 6516. See WOLD.

WISE, *sb.* manner, 1036, 1045, 5780.

WITHOUTEN, *prep.* without, 341, 794, 1171, 3706; WITHOUTYN, 20.

WITHOUTEN, *adv.* without, 3917.

WITTE, *sb.* blame, 869.

WITTELY, *adv.* wisely, 1051.

WOLD, would, 376, 1036. 'And it

wold be' = if it might be, 214, 6432; 'If it wold be,' 6500. WULD, 374.

WOLLE, *v.* will, 4403, 4432.

WONDER, *adj.* wonderful, 501, 1171, 1418, 2074, 4307, 5327; *adv.* wonderfully, 1414, 3447, 4696.

WONNE, *pp.* conquered, 6398.

WOO, *adj.* sorrowful, 915, 2371, 2578, 3484, 6652.

WOODE, *adj.* furious, mad, 2983.

WOOTE, *v. pres.* knoweth, 891; *imper.* know, 6858.

WORLD. 'A world to here,' 2205.

WORTH, in the phrase 'woo worth' = woe be to, 4871.

WOTE, *v.* to know, 2696.

WOWETH, *v. pres.* wooeth, 4442.

WRAUGTH, *sb.* wrath, 1373.

WREKE, *pp.* avenged, 1824.

WULL, *v.* will, 2807.

WURCHIPPE, *sb.* honour, dignity, credit, reputation, 35, 404, 616, 882, 2896, 2911, 3417.

WURCHIPPE, *v.* to honour, 5179.

WYMPELYD, *pp.* wrapped in a wimple or veil, 6858.

WYNNE, *v.* to conquer, 5159.

WYSE, *sb.* manner, 34. 'In lyke wyse,' in like manner, 102.

YAE, *int.* yea, 294.

YCHE, *pron.* each, 698.

YDONYE, a town of Persia, 6964.

YEDE, *pret.* went, 2503, 3458.

YEE, *sb.* eye, 4549, 4984.

YEFERUS, King of Ermonye, 1957. Called also Zeferus.

YEFT, *sb.* gift, 3441; *pl.* YEFTEZ, 3569. YEFTYS, 3094.

YELDE, *pp.* yielded, 4781. YELD, 6620.

YENDER, *adv.* yonder, 1027, 2318, 2425, 2869, 4552, &c.; *adj.* 2777, 3704, 6019.

YMAGENING, *sb.* device, plot, 5747.

YMAGENYNG, *pr. p.* plotting, designing, 963.

YND, *sb.* India, 375, 2505, 5598.

YNDLY, *adv.* 3096.   See INLY.

YOUR, *pron.* yours, 5096.

YOUREZ, *pron.* yours, 2869.

YSORES, son of Sanyk, 4869.

YUELL the Barn, a knight of Egypt, 3618, 4167.   IUELL, 3717.

ZEFERUS, King of Ermonye. Called also Yeferus, 2092.

ERRATUM.

p. 235, col. 2, line 12, under HUDE, *for* hue, colour, *read* hide.

CLAY AND TAYLOR, PRINTERS, BUNGAY.